AFRICAN INSECT LIFE

AFRICAN INSECT LIFE

by

S. H. SKAIFE

D.SC., F.R.S.S.AF.

With Illustrations by the Author

LONGMANS GREEN AND CO.

LONDON   CAPE TOWN   NEW YORK

LONGMANS, GREEN AND CO., LTD.
6 & 7 CLIFFORD STREET, LONDON, W.1
BOSTON HOUSE, STRAND STREET, CAPE TOWN

NEW YORK, TORONTO, BOMBAY,
CALCUTTA, MADRAS, MELBOURNE

Printed in South Africa by Galvin & Sales (Pty.) Ltd., 11 Castle Street, Cape Town

CONTENTS

Chap.   *Page*

I. PRIMITIVE INSECTS 1
The Insect Legion 1; Fish-moths 2; Bristle-tails on the Veld 4; Other Primitive Insects 5; Classification 6

II. COCKROACHES, GRASSHOPPERS AND THEIR KIN 7
The Orthoptera 7; Cockroaches 7; African Cockroaches 14; Praying Mantes 15; Stick Insects and Leaf Insects 18; Locusts and Short-horned Grasshoppers 21; Long-horned Grasshoppers 29; Crickets 33; Classification 35

III. EARWIGS 36
The Dermaptera 36; African Earwigs 37; Classification 38

IV. STONE-FLIES 39
The Plecoptera 39; The Life History of a Stone-fly 39; Classification 40

V. TERMITES 41
The Isoptera 41; The Black Mound Termite 41; Termites as Pets 42; The Workers 45; The Soldiers 49; The King and Queen 50; The Wedding Flight 52; Secondary Kings and Queens 54; Tertiary Kings and Queens 55; Harvester Termites 56; The Snouted Harvester Termites 58; The Wood-inhabiting Termites 60; The Fungus Growers 63; Guests and Parasites 65; Classification 66

VI. BOOK LICE AND THEIR ALLIES 68
The Silken-Tunnel Dwellers 68; Book Lice and Their Allies 68; Classification 70

VII. BITING LICE AND SUCKING LICE 71
Biting Lice 71; Sucking Lice 73; Classification 76

VIII. MAY-FLIES 77
The Epemeroptera 77; The Life History of a May-fly 77; Other May-flies 80; Classification 81

IX. DRAGON-FLIES 82
The Odonata 82; Damsel-flies 83; Dragon-flies 86; African Dragon-flies 89; Classification 89

X. THRIPS 91
The Thysanoptera 91; The Life History of a Thrips 91; African Thrips 93; Classification 93

XI. PLANT BUGS AND THEIR KIN 94
The Hemiptera 94; Shield Bugs 94; Twig-Wilters 97; Pond-Skaters 98; Assassin Bugs 100; Bed Bugs 101; Giant Water Bugs 101; Water Scorpions 102; Water Boatmen 104; Cicades 106; Frog-hoppers 108; Tree-hoppers 109; Leaf-hoppers 109; Lantern Flies 110; Jumping Plant Lice 111; White Flies 112; Aphides 113; Scale Insects 116; Mealy Bugs 122; Classification 123

XII. ANT LIONS AND THEIR KIN 128
The Neuroptera 128; Alder Flies 128; Lacewings 130; Ant Lions 131; Classification 135

XIII. SCORPION FLIES 137
The Mecoptera 137; African Scorpion Flies 137; Classification 138

XIV. CADDIS FLIES 139
The Trichoptera 139; African Caddis Flies 139; Classification 142

CONTENTS

Chap.   *Page*

XV. MOTHS   143
The Lepidoptera 143; Primitive Moths 145; Clothes Moths and Their Kin 146; The Codling Moth and Its Kin 149; Bagworms 151; Carpenter Moths 153; Clearwings 154; Slug Caterpillars 154; Meal Moths and Their Kin 156; Plume Moths 161; Lappet Moths 161; Hawk Moths 164; Emperor Moths 167; Gregarious Caterpillars 170; Cutworms and Their Kin 172; Tiger Moths 178; Brown-Tail Moths and Their Kin 180; Looper Caterpillars 182; Classification 184

XVI. BUTTERFLIES   187
The Rhopalocera 187; Skippers 187; Whites 189; Swallow-tails 191; Mimicry 193; Blues and Coppers 195; Beaked Butterflies 198; Browns 199; The Painted Lady Family 201; Distasteful Butterflies 205; The African Monarch and Its Kin 207; Classification 209

XVII. BEETLES   211
The Coleoptera 211; Tiger Beetles 211; Ground Beetles 214; Water Beetles 216; Whirligig Beetles 218; Ants' Guests 220; Rove Beetles 221; The Cadelle 222; Dried Fruit Beetles 223; The Saw-Toothed Grain Beetle 224; Ladybirds 224; Skin and Horn Beetles 227; Glow-worms and Fire-flies 229; Death Watch Beetles 231; Shot-hole Borers 232; Powder Post Beetles 234; Buprestid Beetles 235; Click Beetles 235; Meal Worms 237; Blister Beetles 239; Pea and Bean Weevils 241; Leaf-eating Beetles 243; Long-horned Beetles 246; Weevils 249; Pinhole Borers 252; Stag Beetles 254; Dung Beetles 255; Classification 259

XVIII. FLIES   263
The Diptera 263; Crane Flies 263; Moth Flies 264; Mosquitoes 265; Midges 272; Gall Midges 274; Fungus Gnats 276; Blood-sucking Midges 276; Worm Lions 278; Horse Flies 280; Robber Flies 282; Bee Flies 282; Hover Flies 284; Fruit Flies 286; Vinegar Flies 288; The Lesser House Fly 289; The House Fly and Its Kin 290; Warble Flies and Bot Flies 297; Tachinid Flies 299; The Sheep Ked and Its Kin 301; The Bee Louse 302; Classification 303

XIX. FLEAS   306
The Aphaniptera 306; Household Fleas 306; Rat Fleas 308; Jigger Fleas 309; Classification 311

XX. WASPS   312
The Hymenoptera 312; Saw-flies 312; Ensign Wasps 313; Ichneumon Wasps 316; Braconid Wasps 318; Fig Insects 320; Chalcid Wasps 321; Velvet Ants 324; Scoliid Wasps 325; Cuckoo Wasps 326; Mason Wasps 327; Social Wasps 328; Spider-hunting Wasps 330; Sand Wasps 332; Bee Pirates 334; Fly-hunting Wasps 335; Crabronid Wasps 337; Classification 338

XXI. BEES   342
Bees and Wasps 342; Primitive Bees 342; Burrowing Bees 345; Leaf-cutter Bees 345; Carpenter Bees 349; Anthophorid Bees 356; Social Bees 357; Classification 359

XXII. ANTS   360
The Formicidae 360; Ponerine Ants 360; Driver Ants 362; Dolichoderine Ants 365; Myrmicine Ants 368; Camponotine Ants 373; Classification 375

INDEX   377

PREFACE

This book, written in language as simple as is consistent with scientific accuracy, is intended mainly for the amateur student of natural history, for the farmer, gardener and householder who wish to know something about the numerous insect friends and foes they see about them. The specialist may criticize some of the omissions in the book, omissions due to the need for keeping its size within reasonable limits. For example, nothing at all is said about wing venation or genitalia, subjects that are essential for an understanding of the finer details of classification but which are highly technical, require lengthy descriptions and many figures and are of little or no interest to anybody but the specialist.

A book of this nature must of necessity consist largely of a selection and compilation of information gained from many sources. Fifty years ago it could not have been written because our knowledge at the time was so incomplete, but during the past half century a great deal of work has been done by entomologists working in various parts of the continent. The results of these entomological researches are locked away in scientific journals that are inaccessible to most people; often they are couched in language that is jargon to the amateur. Full use has been made of these sources of information, but it was considered undesirable to clutter up the text with numerous references to scientists and their publications. I wish, however, to acknowledge here my indebtedness to friends and colleagues who have been responsible for some of the major contributions to our knowledge: to Mr. C. P. Lounsbury, the "father" of economic entomology in South Africa, and the late Dr. C. W. Mally, under whom I worked as a young Government entomologist; Professor J. C. Faure, who laid the foundations of our knowledge of locusts in South Africa and who helped to establish the phase theory; Dr. K. H. Barnard, who worked on stone flies, may flies, caddis flies and dragon flies; the late Dr. C. Fuller and Dr. W. G. H. Coaton, to whom we owe most of our knowledge of South African termites; Dr. A. J. T. Janse, our leading authority on moths; Dr. G. van Son, Rev. D. P. Murray, Messrs. C. G. C. Dickson, R. H. R. Stevenson and C. Gowan Clark who have studied our butterflies; the late Dr. L. Peringuey, Sir Guy Marshall, Dr. F. G. C. Tooke, and Dr. C. Koch, who have turned their attention chiefly to beetles; Dr. A. J. Hesse, Dr. B. de Meillon, Dr. H. K. Munro and Dr. F. Zumpt, who have worked on flies; Dr. G. Arnold and the late Dr. H. Brauns, who specialised on ants, bees and wasps; and to Dr. C. K. Brain, Dr. T. J. Naude, Dr. B. Smit, Dr. R. I. Nel, Dr. F. W. Pettey, Dr. L. B. Ripley, Major R. O. Wahl, and Mr. C. P. van der Merwe who have contributed so much to our knowledge of economic entomology.

There are many younger entomologists deserving of honourable mention, but the list would be far too long if any attempt at completeness were made. Suffice it to say that this book is based largely on the work of all these men.

The insects are dealt with in systematic order, beginning with the most primitive, and the arrangement given in A. D. Imms' well-known *Textbook of Entomology* (Methuen, London) is followed, except for the highest orders. Imms places flies and fleas at the top of his tree, because they are the most highly modified in structure, but I feel that these rather unpleasant insects scarcely deserve this exalted position, therefore I have put the wasps, bees and ants at the top instead. The illustrations have all been specially prepared for this book and consist of drawings and photographs made as clear and distinctive as possible so as to assist in the recognition of the different species.

Cape Town,
    July, 1953.   S. H. SKAIFE

CHAPTER I

PRIMITIVE INSECTS

The Insect Legion

To-day there must be nearly one million different kinds of insects that are known to science, insofar as they have been collected, described and named, and a few thousand more are added to this number every year as new species are discovered and labelled. No other class of living creatures includes such a great number of species, such a diversity of forms and such amazing differences in habits and life histories.

There must be well over one hundred thousand different kinds of insects found in Africa south of the Sahara and they are far and away the most abundant of all living things inhabiting this great continent, if we leave micro-organisms out of account. We encounter them wherever we go and they impinge on our lives in many ways, sometimes to our advantage, often to our disadvantage. Africa has remained the Dark Continent, far behind the other continents in development, mainly because anopheline mosquitoes and tsetse flies have rendered large areas unfit for human habitation. Paludrine, D.D.T., gammexane, antrycide and other new discoveries of science are helping to overcome these major pests and are making possible the rapid opening-up of the interior of the continent that is going on to-day.

Besides being of enormous economic importance, insects are probably the most interesting of all living things because of their astonishing ways, and many an amateur entomologist finds an endless source of amusement in the study of these bizarre little creatures. Despite the great number of species, the classification of insects is comparatively simple and easy to understand: much easier, for example, than the classification of birds. A summary of the classification of the insects dealt with will be found at the end of each chapter.

For the present, it will suffice to point out that insects are divided into two major sub-classes, one very much smaller than the other. The lower and smaller of the two includes the most primitive of all insects, the Wingless Insects (*Apterygota*), comprising only a few thousand species, widely spread throughout the world, but mostly very small and seldom seen. The second sub-class, the Winged Insects (*Pterygota*), includes all the rest, such as cockroaches, grasshoppers, stick insects, stone-flies, may-flies, dragon-flies, termites, beetles, butterflies, moths, ants, bees, wasps, and so on.

A word of explanation is necessary here. Insects are the only invertebrates that have mastered the problems of flight. The only other creatures in the world with true powers of flight are birds and bats: in the distant past there were winged reptiles, but these have long been extinct. The great majority of insects have wings and can fly when they reach the adult stage, but many others have, for some reason or other, lost the power of flight and their wings have become useless and more or less vestigial. There are, for example, many different kinds of ground beetles in Africa that cannot fly, but their structure shows clearly that they come from ancestors which had fully-developed wings and were able to fly. Similarly, female scale insects cannot fly but the males can, most aphids cannot fly but some can, some moths cannot fly and quite a number of parasitic insects have lost all powers of flight—but in all these cases the flightless insects have descended from winged ancestors. Therefore they are all included in the second sub-class mentioned above, the *Pterygota*, despite the fact that they cannot fly. Among the primitive insects, the *Apterygota*, are included only those insects which have never, in all their long history on this earth, acquired the powers of flight and have bodies of much simpler structure than the bodies of the winged insects.

Fish-moths

An example of the primitive insects, *Apterygota*, that is familiar to all of us is the little silver-fish or fish-moth which is so common in our homes throughout the country. It is one of the simplest of all insects in its structure and life history. About half an inch long when fully grown, it is silvery grey in colour and has two long, slender antennae and three bristly "tails" on the hind end of its body—hence the name, "bristle-tails", often given to members of this group.

These insects are found in drawers and cupboards where starched linen is kept, on bookshelves, among stored papers that have been left undisturbed, behind pictures on the wall and underneath wall-paper that has become loose. They feed on starch, glue, and similar substances and may do considerable damage to the bindings of books and to valuable papers, prints and photographs by gnawing holes in them. They are active at night and may often be seen running swiftly over the walls, their hairy antennae and tails held out to warn them if they come into contact with enemies.

The fish-moth has eyes, but they are not very good and it has to depend mainly on the sense of touch, hence the long feelers and the dense coating of hairs on the head and the sides of the body. If the insect is examined under the low power of the microscope, the eyes can be seen as a group of about a dozen small, round, lenses placed close together on each side. With such eyes the little creature must be very short-sighted and able to do little more than distinguish light from darkness.

The gleaming, metallic appearance of the fish-moth, and the greasy feel of its body to the touch are due to the dense coating of

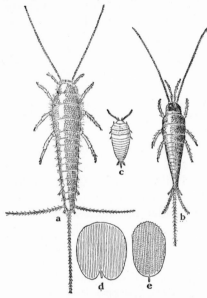

tiny scales that clothe its body, grey above and a beautiful creamy white below. There are thousands of these scales, neatly arranged in overlapping rows and looking very much like the scales on a fish's body. If some of the scales are rubbed off on a glass slide and examined under the microscope they are seen to be flattened, rounded and delicately ornamented with regular ridges. Formerly owners of microscopes used these scales to test the quality of their lenses: a lens that would reveal clearly the ornamentation on a fish-moth scale was regarded as a good one.

Each scale has a tiny peg that fits into a socket in the insect's skin and together they form an elaborate protective coat.

FIG. 1: Bristle-Tails: a. The fish-moth found in houses. *Lepisma saccharina*; b. A bristle-tail common amid decaying vegetation, *Machilis* species; c. A small bristle-tail found in termites' nests, *Trichotriura nigeriensis*; d. A scale from *Lepisma*; e. A scale from *Machilis*.

The scientific name of the fish-moth, *Lepisma saccharina*, may be freely translated as meaning "the scaly insect that likes sweet substances."

There is no difference in the appearance of the two sexes, except that the female is slightly larger and stouter than the male. She lays her oval, white eggs in batches of six to ten in cracks and crevices. These hatch out in one to three or four months, depending on the temperature, into tiny creatures similar to their parents, but without the dense coating of scales.

There are no larval or pupal stages among these primitive insects. The young fish-moth feed and grow and cast their skin at intervals, like all other insects. After moulting five or six times they are adults.

This may take nine months to two years, according to the amount of food that is available and the temperature.

The higher insects do not cast their skin again after the adult stage is reached, but this is not the case with the fish-moth. They continue to moult at intervals after they are mature, and they may live for several months before their ovaries are exhausted and death overtakes them.

The fish-moth is one of the many insects that have been widely spread over the earth by man's commerce. It is thought to have been originally a native of America but it was carried long ago to Europe and from there to other parts of the world. The climate of Africa suits it and it is very common here.

Bristle-Tails on the Veld

There are many relatives of the common fish-moth found on the veld; small, inconspicuous insects that are seldom noticed. A brown bristle-tail (*Machilis* species), with a sheen like bronze, may be seen running over rocks on the sea-shore and on the mountain-side. They are said to feed on lichens and vegetable debris, but very little is known about their habits and life history. Other species are common amid decaying vegetation. The scales from these insects are very beautiful objects when viewed under the microscope.

Another species of fish-moth, silvery white and only about an eighth of an inch long, is found in ants' nests. When a stone is turned over and an ants' nest exposed, several of the little insects may some-times be seen darting about among the ants. The ants take no notice of them at all. If, for some reason or other, the ants trek to a new home, the bristle-tails go with them. They are never found away from the ants and they do not seem to be able to live without the protection and support of their hosts.

From observations made in artificial nests, it seems that they are uninvited guests and live by robbing the ants. As is well known, the worker ants carry food back to the nest in their crops: they do not, as a rule, store any food in their nests. An ant returning with a full crop will stop and feed any of its fellows that happen to be hungry. The two ants put their mouths together and the one with the full crop regurgitates a drop of liquid which is eagerly lapped up by the other. While this is going on a fish-moth that also happens to be hungry will run up and steal some of the food as it is being passed from one ant to the other. Little beyond this is known about the relationship between the ants and their strange guests.

Several different species of bristle-tails are found as guests in termite nests in Africa, but practically nothing is known about their ways or their life histories.

Other Primitive Insects

Many tiny, insignificant insects that are seldom noticed belong to the sub-class *Apterygota*. Tiny, white, soft-bodied insects, the largest not more than one twelfth of an inch long, may be found under stones, amid damp moss and under the bark of trees. These are known to science as *Protura* and are regarded by many entomologists as the most primitive of all insects because they have no antennae and their abdomen consists of twelve segments, a number larger than that found in any other insects.

Campodea is a small white, delicate insect that looks something like a tiny centipede as it wriggles through the damp soil in which it lives. *Japyx* is also very small, white or brown, smooth-bodied and with a pair of pincers on its tail that make it look like a miniature earwig. It is found amid decaying vegetation and is probably predacious, feeding on other creatures as small as or smaller than itself.

The spring-tails (*Collembola*) are small, active insects that may be very abundant at certain seasons of the year in localities that suit them. Some are white or yellow, but most are dark coloured, and they can jump very well, like fleas. But they do not use their legs

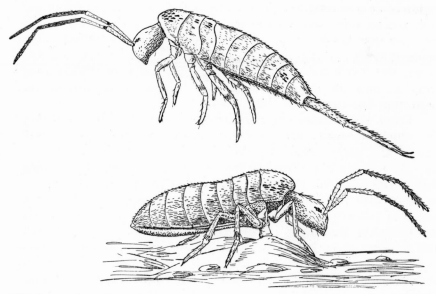

FIG. 2—A spring-tail *Neophorella dubia* that is common amid decaying vegetation. It is greyish yellow and about one eighth of an inch long.

in leaping.   As their name implies, they carry a spring in their tail —a forked appendage that is carried bent forward under the body and reaches almost as far forward as the head.   When the insect wishes to jump it jerks its tail downwards and backwards and this strikes the surface on which it is resting and propels it up and forward. The leaps seem to be haphazard and not aimed in any direction: the spring-tail simply jumps until it lands in a spot that suits it.   On the underside of the abdomen, near the front, there is a short tube or sucker by means of which the insect can fix itself in position when it is tired of jumping.

   Spring-tails may be found in almost any damp situation, in loose earth, among dead leaves, under stones and bark, on the surface of a stagnant pool.   Some species are even found on snow on the tops of mountains.   Most of them seem to feed on dead, decaying vegetation but some gnaw at the tissues of living plants and may do a little damage by thus exposing the plants to the attacks of fungi. Several species live in ants' nests and termite mounds;   these are always blind and they have lost the power of leaping.

CLASSIFICATION

SUB-CLASS APTERYGOTA

   Primitive wingless insects widely distributed over the world.   About 1,500 species known.   No metamorphosis.

ORDER 1: *THYSANURA*—Bristle-tails

   This order includes the well-known fish-moths.   Abdomen with eleven segments. Three many-jointed appendages on the hind end of the body, or, more rarely, a pair of unjointed forceps.   Tracheae (air-tubes) present.

ORDER 2: *PROTURA*

   Minute insects, without eyes or antennae.   Abdomen with twelve segments.   Tracheae may be present or absent.

ORDER 3: *COLLEMBOLA*—Spring-tails

   Small insects with an adhesive ventral tube on first segment of abdomen and a forked springing organ.   Antennae usually with only four joints and abdomen with six segments only.   No tracheae as a rule.

PLATE 1

(b) THE COMMON FISH MOTH. *Lepisma saccharina*, found in houses and widely spread over the world. About four times natural size.

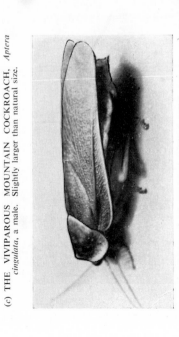

(d) THE VIVIPAROUS MOUNTAIN COCKROACH, *Aptera cingulata*, a female. Natural size.

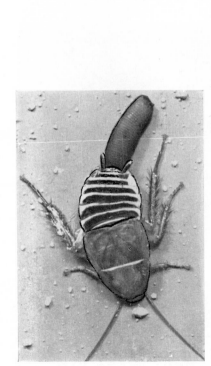

(a) THE SHORT-WINGED MOUNTAIN COCKROACH, *Temnopteryx phalerata*, a female carrying her purse of eggs. About twice natural size.

(c) THE VIVIPAROUS MOUNTAIN COCKROACH, *Aptera cingulata*, a male. Slightly larger than natural size.

PLATE 2

(*a*) THE GREY PRAYING MANTIS, *Epitenodera capitata*. Slightly larger than natural size.

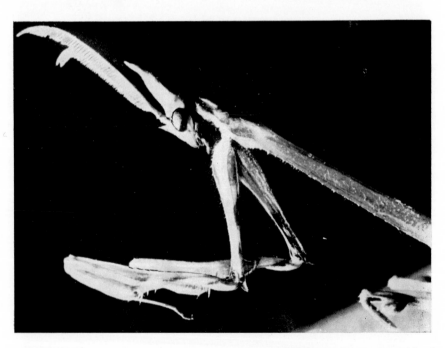

(*b*) The head and elongated first segment of a praying mantis, *Empusa guttula;* note also the elongated basal joint of the front leg that gives the insect its long reach forward when catching its prey. The specimen is a male, as shown by the plumed antennae. Enlarged.

PLATE 3

(a) Egg-masses of four different species of Praying Mantis. These consist of material extruded by the females when laying their eggs which hardens in the air. Natural size.

(b) A young Praying Mantis, *Empusa guttula*, showing the manner in which it carries its abdomen curled up. Enlarged.

PLATE 4

(a) A GREEN PRAYING MANTIS, *Miomantis semialata*, female, well concealed amid the green foliage. Slightly larger than natural size.

(b) THE BROWN LOCUST, *Locustana pardalina*, female in the swarm phase. Nearly twice natural size.

PLATE 5

(a) Eggs of the Green Stick Insect greatly enlarged shown with a match head for comparison

(b) THE GREEN STICK IN-
SECT, *Macynia labiata*, male.
About natural size.

(c) THE GREEN STICK IN-
SECT, *Macynia labiata*, female.
About natural size.

PLATE 6

(a) THE GREEN BLADDER GRASSHOPPER, *Bulla unicolor*, male with inflated abdomen, natural size

(b) THE GREEN BLADDER GRASSHOPPER, *Bulla unicolor*, an immature specimen that has just cast its skin

(c) THE GREEN BLADDER GRASSHOPPER, female with vestigial wings

(d) THE STINKING GRASSHOPPER. *Phymateus morbillosus*, an immature female, natural size

CHAPTER II

COCKROACHES, GRASSHOPPERS AND THEIR KIN

The Orthoptera

We now come to the second and much larger of the two sub-classes, the *Pterygota*, the winged insects or insects that have descended from winged ancestors. The lowest group of these are placed in an order known as the *Orthoptera*, (the "straight-winged" insects) and they include cockroaches, praying mantes ("hottentot gods"), stick insects, locusts and short-horned grasshoppers, long-horned grasshoppers, and crickets.

Cockroaches

There are about twelve hundred different species of cockroaches known in the world. Of these, five have become cosmopolitan, spread

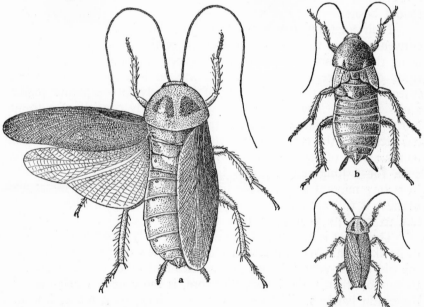

FIG. 3—Domestic Cockroaches: a. The American Cockroach, *Periplaneta americana;* b. The Oriental Cockroach, *Blatta orientalis;* c. The German Cockroach, *Blatella germanica.*

far and wide by man's shipping and commerce. The largest of the five, the American cockroach, *Periplaneta americana*, is about one and a quarter inches long, dark brown in colour and both males and females have wings. This species is very common indeed in the coastal areas of Africa but is less abundant inland. It is found in sewers, kitchens, bakeries and similar places and is thought by some scientists to be a possible agent in the spread of poliomyelitis because of its insanitary habits.

The commonest cockroach in dwellings inland is the smaller German cockroach, *Blatella germanica*, which is only about half an inch long, pale brown in colour and with two dark stripes on the thorax. The well-known and heartily disliked "blackbeetle" in Britain is the Oriental cockroach, *Blatta orientalis;* this is also found in Africa but it does not seem to be as common here as the two first mentioned. It is about three-quarters of an inch long, dark brown in colour and the male has short wings that reach only half-way back along its abdomen, whilst the female is wingless.

Every student of zoology becomes intimately acquainted with the cockroach because it is one of the "types" he has to study. These insects are readily obtainable, they are easily kept in captivity and they are suitable for dissection and for experimentation. They are omnivorous and will eat almost anything that is edible, from bread to old boots.

Their anatomy has been studied in the closest detail and it is convenient here to give a brief account of the structure of an insect, using the common cockroach as our type. The body is divided into three distinct regions, the head, thorax and abdomen; the name, insect, refers to this cutting up of the body into separate regions and segments. The outer covering of the body consists of a tough, horny substance known as chitin (pronounced ki-tin) which is related chemically to the cartilage of vertebrates and which is very resistant to the action of acids and alkalis: it can be boiled in strong caustic soda for a long time without being harmed, although it dissolves in strong mineral acids. This forms the skeleton of the insect and, because it will not stretch to any extent, is the reason why the insect has to cast its skin from time to time.

The insect is doomed to remain small partly because of the nature of its skeleton. When it casts its skin, the new coat of chitin beneath the old one is very soft and the muscles and other organs have little to support them; the insect, therefore, is more or less helpless until the chitin hardens. If an insect were as large as a horse, it would flop down in a shapeless heap when it moulted because of the softness of its skeleton and the weight of its body. The other reason why the largest of insects are only a few inches long is because of the nature of their breathing organs.

FIG. 4 : The anatomy of the cockroach: a. The internal organs in position; b. The alimentary canal, showing the salivary glands, the crop, the gizzard, the caeca, the stomach, the Malpighian tubes, the intestine and the rectum, in the order given from top to bottom; c. The respiratory system, showing the main tracheae: the finer branches and capillary tubes are not shown; d. The heart, with the muscles that cause it to expand and contract; e. The reproductive organs of the female, showing the egg-tubes on each side and the colleterial glands; f. The reproductive organs of the male, showing the testes and the mushroom gland, also the major part of the central nervous system is shown lying along the ventral side.

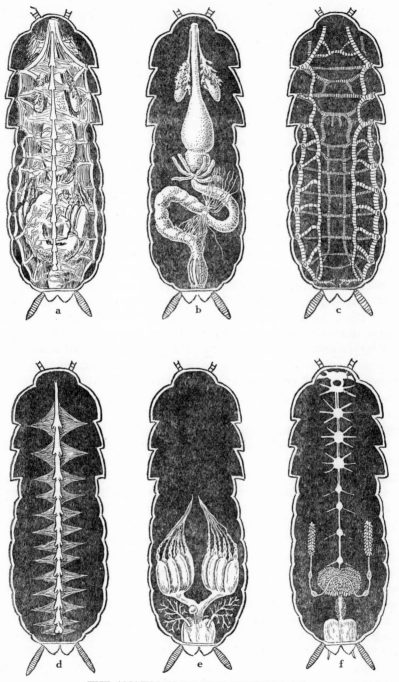

THE ANATOMY OF THE COCKROACH

If you kill a cockroach by dropping it into boiling water and then pin it on a piece of cork and remove the skin from the upper surface of its body by cutting round the edge with a pair of fine-pointed scissors, the first thing you will notice about its internal anatomy is a number of silvery threads branching in all directions through the tissues. These are the tracheae, the breathing tubes by means of which air is carried directly to all parts of its body. The blood of the insect does not play any part in its respiration, as it does in the case of vertebrates. The tracheae appear to be silvery because of the air that fills them.

The cockroach, like most other insects, has ten small round openings along each side of its body. These are called spiracles and they can be opened or closed according to the need of the insect for more or less air. The air is drawn in and out through the spiracles mainly by a pumping action of the abdomen that can be clearly seen in many insects, but the supply in the fine capillary tubes that form the ultimate branches of the tracheae is renewed by diffusion. The renewal of a gas through diffusion is rapid enough in narrow tubes over very short distances but is slow in long capillary tubes. Respiration by means of tracheae therefore is efficient in small insects, but such an air-supply would be inadequate for the needs of a larger animal. Thus we find that the longest of all insects, such as certain stick insects found in Africa, which measure ten inches in length, are still very slender so that the capillaries of the respiratory system are not unduly long. An insect, let us say ten inches long and five inches broad, could not breathe properly; it would need something similar to the lungs and blood system of a vertebrate.

The heart of the insect is situated along its back, just beneath the skin. It consists of a tube, closed at the hind end and open in front near the head. The blood enters the heart through small openings along each side, thirteen in the case of the cockroach, but fewer in most other insects. The openings have valves that prevent the flow of the blood out of the heart so that, when the tube expands, blood is drawn into it and then, when it contracts, the valves close and the blood is driven forwards and out through the opening in front. There are no blood vessels apart from the heart: the blood bathes all the tissues of the body and the heart is simply an organ to keep it in movement. The pulsation of the insect's heart can easily be seen if a large smooth caterpillar is examined. A dark line will be seen along the back, which is the heart showing through the translucent skin, and waves of expansion and contraction can be seen passing from back to front along this line. If the pulsations are timed they will be found to be much more rapid in warm weather than when it is cold, and this is one reason why insects are sluggish at low temperatures. In some insects the heart can reverse its action, pumping the blood forward for a number of beats and then driving it backwards for a time; it is not known how or why this reversal of the flow is brought about. The principal function of the blood is to carry food to all parts of the body and to remove waste products.

The digestive canal of the cockroach consists of an oesophagus that leads from the mouth and expands into a large crop at its hind end. The food is stored and softened in the crop by the salivary secretions. From the crop it passes into the gizzard, a small muscular organ lined with thick chitin and armed with teeth on the inner surface. Here the food is ground into fine particles, after which it passes into the tubular stomach where digestion is completed and the digested food is absorbed by the blood. At the front end of the stomach there are eight short tubes, or caeca, which are simply prolongations of the stomach to increase the surface for digestion and absorption.

At the rear end of the stomach there are a number of fine tubes known as Malpighian tubes, after Malpighi, the Italian scientist who first described them. These act as the kidneys of the insect and through them waste products are removed from the blood and passed into the hind intestine. The hind intestine conveys the indigestible remnants of the food and the excretion of the Malpighian tubes from the stomach to the rectum and thence to the exterior. The rectum has six rectal glands in its walls, the function of which is not known, but they may have something to do with the removal of water from the excrement.

The reproductive organs of the female cockroach consist of eight egg-tubes on each side. These join together at the hind end to form the right and left oviducts which, in their turn, join to form the vagina. An egg-tube consists of a row of eggs, one behind the other, the oldest and largest of the eggs being the one nearest the oviduct; and the eggs mature and grow as they pass along the egg-tube so that an egg is ripe and ready for laying by the time it reaches the oviduct. As the cockroach has sixteen egg-tubes all together, sixteen eggs mature at a time.

There are a pair of glands that open into the vagina, consisting of fine, white, branching tubes. These are known as the colleterial glands and they produce the material that forms the egg-case which encloses and protects the eggs when they are laid.

The male cockroach has a pair of small white testes. From these, slender tubes, one on each side, convey the sperms to the wider, central tube called the ejaculatory duct, which leads to the exterior. Attached to the front end of the ejaculatory duct there is a large, tubular gland, sometimes called the mushroom gland because of its shape. The function of this gland is not known but it is probable that the secretion from it serves as a fluid in which the male cells can live in a vigorous condition and in which they can be conveyed to the female when copulation takes place.

The central nervous system of insects lies along the ventral surface, beneath the alimentary canal. In the head, just above the oesophagus, there is a small brain that gives off nerves to the eyes and antennae. Below the oesophagus there is another mass of nerve tissue, called the suboesophageal ganglion, that gives off nerves to the mouthparts. These two are connected by nerve cords that run round each side of the oesophagus. From the oesophagus a double nerve cord runs back through the thorax and abdomen. There are three swellings on this cord in the thorax, one for each segment, known as the thoracic ganglia, and nerves are given off from them to the legs and wings. There are six ganglia in the abdomen from which nerves go to the various abdominal organs.

The muscles of an insect are far too complex to be described here: there are about two thousand in a caterpillar, and more in a winged insect. The strength of insects is remarkable. It has been shown that a small insect can lift something like twenty-five times its own weight, whereas many men could not lift their own weight. The efficiency of the insect's muscles is related to their small size: if an insect were as large as a horse it would not be any stronger than the latter, if as strong.

The head of the cockroach bears the antennae, eyes and mouthparts. The antennae are regarded as the principal olfactory organs, but many insects can smell with other parts of the body as well—for example, some butterflies can detect odours with their feet. There are many minute pits and sensory hairs on the antennae which are apparently delicate organs of smell and touch.

The mouthparts (Fig. 5) consist of an upper lip, or labrum, a lower lip, or labium, and two pairs of jaws between them, the hard jaws or mandibles, and the soft jaws, or maxillae. The jaws open sideways, and not up and down as do those of vertebrates.

The cockroach has a pair of compound eyes which, if examined under the microscope, are seen to consist of several hundred hexagonal facets so that the cornea, or outer covering of the eye, looks like a piece of honeycomb. Each facet marks the position of a separate lens and the number varies greatly with different insects: there are two to three thousand in each eye in the case of the cockroach, twenty thousand or more in some dragon-flies and only a dozen or so in certain ants. It is difficult to understand exactly what or how an insect sees with eyes so very different from our own. The opinion generally accepted to-day is that insects have what is known as mosaic vision: each facet of the eye receives a small portion of the picture so that the image that reaches the insect's brain is something like

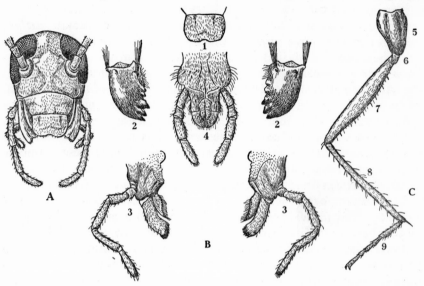

FIG. 5—The American Cockroach, *Periplaneta americana:* a. Front view of head; b. The mouthparts, 1—the labrum or upper lip.   2—the mandibles.   3—the maxillae or second pair of jaws.   4—the labium or lower lip;   c. The hind leg, 5—coxa, 6—trochanter. 7—femur 8—tibia.   9—tarsus.

a stained-glass window.   Because of the shape of the eyes and because of the lack of an efficient means of focusing, insects must be short-sighted, but their eyes are eminently suited to detect movements, even of objects a little distance away, because the image of the moving object shifts from facet to facet in the eyes.   Insects cannot close their eyes; it is, therefore, difficult to know whether or not they sleep in the same manner as we do.   It is very likely that they do, however, although they are much more easily aroused because of their wide-open eyes.

Many insects have simple eyes in addition to the compound eyes, but these are lacking in the cockroach.   The simple eyes, generally three in number on top of the head of the adult, each have one lens only and they are very small and cannot be very efficient organs of vision.   It has been suggested that the light falling on them serves as a stimulus to the compound eyes and other organs of the body.

The thorax consists of three segments and each bears a pair of legs.   Each leg consists of five parts: the coxa, a short, stout joint joining the leg to the body; the trochanter, a small joint connecting the coxa and the thigh, or femur; the shank or tibia follows the femur;

then comes the foot, or tarsus, consisting of five joints and ending in a pair of claws. The cockroach, like most winged insects, has two pairs of wings, on the second and third segments of the thorax. The first segment of the thorax never bears wings. The first pair of wings are more or less stiff and leathery, while the larger second pair are thin and membranous and are the principal organs of flight.

The abdomen consists of ten segments and at the hind end there are a pair of sixteen-jointed tail feelers, known as cerci.

And now, having dealt briefly with the anatomy of the cockroach, let us return to its life history. The female lays her eggs in a curious brown, leathery case that looks very much like a tiny purse with a zip-fastener along one edge. The egg-case is divided longitudinally by a thin membrane into two chambers. Within each of these chambers there is a row of cylindrical pockets, each containing a cigar-shaped egg, generally sixteen in number, eight along each side of the purse.

This striking egg-case is not the product of the female's skill and volition. It is formed inside her body and the eggs pass into it, two by two, each into its own receptacle, as the case is slowly formed and extruded. Finally, when the batch of eggs is complete, the purse-like case sticks out at the rear end of the cockroach and she carries it about with her for some time.

Sooner or later, however, she drops the case in some hiding place and leaves her young to fend further for themselves. When the eggs hatch the purse splits open along one edge and the young cockroaches struggle out, feeble and white, but otherwise very much like their parents. Soon their skin hardens and darkens and they are able to run about and forage for themselves. They moult six or seven times in the course of their life and reach full size in about a year.

African Cockroaches

Besides the cosmopolitan species that are household pests, there are a large number of "wild" cockroaches native to this country. You find them when you tear the bark off trees or fallen logs, beneath stones, amid decaying vegetation, in hollow stems and so on. They are easily recognised for what they are because they are nearly all brown or black, have flattened bodies and the head is bent down under the thorax so that it is scarcely visible from above.

The large brown mountain cockroach, *Aptera cingulata*, is particularly interesting. The female is of a rich shining brown colour. Flat on the underside but rounded and obese above, she is about an inch and a half long when fully grown, and has no wings. She is nocturnal, hiding during the day and creeping forth to hunt for food at night. It is not known what she feeds on. I have kept these insects

in captivity but they have consistently refused to eat the dainty tit-bits I offered them, such as slices of apple, carrot, banana, bits of meat, bread, and so on. On the veld I have seen them feeding on the berries of the parasitic plant, *Cuscuta*, so they are apparently vegetarian. They may eat decaying leaves and dead insects.

If a female is picked up she makes a squeaking sound by rubbing the roughened edge of one segment of her body against the surface of the segment behind. The male is winged, of slender build and quite different in appearance from his mate, looking very much like the American cockroach. Like the rest of their kind, they can produce an unpleasant smell if disturbed, by giving off a fluid from glands on the back.

The female of this species does not lay eggs, but retains them inside her body until they hatch. Then she deposits the living young, some eighteen to two dozen of them in a batch. At first all the little ones are white but they soon turn black and they remain with their mother for a time, like chicks with a hen. During late summer and early winter family parties of these insects may sometimes be found, beneath loose bark, under stones and amid dead leaves. Each party consists of a number of black young ones, together with one, two or more adult females and perhaps a winged male or two. Later on they scatter and live more or less solitary lives until the next breeding season—that is, if they survive for more than one season, although it is not known whether or not they do. We still have a great deal to learn about these interesting insects.

About twelve hundred different species of cockroaches are known in the world. They are insects of ancient lineage, for fossil cockroaches, similar in form to those we know to-day, have been found in rocks of the Carboniferous era.

Praying Mantes

Everybody is familiar with the interesting insects known as praying mantes, or hottentot gods. They are abundant in Africa and many are striking in form and colour. This large family is composed of insects that are all carnivorous and the members of it are easily recognised by the peculiar form of the front legs, which are adapted for seizing and holding their prey.

The slender, rather delicate-looking insect shown in the photograph is the common grey mantis. This particular specimen was kept as a pet for two months before she died and during that period she devoured fifteen grasshoppers nearly as big as herself, twenty-four flies and two males of her own kind. She took very little exercise to justify her gluttony, for she remained motionless,

C

apparently quite content, clinging to the side of her roomy cage of wire gauze, in an attitude of dreamy contemplation, until an insect was put in the enclosure with her.

Her small, triangular head, with the two bulging compound eyes and the three simple eyes between them, swung round on her flexible neck as she watched the movements of her victim. This ability to turn its head, to look over its shoulder, as it were, is a curious characteristic of all praying mantes. The great majority of insects have short, stiff necks and they cannot twist the head round to look in another direction: they have to move the whole body. But the praying mantis can cock its head in an engagingly pert and intelligent-looking manner.

Slowly she stalks her prey, moving cautiously with a slight swaying motion on her four hind legs, until she is close enough for those deadly front legs to make a lightning grab at the insect. Once grasped, the victim has no chance to escape from those legs armed with double rows of spikes, and the mantis proceeds at once to nibble at it with her small jaws, reducing it to a pulp and swallowing it, except for the tough legs and wings, in an amazingly short time.

The name *mantis* is a Greek word meaning a prophet or soothsayer and was given to the insect because of its deceptive, meek appearance, with those front legs lifted as though in an attitude of prayer when they are at rest. The South African name, hottentot god, seems to have been given for a similar reason.

If you examine a praying mantis you will see that the front part of its body, between its head and the base of its wings, is long and slender. The first pair of legs are articulated to the front of this elongated segment and the first joint of the legs, the coxa, is much longer than is the case with other insects. All this gives the mantis a very long reach so that those grappling irons, toothed like a saw, can strike swiftly and surely at the unsuspecting victim some distance in front.

Anybody who has caught hold of a praying mantis will know how it claws at the fingers of the captor with those long front legs, but it is too weak to do any damage to the human skin. One gets the impression that it is a fearless, impudent little creature. It certainly does not hesitate to attack insects as big as itself and it will tackle spiders, honey bees and other armed foes if they come its way.

As a result of her gargantuan meals the mantis in the photograph laid five lots of eggs before she was spent—then she became lame, refused to feed any more and finally gave up the ghost. The female mantis has special glands inside her body which consist of a number of twisted tubes that secrete a gummy liquid something like the silk produced by silkworms. When she is about to lay her eggs, she pours out the liquid from her genital opening and whips it into a foam with the tip of her tail. By some means or other she shapes the foamy mass, with only the tip of her abdomen and the two cerci on her tail to serve as tools.

Down the middle of the mass, before it hardens, she forms a series of neat little receptacles in which she deposits her eggs, side by side, with the head end uppermost. Not only is each of the sixty or so eggs enclosed in its separate compartment, but there is a valve at the top of each receptacle that affords an easy mode of exit for the young one when it hatches but which prevents the entry of enemies from outside. These valvular openings can be seen in the photograph in a double row along the middle of the top of the egg-mass.

This is an extraordinary product for an insect, but when it is remembered that the work is performed in the dark, with a foamy material that hardens quickly on contact with the air, and that she has as instruments only the tip of her tail and her hind legs, then the amazing nature of her work becomes apparent. If you put a match to the egg-mass you will find that it burns with a smell like that given off by burning silk.

The hatching of the eggs presents another curious feature of the mantis's life history. When the little ones emerge from the eggs, after about a month, each one is enclosed in a tight-fitting membrane so that it looks like a tiny fish without any fins. It wriggles its way up out of the cell, passing easily through the door at the top that opens only outwards, and stopping when its body projects about half-way out of the opening. There it remains motionless for a time and the blood is now pumped into its head so that it swells and pulsates as though it is about to burst, but it is only the membrane that splits as a result of the pressure, and the little creature struggles out of the hole, leaving its cast skin behind it. Now it can be seen as a miniature mantis, like its parents, only much smaller, of course, and without wings. The little ones scatter soon after hatching, each to make its own way in the world.

The newly-hatched young are black and each carries its abdomen curled up over its back, a peculiar custom that seems to be common to all young mantes, but it is not known why they adopt this posture. The process of hatching is more complicated in the case of some species of mantes because the young, whilst still enclosed in their swaddling membrane, drop from the exit-holes in the egg-case and hang suspended for some time by silken threads before moulting and dropping to the ground.

The above account applies in general to all mantes, of which there are a large number of different species found in Africa. Most of them resemble their surroundings in a remarkable manner and they offer excellent examples of what is known as protective resemblance. The large green mantis (*Sphodromantis gastrica*), for example, is common and is always found on bushes and trees where the green foliage hides it. Its food consists chiefly of caterpillars and it must be regarded as a beneficial insect. The common brown mantis (*Tarachodes perloides*), on the other hand, is dull brown, speckled with darker brown, and is always found on the trunks and branches of trees where its colouring and markings match perfectly those of the bark.

Some of them are marked and coloured in such a way that they may easily be mistaken for flowers as they rest on a plant. The yellow, green and red mantis, *Harpagomantis tricolor*, is green and yellow with a dark red patch on the hind wings. The projecting points on the sides of its abdomen and its colours make this insect resemble the flowers among which it likes to rest and hunt. Some mantes have a quaint appearance because of the flattened areas on their limbs and the strange projections on their bodies. The mantes known as *Empusa* species are of this type, with a conical projection on the front of the head that looks something like a miniature bishop's mitre, with knobs and projections on the legs and abdomen that give it the appearance of a piece of gnarled bark, and with striking plumed antennae in the males.

The males are in every case more slender and somewhat smaller than the females and the reprehensible habit of mate-eating seems to be prevalent among female mantes. The gruesome creatures even chew off the heads of the males while copulation is in progress.

Stick Insects and Leaf Insects

The members of this family are among the most helpless of the Orthoptera: most of them cannot fly and they cannot jump; they can only creep about slowly on the plants upon which they feed. As they are very edible they are eagerly sought for by birds and other insect-eaters and their sole means of protection from their many enemies is their close resemblance to their surroundings, which makes them difficult to find.

The stick insects, as their name implies, closely resemble sticks or grass stems when at rest and, when disturbed, they remain stiff and motionless, "shamming dead". It requires a keen eye to detect them amid the foliage. The insects do not voluntarily feign death: they are quite incapable of reasoning, as we would do, that they are hard to see as long as they remain quite still. Involuntarily and instinctively they fall into a cataleptic state when disturbed, and remain with body rigid and the long front legs held stiffly out in front for some time, until the fit passes off and they can creep about once more.

Some of the largest stick insects in Africa may reach a length of eleven inches and they are among the longest of all insects, but they are not very bulky because their bodies are slender. Much of their length is due to the elongation of the middle segments of the thorax. Some species have wings but in all cases the first pair is small and often reduced to useless scales. The second pair serves for flight. All are vegetarians and usually the male is smaller and more slimly built than the female.

The leaf insects have broad, flattened bodies and curious membranous expansions on their legs. Usually the female has the first pair of wings large and flattened, to add to her leaf-like appearance, but the second pair of wings is small and vestigial and she cannot fly. The male, on the other hand, has a small first pair of wings and a large second pair and he can fly quite well. Nearly all the leaf insects are found in the tropical regions of the Far East.

The common green stick insect of the Cape (*Macynia labiata*) may be taken as our example of this group. The fully grown female is about two and a half inches long and the male is a little shorter and slighter in build. Both are green to match the colour of the foliage amid which they live and both have pink mouthparts and a pink tip to the tail when mature. The male has a pair of claspers on the end of the abdomen; the abdomen of the female ends in a blunt point.

These insects rest motionless on their food-plant throughout the day, but are active and feed during the night. During the hours of daylight they remain still and rigid for hours at a time looking like a piece of green, leafless twig. What looks like a pair of feelers on the front of the head is really the first pair of legs: the antennae are comparatively short and inconspicuous.

The egg-laying starts in late spring, at the end of October, and goes on until January, after which the spent insects die. It is as careless and casual an egg-laying as it is possible to find among insects. Most female insects show remarkable instincts and labour prodigiously to provide for their offspring, but the female stick insect simply drops her eggs light-heartedly behind her, one at a time, letting them fall unheeded to the ground which may be far below her. Her maternal duties are very light indeed and she hardly seems to be aware that she is laying an egg as she goes on nibbling at a leaf.

Each female seems to lay at the rate of about one egg every twenty-four hours and, as the oviposition extends over three months or longer, she may lay one hundred eggs before her ovaries are exhausted. The egg is a remarkable object and looks exactly like a hard, shiny green seed. It is about the size of a cabbage seed and has a beautiful ornamental white cap at one end which is pushed off by the young insect when it hatches. Down one side of the egg there is a white mark, like the mark you see on a pea or bean where the stalk held it in place inside the pod. Most people, if shown some of these eggs, would unhesitatingly declare them to be seeds.

The eggs lie on the ground all through the hot summer months, sheltered perhaps by the bush on which the mother lived, or by dead leaves. They take six months to hatch, the young emerging in the following autumn, late in April and during May. The baby stick insect is exactly like its parents, a long-legged green thread about half an inch long. As its parents did before it, it rests motionless during the day and feeds at night on the tender young leaves brought out by the autumn rains.

After feeding and growing for a few days, its tough outer skin will not stretch any more and the little creature rests and prepares for the difficult and trying process of moulting. It hangs, head downwards, clinging by its four hind legs. A split appears in the skin along its back, just behind the head, and slowly and laboriously the insect pulls itself out of its old skin, emerging clad in a new suit a size larger than the one it discards.

It is not only the outer skin that is cast off, but also the lining of the front and hind parts of its alimentary canal, of its main tracheae and of certain glands. If you watch a stick insect whilst it is moulting (and they are easy to keep in captivity), you will see two crystal globules of liquid at the bases of its front legs. This is the lubricating fluid produced by special glands to aid in the difficult task of extracting itself from its old skin. The little creature rests for a while beside its cast-off skin and then, before moving off, it frugally eats the empty husk. It has to moult in this way five or six times before it is fully grown and adult.

Sometimes in the course of its perambulations, the stick insect loses a limb—maybe as the result of an unsuccessful attack by an enemy. This is not a serious matter if the insect is still immature because a new limb grows out to replace the lost one, appearing as a stump at the next moult and rapidly increasing in size with the succeeding moults. If the insect is adult when it loses a leg it cannot grow a new one because it does not cast its skin again.

Ants, frogs, lizards and birds are among the many enemies. The red-winged starling is a particularly formidable foe because this bird feeds its young mainly on stick insects and it destroys them in large numbers. A fly that looks like a small, hairy house-fly (*Tachinid*) lays its eggs on stick insects and the grubs burrow into the living victims and devour them.

Parthenogenesis is known to occur among some stick insects. Parthenogenesis means "virgin birth" and is the name applied to cases where unfertilised eggs develop and hatch in the normal way. It occurs among many insects, such as bees, aphides and some moths. The males of some species of stick insects are very rare and, with these species, parthenogenesis must be common.

Stick insects and leaf insects belong to the family of the Orthoptera called *Phasmidae*, from the Greek word meaning a ghost.

Locusts and Short-Horned Grasshoppers

There is a tendency in Africa to speak of any large member of the grasshopper family as a "locust", whilst the smaller species are called

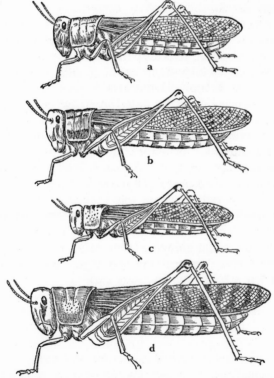

FIG. 6—The four species of Locusts found in Africa: a. The Brown Locust, *Locustana pardalina;* b. The Desert Locust, *Schistocerca gregaria;* c. The Migratory Tropical Locust, *Locusta migratoria;* d. The Red Locust, *Nomadacris septemfasciata.* All approximately natural size.

"grasshoppers". Strictly speaking, the term locust should be applied only to those grasshoppers that gather together in swarms and migrate from place to place. Using the name in this sense, there are fewer than a dozen species of locusts in the whole world.

The brown locust, *Locustana pardalina*, is the most important species found in South Africa. Its permanent home and natural breeding grounds are mostly within the borders of the Union, but when it is abundant and migrating in swarms it often spreads into South-West Africa, Bechuanaland and Southern Rhodesia.

The red locust, *Nomadacris septemfasciata*, is the well-known pest of tropical Africa including Portuguese East Africa, both the Rhodesias, Angola, the Belgian Congo, Nyasaland, Tanganyika, Kenya, Uganda, Abyssinia and Southern Sudan. Its permanent home is in the region of Lakes Tanganyika and Rukwa, but when it is swarming it may extend its range as far as the Sahara Desert in the north and Natal and the eastern Cape Province in the south.

The desert locust, *Schistocerca gregaria*, is the insect referred to in the Bible as one of the plagues of Egypt and to this day it occurs in vast swarms and may do great damage to crops in north and east Africa and Asia Minor. It is also found in South Africa but only forms comparatively small swarms in the Kalahari after exceptionally good rains, and these soon disappear.

The fourth species of locust found in Africa is that known as the tropical migratory locust, *Locusta migratoria*. Its headquarters are in North Africa and it frequently gives trouble in Nigeria, the Sudan, Kenya and Tanganyika. Scattered individuals of this species may be found in some parts of South Africa and occasional swarms may invade South-West Africa and the north-west Cape.

Let us take the red locust as our example. It is the largest of them all, the adult reaching a length of three inches from the front of the head to the tips of the folded wings. The full-grown winged insect lives for about nine months, from April to January, and during this period its colour changes considerably. At first it is greyish brown, but a few weeks later its body turns to a reddish brown, the front wings have distinct brown stripes on them and the hind wings are red at the base. Later still, in December and January, when the eggs are being laid, the colour changes to a greenish or pinkish yellow.

Red locusts, when they are numerous and overcrowded in their permanent home, form huge swarms which migrate in all directions. There have been reports of swarms that were twenty to forty miles in length and two to five miles wide when the insects were in flight. As a rule, the swarms fly during the daytime, with pauses for rest and feeding, and they sleep at night in dense clusters on trees and bushes. The hungry hordes may travel for about eight months in

this way, searching for feeding grounds and suitable climatic conditions, and they may cover hundreds of miles.

In November or December the egg-laying begins. This takes place at night and the females deposit their eggs in the ground. Each female that is ready to lay her eggs rests on the ground and forces the tip of her abdomen, armed with four, hard, horny points, to a depth of two or three inches into the soil. She deposits a neat package of sixty to eighty eggs in the hole and then squirts a frothy liquid on top of them which hardens and forms a plug to the hole.

FIG. 7: A Red Locust female in the act of depositing her eggs in the ground. She can extend her abdomen to more than twice its normal length.

After the egg-laying is over the swarm moves on again, but about a fortnight later the females are ready to deposit more eggs and the process is repeated, probably several hundred miles from the spot where the first lot of eggs were laid. Each female may lay three or four packages of eggs before she dies, totalling an average of some two hundred eggs per female.

The eggs hatch in about a month. The newly-hatched hopper is greenish grey in colour and it wriggles its way up out of the ground, looking very much like a small worm at this stage. Within a minute or so of emerging it casts its skin, leaving this behind as a crumpled white speck at the mouth of the hole. Slowly the little insect's new skin hardens and the colour changes until by the time it is a few hours old, it is brown with black and yellow markings and it can hop about and feed.

The young hoppers gather together in swarms and, when they are a few days old, they begin to move off across the veld in their ceaseless search for food. They feed chiefly on plants of the grass family, including maize, wheat, sorghum and sugar cane, but they will also devour other kinds of plants if they cannot find sufficient grasses.

For a period of two or three months the young locusts must travel on foot as they have no wings. They grow rapidly and cast their skin six times during this period. Their colour varies but mostly they are handsome creatures with red, black and yellow markings. After the sixth moult they are adults, with four strong wings, and they are able to fly great distances during the eight or nine months they spend in this stage before death overtakes them.

D

The red locust, like all other members of the family, has many natural enemies. These include locust birds, such as the white stork and wattled starling, and kestrels, which follow the swarms and eat great numbers of the insects. The larvae of many different kinds of blister beetles and of certain kinds of flies destroy the eggs in the ground. Other kinds of flies are parasitic on the locusts themselves. There is a disease caused by a fungus which kills off enormous numbers of the locusts during warm, wet weather. The dying locusts creep up on grass stems and bushes and there they die. Their dead bodies may often be seen hanging on the stems and covered with the furry growth of the fungus. Finally, man himself must to-day be regarded as the most deadly of all the locusts' enemies because he now fights them in their breeding centres with very effective modern insecticides.

When the locusts are abundant and travelling over the country in swarms, their natural enemies also increase greatly in numbers because the insects provide them with an abundance of food. Steadily but surely the balance of nature is restored and the locust plague diminishes. The areas overrun by the swarms far from the natural breeding grounds are, for reasons that are not understood, unsuitable as a permanent home for the locusts and after a time they die out in the invaded areas.

But in the region of Lake Tanganyika and Lake Rukwa and Lake Tchad the red locusts do not die out. Their numbers may be so reduced that they are no longer overcrowded and they no longer form swarms, but they remain as solitary grasshoppers, scattered over the veld. Their habits change. They no longer move about from place to place and they differ in colour and markings from the locusts that flew in swarms. They are living in what is known as the solitary phase and the surrounding regions are, for a time, free from the plague.

Within a few years, however, conditions favourable for the locusts may return and they may begin to increase enormously in numbers, because good rains have brought forth abundant food and there are few natural enemies to keep them in check. As soon as their permanent home becomes overcrowded, the locusts enter upon what is known as the swarm phase. They begin to gather together in large numbers and soon they start migrating in all directions from their breeding centres—and so the trouble begins all over again.

It is now known that all locusts go through these two phases, the solitary and the swarm phase. During the years when there are no swarms travelling far and wide and causing great losses to farmers, the locusts are living as solitary grasshoppers in their restricted natural breeding grounds. Nowadays concentrated warfare is waged on them in their breeding centres in the attempt to keep down their numbers sufficiently to prevent them from entering upon the swarm phase. At Abercorn, for example, at the southern end of Lake Tanganyika, there is a research station with a number of entomologists stationed there whose job it is to keep constant watch on the permanent homes of the red locust in that region and to take steps to deal with any swarms that may begin to develop.

As an example of the short-horned grasshoppers that are not locusts we may take the common black and red grasshopper, *Phymateus morbillosus*, or *stink-sprinkaan*, as it is called in Afrikaans. This heavily built member of the family, red, yellow and black in colour, can scarcely hop and does not fly far. Its favourite food is plants of the milkweed family (Asclepiads) and it is therefore rather a misnomer to call it a grasshopper. Furthermore, it goes about in small bands when young and in this respect may seem to resemble the locusts, but the insects do not travel far and the bands may break up before the adult stage is reached.

The bright red head, thorax and legs, the purple, yellow-spotted wings and the yellow and purple abdomen of the adult make this one of the most striking and conspicuous of all our grasshopper tribe. It is an excellent example of what is known as warning coloration. Of sluggish habit and never attempting to hide itself, this insect could easily be caught by any toad, lizard or bird that desired to make a meal of it. But it has a decidedly unpleasant smell and an equally unpleasant flavour. A young and inexperienced insect-eater might be tempted to rush at and seize such an easily-caught victim, but it would quickly drop it because of the evil taste and it would learn to associate the nauseating smell and flavour with those bright colours. Hence the value of the warning colours to the insect: they induce such creatures as might be tempted to eat it to leave it severely alone.

This grasshopper is also protected by a frothy yellow liquid that oozes from openings situated near the base of the hind legs. This liquid is the insect's blood and it has the same distasteful properties as the rest of the body, but in greater degree. The froth is only given off if the grasshopper is roughly handled, and at the same time it ejects a drop of dark green fluid from its mouth—so it is little wonder that few, if any, animals will eat this insect.

Although these particular grasshoppers do not produce any sound, so far as I am aware, they, like the rest of the family, have well-developed ears, or tympanal organs, as they are called. These are not situated on the head but on the abdomen, just above the base of each hind leg. They are clearly visible to the naked eye if the wings are lifted, as circular depressions in the skin, about a tenth of an inch in diameter, with a tightly-stretched membranous ear-drum in each.

Most of the short-horned grasshoppers that chirrup do so by rubbing their hind legs against their wings. Each thigh has a row of tiny pegs on it which catch in the raised vein on the wing and cause it to vibrate. Only the males can do this: the females are quite silent or capable of producing only a very faint sound. But the front wings of the red and black grasshopper are comparatively soft and there is no prominent vein on them, nor are there any pegs on the hind thighs, so it is obvious that this particular grasshopper cannot produce sounds in the same manner as other members of the family.

Like other short-horned grasshoppers, the female *Phymateus* lays her eggs in the ground. She has the four hard, horny points on the tip of her abdomen that are the mark of the female in all this family— the male has a soft, rounded tip to his tail, without any points, because he does not need to do any digging. When she is ready to lay her eggs she presses the tip of her abdomen against the soil and by steady pressure and a slow turning movement she forces it into the ground. Her abdomen is more or less telescopic and she can elongate it to about one and a half times its normal length. When she has thrust her abdomen right into the soil, so that only her head, thorax, legs and wings are above the surface, she lays her large, yellow, cigar-shaped eggs at the bottom of the hole. Then, like the female locust, she emits a frothy fluid that binds the soil particles together and forms a case or pod enclosing the fifty or so eggs. Finally she scrapes a little soil into the top of the hole and the egg-laying is complete.

A week or so later the female may lay another batch of eggs, and so on until three or four egg-pods complete her contribution to the next generation. She may linger on for a time after this, more sluggish than ever and feeding very sparingly, but the cold and rain of the late autumn put an end to her existence.

An egg-pod is about an inch and a half long and half an inch thick and is buried two or three inches deep in the ground. The eggs are yellow at first but soon turn brown. They lie in the soil all through the winter and only hatch in the following spring, or early in the summer. Something like five or six months are spent in the egg state below the ground. The eggs begin to develop as soon as they are laid, but after a time development stops and there is a long dormant period, until development recommences in the spring and proceeds then without a check until the young hatch. This embryonic diapause, as it is called, is common among the short-horned grasshoppers. It is not due to a drop in temperature or, apparently, to any other external cause, for, if the eggs are put in an incubator and kept under favourable conditions, the pause in the development still occurs. It is a provision of nature to enable the eggs to pass unharmed through prolonged periods of unfavourable weather conditions.

The eggs are placed head-end downwards when they are laid in the soil, but as development proceeds, a remarkable change takes place. The embryo inside the egg slowly creeps round, as it were, until its head is uppermost, in the best position for hatching. This slow movement inside the egg-shell can be watched if some egg-pods are kept on damp soil in a box and if the eggs are examined from time to time. The black eyes of the embryo are visible through the thin, translucent covering of the egg and they can be seen to move slowly from the lower end on one side to the upper end on the other.

When the embryo is fully formed and ready to emerge, a swelling appears in the back of its neck, in the joint between the head and the thorax. This swelling throbs and causes the egg-shell to burst to allow the young grasshopper to wriggle its way out.

It is still enclosed in a thin membranous covering, like the newly-hatched locust, and it has to struggle up through the frothy plug and then through the soil until it reaches the surface. The first youngster has the hardest task as the others usually follow the route made by the first one. The membranous coat is shed as soon as the little insect reaches the outer air and the cast-off membrane shrivels up at once. The tiny white objects strewn around the hole after the young have emerged are their discarded first coats, intended only to protect them during their struggle to freedom. The skin of the larva soon hardens and turns black and the larva is then ready to move off and feed in company with the rest of the family. It moults six times in the course of its growth and is fully grown when about three months old.

Another very interesting group of short-horned grasshoppers, found only in Africa, are the bladder-grasshoppers, *Pneumorinae*. They are fairly common in some parts of the country but are much less numerous than they once were because of the interminable veld fires that are helping to turn Africa into a desert. The young stages and the females cannot fly and so are wiped out when a fire rages through their haunts.

The bladder grasshoppers are mostly green in colour but some have a pinkish tinge and others, like the one shown in the photograph are beautifully mottled with silver markings. Their colouring is such that they harmonise very well with their surroundings and are difficult to find. In Afrikaans they are known as *hekiejees*, and a name given to them by natives sounds like *groonia* or *gonnia*, with a guttural *g*. Both names seem to be an attempt to reproduce the strange call of the males.

Nothing is known about the life history of these insects. It is a remarkable fact that, although you will see many specimens of different species in our museums, there are no immature males among them. All the males in the collections are full-grown adults, with bodies like bloated bladders. Consequently we have no idea of how they acquire their strange form.

The voice of the male bladder grasshopper is so loud and so unlike the sounds made by other insects that few people hearing it during the night would recognise it for what it is. Most would declare without hesitation that it is the croaking of a large and noisy frog. It is impossible to describe the sound in words but the call may be said to consist of a long, loud rasping noise, with deep resonance, repeated at intervals of a few minutes. The volume of the sound suggests that the owner of such a voice must be at least as large as a bull-frog, yet it is the call of a puny insect about two inches long, an insect which looks like a grasshopper that has been pumped up with air until it is on the point of bursting. It sometimes comes flying into the room and round the lamp at night and it may be picked up and handled freely because it is quite harmless and cannot bite.

If the insect is held up to the light it will be seen that its body is almost completely hollow and filled with air. A dark line along its belly, about the thickness of a match-stick, marks the position of the digestive organs, the reproductive organs and the nervous system, while a thin line along the back indicates the position of the insect's heart. The rest of the body consists of nothing but air contained in the enormously dilated tracheae. The whole structure of the insect has been profoundly modified so that its body may act as a resonance box to give volume to its call. The sound-producing apparatus, or stridulating organ, as it is called, is lodged on each side of the bloated body and consists of a row of raised, hardened spots, yellow in colour and looking something like the miniature backbone of a fish when viewed through a hand lens.

On the inner side of each hind leg a tiny comb of about a dozen stiff points juts out and is so situated that, when the insect moves its hind legs up and down, against the sides of its body, these combs rub against the raised dots on the sides and set up the vibrations that are magnified by the hollow body, so producing the loud call. The male might well be called a perambulating love song, for his loud, far-reaching call is apparently meant to attract his fat, wingless mate.

The female is quite different. She has a stout, solid body of the ordinary grasshopper type, except that her hind legs are not adapted for leaping and her wings are reduced to small stumps, so she cannot jump and she cannot fly. She creeps about in the bushes, not far from the ground, and her colour harmonises so closely with the foliage that she is extremely difficult to find. It is not known where the eggs are laid and the general habits and life histories of these interesting insects have still to be investigaged.

The family of short-horned grasshoppers, *Acridiidae*, includes a very large number of species, several thousands of which are found in Africa. They range in size from small insects of less than half an inch in length when fully grown to some of the giants among our insects. The antennae are always shorter than the body and this is an easy means of telling members of this group from the next family, the long-horned grasshoppers, *Locustidae*. Their ears are found on their backs, beneath the wings near the base and the females have only a short ovipositor, consisting of four hard, horny points at the tip of the abdomen.

Many are wingless and of particular interest are the toad grasshoppers, *Batrachotettix* species, that are found in the drier regions and closely resemble the ground on which they live. In striking contrast to these are the species with warning colours, such as the red and black grasshopper described above and the elegant grasshopper, *Zonocerus elegans*, which is yellow, green, blue and black, and which, instead of having to hide from enemies, flaunt their bold colours in order to advertise their disgusting taste and smell.

Long-Horned Grasshoppers

As their name implies, the members of this family, *Locustidae*, all have long, slender antennae of more than thirty joints, longer than the body. The females can, as a rule, be readily recognised by the conspicuous sword-like ovipositor on the tail. Many different species are found in this country but they are not so commonly seen as the grasshoppers because of their concealing colours and because they are mostly nocturnal in habit. There are quite a number of green species that are found in bushes and trees and the females lay their flattish eggs in slits they cut in the bark by means of their ovipositors. Some haunt fruit trees and may do damage to the fruit by nibbling holes in the skin and by depositing their eggs in the unripe fruit.

The males are often loud and persistent singers. They do not stridulate in the same way as the short-horned grasshoppers, but rub their wings rapidly one over the other. When closed, the left front wing usually overlaps the right one and, in the male, the underside of the left wing, near the base, has fine teeth on it to form a rasp. This rubs against a special roughened area on the under wing and the vibration so set up is magnified by the wing acting as a resonator. The call of certain kinds of these insects in the United States is thought to sound like "Katy did, she did!", hence the name, "katydid," given to them in America. Some *Locustidae* have lost the power of flight but the males retain the stumps of their first pair of wings so that they can still produce their shrill, nocturnal calls.

The long-horned grasshoppers have ears, not on their backs, as the grasshoppers have, but on their front legs. On the shank or tibia of each front leg, just below the joint between it and the femur, a slight swelling may be seen. The tiny ear-drum or tympanum is lodged in a depression in this swelling. Such ears are not nearly as efficient as our own and they can probably do little more than pick up the shrill trillings of their own kind.

Some are vegetarian in their diet, others are carnivorous and are fierce slayers of other insects, whilst some seem to indulge in a mixed diet and to devour anything that comes their way that is edible. The *Locustidae* are divided into fifteen sub-families and they show a great variety of form, colouring and habits. We know very little indeed about the life histories of African *Locustidae*.

The fat, ungainly insects known in Afrikaans as *koringkrieks* or *dikpens* are sometimes spoken of as armoured ground crickets, but they are not true crickets. These insects, of which there are about two dozen species found in Africa, are widely spread, but they are most abundant and most noticeable in the drier areas. They are all very similar in appearance and habits, differing mainly in size and the spiny armour of their bodies. A very common species, *Hetrodes pupus*, is about an inch and a half long and has a stoutly built body, dark brown in colour, with two narrow yellow stripes and five rows of spines along the back of its abdomen. On the back of its thorax it has a strong armour-plate with sharp spines bristling round the edges. If this insect were magnified a thousand times it would look rather like one of those fearsome reptiles that became extinct long, long ages ago.

Many people in South Africa fear the koringkrieks because they have the reputation of being poisonous. If one of these insects is handled roughly, it squirts a liquid from a hole on each side of its thorax. This liquid is the insect's own blood and it is obviously ejected as a means of defence. It is said that the liquid, if it falls on the human skin, causes painful sores that take a long time to heal, but I have frequently handled koringkrieks and got the liquid on my fingers and have so far suffered no ill effects at all. The koringkriek can and will, however, inflict a sharp bite with its strong jaws.

Although these insects cannot fly or jump—they can only amble

PLATE 7

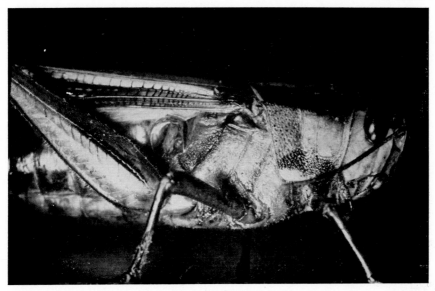

(a) Head and thorax of the Common Garden Grasshopper. The ear can be seen just above the base of the hind leg. The right wings have been removed to reveal the ear. Enlarged.

(b) A WINGLESS TOAD GRASSHOPPER, *Batrachotettix* species. Slightly enlarged.

PLATE 8

(a) A LONG-HORNED GRASSHOPPER, *Tylopsis continua*, female; her antennae are longer than her body. Natural size.

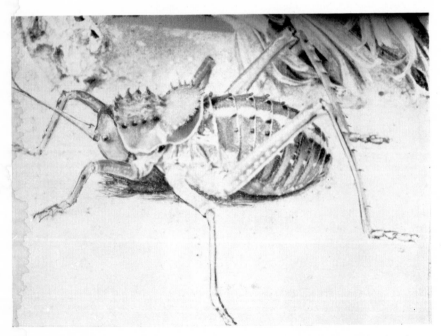

(b) THE ARMOURED GROUND CRICKET, *Hetrodes pupus*, adult male. Slightly enlarged.

along rather clumsily—they appear to be more or less immune from the attacks of insect-eaters. This immunity seems to be partly due to the irritant fluid and partly to the spiny armour.

If the male koringkriek is taken—he is easily recognised because he lacks the long, sword-shaped ovipositor that adorns the tail of the female—and the shield on the back of his thorax is lifted up, the remnants of his wings can be seen, in the form of a pair of stout, membranous stumps that can move one over the other. By rubbing these stumps rapidly together he can produce a loud, rasping note. The female has not got these stumps and is, therefore, voiceless. The ears can be seen just below the knees on the front legs.

The koringkriek has a curious pair of eyes. Each one is small and hemispherical and projects from the head on a short stalk, something like a crab's eye, except that the stalks are not movable. The insect has thus a goggle-eyed appearance, as though its eyes were popping out of its head in a perpetual state of surprise. It is difficult to conceive what sort of view of the outside world such a pair of eyes convey to their owner. They must be very short-sighted, but their shape and position must give the insect a wide angle of vision which makes it unnecessary for the creature to turn its head to see behind.

Apparently the female uses her long ovipositor to thrust her eggs deep in the soil. Her eggs are large, measuring nearly a quarter of an inch in length, oval in shape and white. If a gravid female is killed and dissected only about fourteen of these large eggs are found inside her. The eggs hatch into small koringkrieks exactly like their parents, but black. They seem to be omnivorous. Travellers in regions where these insects are abundant complain that they will even nibble at harness, leather boots, the canvas tent of a wagon, clothes and similar articles. Those that I have kept in captivity have attacked and eaten other insects put in the cage with them, particularly if they are injured. They are also not averse to cannibalism on occasion.

It is not known how long they live or how long they take to reach full size, but it seems almost certain there is one generation per year. At the Cape young individuals may be found in the spring and these are adults by the following February. They lurk amid dead vegetation during the day and come out at night to feed. Some of the species found inland are more diurnal in their habits and can often be seen resting on bushes in the full glare of the sun.

One of the most extraordinary and bizarre of all the insects found in this country is the male monstrous cricket, *Henicus monstrosus*, which is not a true cricket but something halfway between the *Locustidae* and the cricket family. If he were magnified to the size of a dog

E

and you were to see him coming along the road, he would look like something out of a particularly hideous nightmare.

He is a little less than an inch long, brown in colour and there is nothing out of the ordinary about his body and legs, but his head is quite unique, making him one of the weirdest-looking creations in nature. First of all, his head is much too large for his puny body, having a diameter about equal to that of a sixpenny-piece, and it is armed with a pair of jaws that are quite ludicrous. They are long and curved, like a pair of bandy legs, and furnished with four small teeth at the tips. Although he looks fearsome, his jaws are so weak that he cannot even administer an effective nip with them. They are so long, and they will not bend and their tips are so far away from his mouth that it is difficult to understand how he manages to eat at all with such ridiculous jaws.

He has, however, a second pair of jaws, like all other insects. They are smaller and softer than the mandibles and they are hidden in the photograph by the large, shield-shaped upper lip that hangs down in front of the mouth. These second jaws are armed with sharp points at the tips. Possibly he uses his absurdly long mandibles for holding his food while he nibbbles at it by means of the second pair of jaws. We know nothing at all about the nature of his food or how he feeds.

On his forehead there are two quaint horns which curve slightly downwards and add to his grotesque appearance. The function of these horns is also unknown. His eyes are small but prominent and he seems to have quite good sight as far as insects go, despite the fact that he lives in almost perpetual darkness, deep in the ground or under a large stone by day, venturing out at night. Instead of the three simple eyes on the centre of the head, between the feelers, he has only three faint white dots, showing where they were situated before they were lost by his ancestors long ago.

The female monstrous cricket looks more or less like an ordinary wingless long-horned grasshopper. Her body is about three quarters of an inch in length and she has a long ovipositor on her tail, shaped like a scimitar and consisting of six slender blades closely applied and locked together to form a flattened tube. Her head is quite normal in shape and size and very different from the grotesque cranium of her mate.

The male makes a rasping noise by rubbing his mandibles and second pair of jaws together and it has been suggested that this gnashing of the teeth constitutes his love song. If this is so, and if his head is the result of sexual selection, then there is certainly no accounting for the taste of the female.

The monstrous cricket and its relatives are placed in a family by themselves called the *Gryllacridae*, a name which may be interpreted as "cricket-grasshoppers" and which indicates the relationship of these strange creatures. Popularly they are sometimes spoken of as king crickets because some of them are of large size, nearly three inches in length. Like the rest of the *Locustidae*, they have four joints to each foot, while the true crickets have only three.

There are a number of different species of king cricket found in Africa and in many of them the males are as extraordinary as the male of the monstrous cricket. They form an ancient group of insects, limited to the Southern Hemisphere and affording an indication that Australia, India, Africa and South America were once linked together in some way. Gardeners often unearth members of this family when digging. One common species is a big, bloated insect about two and a half inches long, brown in colour, with very long, slender feelers and no wings. It makes a slight squeaking sound when disturbed and tries to bury itself again as quickly as possible. This is the pallid king cricket, *Maxentius pallidus*, and it is often regarded with fear because of its size and formidable appearance, but the worst it can do is to give a sharp nip with its jaws. It spends the day in its burrow underground and emerges at night to feed on some of the gardener's most cherished plants.

Crickets

This family of well-known insects is closely related to the preceding one. Its members also possess long, slender antennae, a long ovipositor, ears on their front legs and a stridulating organ on the wings of the male. Their feet, however, are more like those of the short-horned grasshoppers because they have only three joints.

We have several species of crickets in this country that are closely allied to the common household cricket, the cricket on the hearth, *Gryllus domesticus*. In fact, it is said that this little insect's original home was North Africa, but it has been widely spread over the world by man. They are the tireless singers we can hear on any warm evening even in the heart of our largest towns. If you try to track down a male cricket by the noise it is making you will soon learn that it is a practised ventriloquist. When he is chirping, by rubbing one wing over the other, he raises his front wings so that they are free of his sides and there is nothing to interfere with the vibration—consequently the sound is loud and clear. But if he becomes suspicious, he can lower his wings so that the bent-down edges touch his sides: this dampens the vibration and muffles the sound, causing it to seem to come from a distance away—hence the ventriloquial effect.

If you listen to the chirping of crickets on several evenings and time the rate at which they chirp, you will find that temperature has a considerable effect on the speed and vigour of their song. Careful observations have been made and it is calculated that if the number of chirps made by a cricket in fourteen seconds be counted and the number forty added, the answer will be, in nine cases out of ten, the correct temperature within a couple of degrees Fahrenheit. So, if you have no thermometer, here is an easy way of determining the approximate temperature on any warm night.

Crickets sit at the entrances to their burrows and chirp defiance to any other males in the neighbourhood, but their song also serves to attract females that are looking for mates. It has been found that a female cricket will approach a telephone or loud-speaker from which the sound of a male cricket is issuing. If two males meet when there is a female about they will fight, but such combats cause little harm on either side: there is some biting, butting and buffeting and then one gives up and runs away before any serious hurt is inflicted, leaving the victor to chirp triumphantly and to court the female.

The eggs of most species of garden and household crickets are laid singly in the ground and the young that hatch from them moult six or seven times before they reach full size, a process that takes several months. In many cases the young emerge in spring and are full-grown by the following autumn.

Crickets are normally plant feeders but at certain times of the year some species may come into houses for shelter and get into cupboards and drawers. They often chew holes in clothing and linen and may on occasion do much damage.

Mole crickets are very common in Africa and they are often attracted to lights at night, causing consternation by flopping down on the floor and then scurrying about. These insects have their front legs highly adapted as digging implements, being very stout and armed with strong teeth. They burrow in damp earth and often disfigure lawns and bowling greens by throwing up small mounds of earth during the night. A male mole cricket beneath a stone in a damp spot in the garden will keep up a low, dull whirring song for minutes at a time and it will puzzle anybody who tries to locate him to find out exactly where the sound is coming from. These insects seem to feed principally on roots but they may also be carnivorous. Some-times they do damage in the garden by eating holes in potatoes and strawberries. If they are causing trouble in this way they can be caught in large numbers by placing half pumpkins, cut side downwards, on the ground where they occur and leaving overnight. The insects creep under the pumpkins for shelter and food and may be collected in the morning.   The females lay their oval, white eggs in groups in holes in the ground.

There are a number of different species of delicate tree crickets that look like pale green ghosts when they come out at night to feed. Despite their weak appearance some of them are carnivorous and feed on small insects such as aphides and young caterpillars.   The males are persistent and rather pleasing, although monotonous, singers. The females cut slits with their ovipositors in the tender young twigs of bushes and trees and deposit their eggs in them.   The punctures are in a neat, regular row along the twig and often they are so deep that the twig dies as a result.   Fruit trees, particularly peaches, may be injured in this way.

There are tiny little dark brown or black crickets that may be seen jumping about in numbers on damp soil beside a stream or pond, but we know very little about them.   There are also a few species of small crickets that are found only in ants' nests.

CLASSIFICATION

SUB-CLASS PTERYGOTA

Winged insects, or, if wingless, insects that have descended from winged ancestors. Metamorphosis slight among the lower orders but pronounced among the higher orders.

ORDER 5: *ORTHOPTERA* (Straight-winged insects)

The members of this order, when wings are present, have long, narrow fore-wings and much broader membranous hind-wings.   Mouthparts of the ordinary biting type. Cerci are present.   Young are like the adults, but a slight metamorphosis occurs as the wings develop.

FAMILY 1: *Blattidae*—COCKROACHES

Flattened insects with legs well developed for running.   Eggs laid in purse-like cases which may at times be seen protruding from body of female.

FAMILY 2: *Mantidae*—PRAYING MANTES

Fore legs highly modified to serve as traps for capturing prey.   First segment of the thorax elongated.   Eyes large, three simple eyes present.   Head jointed to thorax so that it can turn.   Eggs laid in cases made of viscid material that hardens in air.   All are carnivorous.

FAMILY 3: *Phasmidae*—STICK AND LEAF INSECTS

Normal walking legs, not modified in any way.   Middle segment of thorax elongated.   Eyes small, simple eyes usually absent.   Eggs resemble seeds in appearance and are dropped loosely on the ground.   All are vegetarian.

FAMILY 4: *Acridiidae*—SHORT-HORNED GRASSHOPPERS AND LOCUSTS

Antennae shorter than body.   Feet three-jointed.   Stridulatory organ on hind legs and front wings.   Ears situated at base of abdomen.   Ovipositor short.   Eggs usually laid in the ground.   Most are vegetarians.

FAMILY 5: *Locustidae*—LONG-HORNED GRASSHOPPERS

Antennae longer than body.   Feet four-jointed.   Stridulatory organ on wings only.   Ears on front legs.   Ovipositor long.   Eggs laid in various situations, often in stems of plants.   Many are carnivorous.

FAMILY 6: *Gryllidae*—CRICKETS

Antennae long, feet three-jointed (rarely, with only one or two joints).   Stridulatory organ on wings only.   Ears on front legs.   Ovipositor long and slender.   Eggs laid in various situations.

CHAPTER III

EARWIGS

The Dermaptera

This is a small order of insects, including only about five hundred species from all over the world. They are not well represented in Africa and are of little importance. The name, *Dermaptera*, means "skin-winged" and refers to the membranous second pair of wings which are carried neatly folded beneath the small, leathery pair of

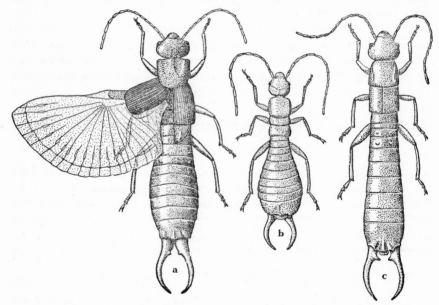

FIG. 8—Earwigs: a.The European earwig, *Forficula auricularia*, with the left wing expanded; b. An African earwig, *Esphalmenus peringueyi*; c. Another African earwig, *Apterygida coloniae.*

front wings. In some textbooks this order is referred to as the *Euplexoptera*, a name which refers to the rather elaborate folding of the hind wings. The popular name "earwig" is said by some to be derived from "ear-wing" and to refer to the hind wing which has something of the shape of the human ear when it is spread out. But in several European languages the insect is referred to as an ear-worm or ear-borer; the belief (quite unfounded) that these insects have the habit of creeping into ears seems to be ancient and widely spread.

The characteristic mark of an earwig is the curious pair of pincers on its tail: these correspond to the cerci of the cockroach but, in the case of the earwig, they have been modified to form nippers. The use of these pincers has not been discovered, although it has been suggested that they are used by the insect when folding its wings. But many earwigs are wingless, like the one in the photograph, and yet these wingless species have the nippers quite as well developed as the others.

In the winged species the second pair of wings is carried neatly folded beneath the short, protective first pair. They are folded first like a fan and then back upon themselves twice, so that they occupy very little space and are covered by the small, square first pair. No other insects fold their wings in this complicated manner and it is said that the earwig uses its forceps when packing its wings away. But, in any case, the wingless species cannot possibly use their pincers in this way and one would have expected them to have disappeared or become small through lack of use, although this has not happened. In most species the male earwig has larger forceps than the female and here again we do not know why. It is just another of those secondary sexual characteristics that are useful to the field naturalist in enabling him to distinguish the sexes with ease.

African Earwigs

Gardeners in this country are not bothered with earwigs as they are in Europe. The common earwig of Europe, *Forficula auricularia,* has found its way to Africa but it does not seem to thrive here and has not become numerous or widely spread. As nothing is known about the habits and life histories of our indigenous earwigs, we must turn to what is known of the European species in order to learn what may be expected.

The female of the common earwig lays in spring some twenty-five or so oval white eggs in a heap beneath a stone, or in some other secluded spot. She watches over them until they hatch and it is said that, if the eggs are scattered, she will carefully collect them again, one by one, and replace them in a heap. The newly-hatched young are like their parents, except that they are white and wingless, with fewer joints to their antennae (eight instead of fourteen) and two simple cerci instead of the forceps. They stay with their mother for a time and then scatter to look after themselves.

Although many gardeners report earwigs as distinctly harmful insects, and it must be admitted they do eat petals of flowers, it would seem that they are largely scavengers, feeding on dead and dying insects and on organic debris of various kinds. They cast their skin four or five times before reaching the adult state and there is only one generation a year in Europe. The males die in the autumn but the females live on through the winter and lay their eggs in the spring, dying soon after the young hatch.

It is probable that the indigenous earwigs of Africa have many interesting ways and habits that await investigation. Here is a virgin field of study for some enthusiast. The species shown in the photograph is found in hollow stems: it is about three quarters of an inch long, narrow and wingless. The well-developed nippers on the tail show that it is a male; the nippers of the female are much smaller. Other species are to be found beneath the bark of trees, in dead, rotting logs, and beneath stones in damp places.

CLASSIFICATION

ORDER 5: *Dermaptera*—EARWIGS

Elongated insects with biting mouthparts. Wings, when present, consist of a short, leathery first pair covering a folded membranous second pair. Tarsi three-jointed. Cerci modified to form a pair of pincers. No ovipositor. Metamorphosis slight: young have fewer joints in antennae than adults and the cerci are straight and unmodified.

PLATE 9

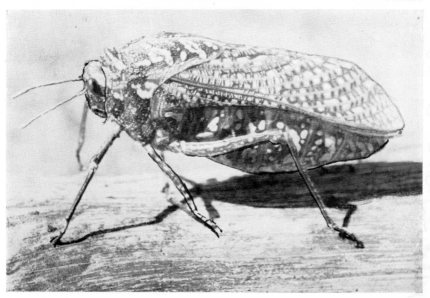

(*a*) THE MOTTLED BLADDER GRASSHOPPER, *Pneumora variolosa*, male. About twice natural size.

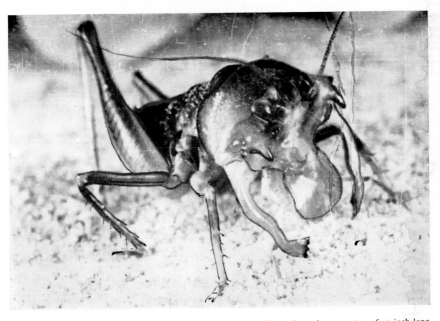

(*b*) THE MONSTROUS CRICKET, *Henicus monstrosus*, male. He is about three quarters of an inch long.

PLATE 10

(*a*) THE MONSTROUS CRICKET, *Henicus monstrosus*, adult female. About twice natural size.

(*b*) THE MONSTROUS CRICKET, *Henicus monstrosus*, enlarged view of head of male

CHAPTER IV

STONE-FLIES

The Plecoptera

This is a small order of inconspicuous insects of moderate size, with two pairs of wings, long, slender antennae and weak jaws. They are usually found near water, on the margins of streams and lakes, particularly in mountainous regions. As they are feeble fliers they spend most of their time resting on stones, the trunks of trees and amid foliage. The name, *Plecoptera*, means "folded wings" and refers to the fact that the hind wings, which are larger than the first pair, are folded when the insect is at rest. They have been little studied in this country and so far only about thirty species are known, but there are undoubtedly a number more that await discovery, description and naming.

The Life History of a Stone-Fly

In streams, especially clear, mountain streams with stony beds, the larvae of stone flies are common. If a stone is lifted from the bed of the stream and the underside examined, as often as not a few

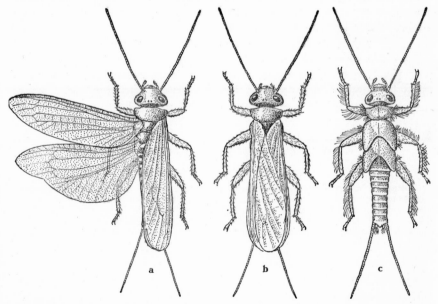

FIG. 9—A Stone-Fly, *Ochthopetina transvaalensis*: a. Adult, with left wings spread; b. Adult with folded wings; c. Nymph, found beneath stones in mountain streams, about half an inch long when fully grown.

dark grey insects, rather like small shrimps, will be seen to run round to the side of the stone away from the light. These may be the larvae of may-flies, which are described later (page 78), or they may be the larvae of stone-flies. The former have three slender tails, while the stone-flies have only two.

A fully grown larva (or nymph, as the immature stages of insects with slight metamorphosis are usually called) may be about half an inch to an inch in length, depending on the species, and it has six legs, long, slender antennae and a pair of compound eyes. Along each side, just above the bases of the legs, there are six or seven tufts of gills: these are tracheae, projecting from the surface of the body, and the oxygen in the water passes through their thin walls into the insect's respiratory system. The stumps of the wings of the future fly can be clearly seen on the back of a well-grown nymph.

The larva creeps actively about among the stones on the bottom of the stream, capturing and devouring any small creatures it can overcome. When it is fully grown it leaves the water and creeps up on to a stone above the surface. Here it rests for a time, a split appears along the back of the thorax and the adult fly pulls itself out of the nymphal skin. The cast skin that is left behind, clinging to the rock, is a fascinating object for study under the microscope: the eyes, legs, jaws, wing-sheaths, the great air-tubes and the front and hind part of the alimentary canal, including the gizzard, can all be clearly seen in the transparent husk.

Although stone-flies are poor fliers, they can run quickly. Mating takes place soon after the emergence of the flies and is accomplished whilst resting on the ground or on a stone or tree-trunk. The eggs, large in number, are dropped by the female into the water where they get dispersed by the current and fall to the bottom.

CLASSIFICATION

ORDER 6: *Plecoptera*—STONE-FLIES

Primitive insects that are aquatic in the immature stages. Soft-bodied, of moderate size, long, threadlike antennae, weak mouthparts of the biting type, four membranous wings held flat over the back in repose, hind pair of wings the larger and folded like a fan when at rest. Some males have small wings and are unable to fly. Two long cerci on tip of abdomen. Metamorphosis slight. Nymphs usually have tufted tracheal gills.

CHAPTER V

TERMITES

The Isoptera

Termites, or white ants as they are often miscalled, are placed in an order by themselves known as the *Isoptera*, or insects with similar wings, the name referring to the fact that both pairs of wings are alike. They are perhaps the most mysterious and most interesting of all insects. They are certainly of vast importance in Africa, where something like four hundred different species are found and where they do enormous damage. Their fortress homes, the "ant-heaps", are abundant over large areas of the continent and they are far and away the most numerous of all living creatures in Africa, if we exclude the micro-organisms.

From the structure of their bodies and from their development it is plain that termites are rather low in the scale of insect life: much lower than the true ants. Cockroaches appear to be their nearest relatives, yet they have evolved an amazingly complex and efficient social life with hundreds of thousands of individuals living in close, interdependent association in colonies that are run on absolutely totalitarian lines. They are very ancient insects. They existed perhaps one hundred million years ago, just as we see them to-day—fossil termites are very similar to existing species, and they have obviously changed little in the course of ages. The termite mound is by far the oldest type of organised community found on this earth. Ants, bees, wasps and human beings are modern upstarts compared with the termites.

No known termites are able to live solitary lives; all are social insects and perish quickly if they are removed from their fortress homes.

The Black Mound Termite

As our example of the wood-eating termites we may take the common black mound termite, *Amitermes atlanticus*. It is a convenient species for study; there are many closely related species widely spread over the continent that have similar habits and it happens to be the kind I know most about as I have had the opportunity to study it for the past fifteen years.

This termite is small, the full-grown worker being only about one-sixth of an inch long. It lives in black mounds, the largest of

41

which are only about eighteen inches in height and two feet in diameter at the base. The mound is built of soil particles bound together with a cement that consists of the insects' excrement, and it is a strong, weather-proof structure capable of excluding most of the termites' enemies. Ants are the bitter, age-long enemies of termites and these soft-bodied, slow-moving insects would have no chance of survival against their agile, aggressive foes if they did not live within the shelter of their fortress homes.

Compared with the size of the puny creatures that make it, the mound is a colossal structure and the architectural wonders of man, such as the pyramids of Egypt or the skyscrapers of New York, are, relatively speaking, feeble efforts. A large mound may contain a population equal to that of some of our largest cities. As a general rule, the inhabitants never venture out into the open air. They live in perpetual darkness and, in consequence, the great majority are blind. The sun never shines on them, no breeze ever stirs the still atmosphere of their corridors and the rain never reaches them. Their home is air-conditioned in a way that we can never equal. They move from one part of the nest to another according to changes in temperature. If you break open a mound on a blazing hot summer afternoon you will find the cells near the surface are all empty because they are too warm and the inhabitants have crowded into the cooler lower part of the nest. On the other hand, these same cells near the surface are all densely occupied at night during the summer and by day during the winter. The air inside the nest is invariably humid and always contains a higher percentage of carbon dioxide than the outside atmosphere, because of the many thousands congregated in their ill-ventilated home.

Because they have lived for countless generations in these air-conditioned homes, where there are no extremes or rapid changes, termites are very delicate creatures when removed from their normal environment and they are extraordinarily difficult to keep under artificial conditions in the laboratory, for observation purposes. That is the main reason why, although many volumes have been written about them, we still have a great deal to learn about them and their strange, totalitarian ways.

Termites as Pets

The easiest way to keep a number of termites alive for some time when removed from their nest is to put them in a glass tube, with a strip of filter paper in the tube to afford them a foothold. One or two drops of water on the paper will keep the air in the tube humid and it must be tightly corked after the termites are inside. Instead of a glass tube, an ordinary petri dish may be used. Under such conditions the termites remain alive for some weeks, provided the receptacle is kept in the dark in a place where the temperature does not vary too widely. They nibble a little at the filter paper because it consists of cellulose, one of the principal constituents of their wood diet, but for the most part they just sit and do nothing during the long hours of captivity.

Obviously one can learn very little about the ways of these strange insects when they are kept under such conditions. A better type

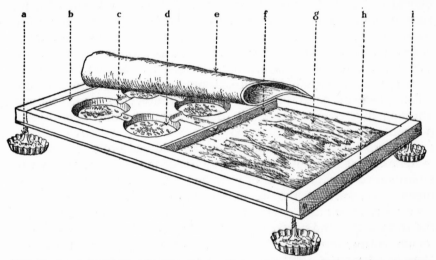

FIG. 10—An Artificial Nest for Termites: a. Crown cork with D.D.T. powder; b. Glass cover of nest; c. One of the grooves connecting the cells; d. A cell, one and a quarter inches in diameter; e. Felt cover to exclude light; f. Cork lino sheet in which cells are cut; g. Layer of humus, with decayed twigs, kept moist to provide food and water; h. Plywood base of nest; i. Wooden frame to stiffen base and form sides of tray. The nest can be made any convenient size. That shown in the diagram is 9 x 4½ inches and suitable for a young queen and a few dozen workers.

of artificial nest is needed in which the insects can live under more normal conditions. After many unsuccessful attempts I succeeded in devising a nest that proved satisfactory. It consists of a sheet of cork lino, the size of which depends on the number of termites to be kept in the nest. Twelve inches by eighteen is a convenient size. Holes one and a quarter inches in diameter are punched in the lino with a leather punch, nine rows with ten holes in each row, making ninety holes altogether. The cork lino is then glued quite flat on one half of a sheet of three-ply wood measuring eighteen inches by two feet. Plastic resin glue is used for this as it is very strong, easily applied and quite water-proof. Strips of wood are glued round the edges of the three-ply base so that it forms a tray.

Grooves about an eighth of an inch wide and the same depth are then cut in the cork lino to form runways for the termites, connecting the cells with one another, as shown in figure 10. A deeper groove is cut from the middle cell in the front row to the exterior so that the termites may run in and out of the nest.

Four one-inch screws are screwed one in each corner on the underside of the tray. These form four short supports on which the tray stands. To keep the termites in the tray and ants out of it, each screw should be stood in an inverted crown cork containing D.D.T. powder. This forms a very effective barrier that needs renewal only every few months. In order to get the termites to enter the nest and take up their abode in it, a little of the material of their mound is taken and ground to a powder with pestle and mortar. The powder is moistened with a few drops of water and then a little of the paste is put into the bottom of each cell and pressed down firm and flat. When the nest is baited in such a way the termites go in readily enough, seeming to recognise the smell of the material from their original home.

A small mound is brought from the veld and broken up and the termites are shaken out on to the tray beside the cork lino nest, which is now covered with a sheet of glass and a piece of felt to exclude the light. A glance at the figure should make all this quite clear. For food, some dead, decaying sticks and leaves are put in the open half of the tray and covered with a thin layer of humus. This is kept damp and the termites come out of the nest and burrow into it quite freely in search of food and moisture. A little sugar added to the water makes the food more attractive. I have kept the black mound termite, *Amitermes atlanticus*, alive in such nests as these for several years now and the account that follows is based on observations made from them.

Smaller nests of the same type, consisting of only one or two cells, may be made for young kings and queens just starting new colonies, or for young queens with only a few dozen workers. Interesting physiological experiments may also be carried out in these nests. For example, I made one nest of a strip of cork lino, eighteen inches long by two inches wide. Two cells, one at each end, were punched in the lino and they were connected by a long, narrow straight groove through which the termites could run from one cell to the other. A thermometer was also embedded in the cork so that the temperature could be easily read, and the whole was covered with a sheet of glass. With this apparatus it was easy to time the speed at which the insects ran at different temperatures and I found that their speed varied directly with the temperature. At 0 degrees Centigrade they did not move at all; they were moribund with the cold: at 10 degrees they moved at a speed of approximately ten yards an hour, at 20 degrees at twenty yards an hour and at 30 degrees at thirty yards an hour. Like the chirping of a cricket, the speed of a termite can be used for a rough determination of temperature.

The Workers

The great majority of the inhabitants of the termite mound are workers, males and females that are stunted in growth and whose sexual organs have failed to develop. They are, in consequence, sterile, and can devote all their time and attention to unremitting labour for the state, without the distractions of sex. Among ants and social bees all the workers are females and it is known that, in the case at least of the bees, the workers develop from eggs similar to those that give rise to queens, but the larvae are fed in a special way that stunts their growth and prevents the development of the sexual organs. It is not known whether it is the same with termites, or whether the queen lays different types of eggs that give rise to workers, soldiers and sexed individuals.

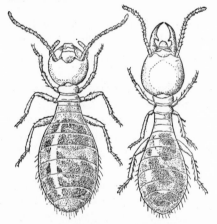

FIG. 11: The Black-mound Termite, *Amitermes atlanticus*. Adult worker on the left, soldier on the right. These insects are about one-fifth of an inch in length.

Another baffling problem about the termite mound is the means by which discipline is maintained in their complex, crowded homes. How are the manifold activities organised? Who or what decides that this or that must be done and these or those individuals among the thousands of inhabitants must do it? None among the multitude has any authority over the others, as far as we can see, yet everything is done in an orderly fashion as it needs to be done.

When more inhabitants are needed and when conditions are appropriate, the queen is given special food so that her ovaries are stimulated and she lays the required number of eggs. These and the young that hatch from them are treated in the appropriate manner to give rise to the required number of workers, soldiers and sexual individuals. When the mound has to be enlarged the requisite number of workers undertake the labour. Food-gathering goes on unceasingly. It is all regulated with the utmost precision, but how, or by whom, nobody knows. The whole colony is dependent on the workers, for they do nearly all the work and without them the others would soon perish; yet they are all on a footing of complete equality with no authority over them. A human city run on the same lines would soon be in a state of chaos.

There are runways under the ground—narrow tunnels radiating in all directions from the mound, which the workers excavate and use in their search for the decaying wood and humus that form their food. As soon as a source of food in any spot is exhausted, the runway leading to it is deserted and falls in and the workers drive new tunnels in other directions. Only the adult workers gather the food. The black-mound termite does not attack sound wood: it seems to require wood that has been partly broken down by the fungi and bacteria that cause decay.

Cellulose, the chief constituent of wood, cannot be digested by the higher animals, including insects, without the aid of micro-organisms in their intestines: the protozoa and bacteria break down the cellulose into constituents that can be dealt with by their hosts. The termites that attack sound wood have large numbers of intestinal protozoa and bacteria that help them to digest their food, but the black-mound termite seems to be able to do without their aid. Although it has some curious protozoan parasites in its intestine, they are comparatively few and can play but a small part in the termite's digestive processes.

The abdomen of the adult worker is brownish-grey in colour because the dark-coloured contents of its alimentary canal show through the translucent body-wall. Inside the nest it passes on this partially digested food to any of its companions that may be hungry. The transference of food takes place from either end of its body: it may feed another termite by regurgitating some of its food from its mouth, or it may present its tail end and the second termite swallows its excrement. So the food passes through the alimentary canal of several individuals until all the nourishment is extracted from it and nothing but an indigestible dark-brown paste remains. This is used by the termites as the cement for building their home, and thus there is no sewage problem in this crowded community. Furthermore, all corpses and all cast skins are devoured, so that the inside of the nest, densely populated and shut off from the exterior though it is, is always spotlessly clean.

The workers are active throughout the twenty-four hours of the day: in the impenetrable darkness of their surroundings there is no difference between night and day. In my artificial nests I see them taking short rests in some of the cells, a group of them with their

PLATE 11

(*a*) The head of the Pallid King Cricket, showing the powerful jaws

(*b*) THE PALLID KING, CRICKET *Maxentius pallidus.* About twice natural size.

PLATE 12

(b) AN AFRICAN EARWIG, that lives in hollow stems; male, the females' pincers are smaller

(d) THE TWO-SPOTTED FIELD CRICKET, an immature specimen

(a) THE TWO-SPOTTED FIELD CRICKET, *Liogryllus bimaculatus*; male on left, female on right

(c) THE MOLE CRICKET, *Gryllotalpa africana*

heads together something like a lot of sheep, but these pauses are of brief duration during warm weather. In the winter all activities slow down. There is no breeding and little food-getting and the termites spend the greater part of their time in doing nothing.

Early spring is the time for building, for enlarging the mound. This work is carried out after rain, when the surface of the mound is moist and soft. Patches of black, crumbly material appear on the surface and, if you break away a little of this material, you see large numbers of workers toiling away below, each one bringing up particles of soil from below and adding them to the ceiling above its head. Silently and unseen the workers build from the inside outwards, and the additions, frail and easily broken at first, are quickly strengthened by their strange cement until the extension to their premises is as strong as the rest.

If you break a hole in the side of the mound, you will throw the termites into a state of great excitement because they know that their enemies, the ants, are always lurking somewhere in the vicinity, ready to pour into the breach to slaughter them and carry them off as food. You will see them signalling in a manner that is common to all termites: they jerk their bodies backwards and forwards, seeming to tap their heads and their tails on the ground as they do so. They are too feeble to produce any sound by this tapping and it is not known what this jerky motion means, or how the termites communicate with one another, but as they all indulge in this curious action when disturbed it seems obvious that they must, by some means or other, be spreading the alarm. The rapid restoration of the broken wall is a matter of life and death for them. If you watch after the hole is made, you will see soldiers come up, ready to defend the breach with their lives whilst the workers get on with the urgent work of repairing the holes. Usually this is done below the surface and you cannot see much, but sometimes the workers close small holes on the outside of the mound. Each worker, as it appears at the opening, shakes its head from side to side in a peculiar manner and then it vomits up a gobbet of dark-coloured slimy material which it deposits on the side of the hole, and withdraws immediately, to be replaced by another worker that carries out the same operation. Before your eyes the barrier is erected in a matter of seconds, damp and soft at first but rapidly hardening and drying. Each worker, then, carries a supply of building material with it that can be used in an emergency and this material seems to consist of partially digested food, soil particles, humus and chewed wood, mixed with digestive juices. If the hole is too large for this quick treatment, the workers carry up fragments of building material from below, sand grains or bits broken from

G

the inside of the mound itself, and fasten them in position with the slimy material described above.

The hole is walled up as quickly as possible, regardless of the fact that a number of workers and soldiers may be running about outside in confusion: these are ruthlessly shut out and left to their fate. The safety of the colony as a whole demands this sacrifice.

The workers collect the eggs as they are laid by the queen and carry them to that part of the nest where temperature and other

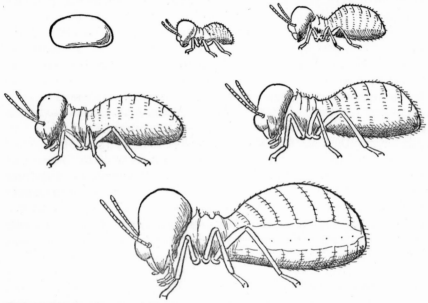

FIG. 12—The Development of the Worker, *Amitermes atlanticus*, from egg to the penultimate stage

conditions are best suited to them. Here the eggs are placed in white heaps and carefully tended and licked by the workers. I find that, if they are removed from the nest, the eggs invariably fail to hatch; without the workers to look after them they die and go mouldy or, if the air is dry, simply shrivel up. They hatch in about a month into tiny, six-legged creatures similar to the workers in form, but pure white in colour. Here we see one of the biggest differences between white ants and true ants. The eggs of ants hatch out into legless grubs, but the young of termites, like other primitive insects, go through only a slight metamorphosis and they are like their parents when born.

It is impossible to tell, when they are first hatched, whether any particular young are destined to develop into workers, soldiers or sexual individuals: they appear to be alike and the differences show only later in life, when they are about two-thirds grown. The young are fed by the adult workers on digested food, and their bodies, therefore, remain pure white until they are nearly fully grown, having no decayed wood or humus in their intestines to show through their translucent body-wall. They cast their skin five or six times and are mature when they are three months old. It is not known how long the workers live but I have kept them alive in my nests for over a year and it seems that, barring accidents, they can live for perhaps four or five years, like the workers of true ants.

Much has been made by some writers of the problem of the termites' water-supply: they point out that these insects must live in a humid atmosphere, that they quickly die in dry air, and yet many species are found in arid regions where temperatures are high and rainfall is low. It has been suggested that such termites must burrow deep into the earth in order to reach water far underground. The problem is not as difficult as it seems—at least, not in the case of the black-mound termite. The workers are most active in collecting food immediately after rain and so they get much moisture in the sodden wood and humus. Inside their crowded, ill-ventilated home the loss of water must be very small and the air is saturated with vapour from the bodies of the insects themselves. Thus, in the case of this particular species, they get all the water they want from their damp food and they do not need to burrow after some deeply-hidden source of water.

The Soldiers

The soldiers, like the workers, are males and females that have failed to grow up properly. They are sterile and they are unable to feed themselves, but have to be fed by the workers. Their job is to defend the colony, principally against their main enemies, the ants. They have huge jaws and a swollen head in which is lodged a large gland that produces a sticky, irritant fluid. When the black-mound soldier bites it grips like a bulldog and you can pull off its body before it will let go. If you tease a soldier with a piece of thread and get it to grip the thread in its jaws you will find that it can lift a stone much larger than its body by its legs whilst hanging on only by the jaws. As it bites it gives off a fine stream of the irritant fluid from the pore between the base of its jaws. If this fluid gets on to an ant it causes it to curl up and may kill it.

The soldiers are blind, like the workers, and they seem to detect friend or foe by smell and touch. When the mound is broken they come running out of the breach with jaws wide open and antennae waving in the air and they are quite ready to sacrifice their lives in defence of the colony. A few soldiers always accompany the workers when they go out foraging for food, although the soldiers take no part at all in the food-getting. Their job then is to defend the workers if ants or other enemies should happen to break through into the tunnel. The workers themselves are also quite capable of fighting and will defend themselves and their home as doggedly as the soldiers, but their first care is to exclude the enemy by the repair of any holes.

Only about five per cent of the inhabitants of a mound are soldiers. The workers seem to decide that this is enough and that more would be too great a drain on the colony. If, in my artificial nests, I deliberately change the proportion by taking away a large number of workers so that soldiers form, let us say, ten per cent of the population, then the workers kill off the surplus and reduce their numbers to about five per cent once more.

The King and Queen

Among ants, bees and wasps the males die soon after mating, but this is not the case with termites. Male termites live on beside their mates and become the so-called kings of the colonies. The titles, king and queen, are misleading because, as far as we can see, they are not rulers in any sense of the word, but simply the parents of the teeming horde and they are usually spoken of in technical works as the "reproductives".

The king is much smaller than his mate because he does not increase in size after he has cast off his wings, but she does. He is brown and easily recognised although difficult to find, being a timid creature. He hides himself under the bulky abdomen of the queen or in some crack or crevice if the nest is disturbed. His only function is to mate with the queen from time to time in order that she may keep up the supply of fertile eggs. It is said that mating takes place tail to tail, with the heads of the pair pointing in opposite directions.

Normally there is only one pair of reproductives in a mound, the founders of the colony known as the primary king and queen. They each have a pair of well developed compound eyes, although they use them only once for a brief period, during the wedding flight, and they have the triangular stumps of their discarded wings on their backs. The abdomen of the queen swells up enormously when her ovaries begin to develop so that she looks something like a bloated sausage with a small head and thorax in front. The black-mound termite is a small species; the queen is only about three quarters of an inch long when she is fully grown, and the king is only about a quarter of an inch in length.

An oft-repeated statement about the termite queen says that she lays an egg every second for twenty-four hours a day—86,400 eggs a day. This example of prodigious fecundity is quoted in book after book, but I doubt whether it is true. A vigorous queen can probably lay one egg each second for a limited period, but she certainly cannot keep this up for long. If she maintained this rate for one month there would be more than two and a half million eggs in the nest, far too many for the workers to care for.

The queen of the black-mound termite does not lay at all during the winter months. Her food supply is cut down at this time of the year and she becomes comparatively slender. But when the spring arrives the workers give her more food and she begins to bulge in a peculiar fashion. Her abdomen does not swell uniformly, but a bulge that looks like a deformity appears on one side or the other and this is a sign that her numerous egg-tubes are beginning to function again. The workers pay her increased attention and there are always a number around her, licking her assiduously, for the sake of the fatty exudation given off from the thin, distended skin of her abdomen.

The saliva of the black-mound termite has the peculiar effect of blackening anything it touches. They blacken in this way the wood upon which they feed, and the light-coloured soil of which the mound is made turns black because it is mixed with saliva and excreta used as cement. The young queen has a pure white abdomen but, as she grows older, her distended body slowly turns yellow and then a chocolate brown. This change of colour is apparently due to the staining effect of the saliva of the workers and it is an easy way to tell old queens from young ones: a white queen is young and a brown queen may be ten years of age or more.

The queen starts laying in the spring and she lays several hundred oval, white eggs that are carried away by the workers as fast as they are laid. Then she rests for a period and no more eggs are laid and her abdomen returns to its normal shape. But if all is well with the nest and plenty of food is coming in, she soon begins to bulge again and another lot of eggs are laid. And so it goes on throughout the summer: spurts of egg-laying with rests in between. If conditions are unfavourable and little food is coming in, egg-laying may cease altogether and the eggs that have already been laid may be eaten by the workers.

When the queen grows too old and her fertility wanes, the workers kill her by licking her to death. She is surrounded day and night by as many workers as can get at her and they all have their mouthparts applied to her skin. Gradually she grows thinner and thinner until finally only a shrivelled skin is left and this is finally covered with mound material and hidden from sight. This has happened on a few occasions in my artificial nests.

The Wedding Flight

If you break open a mound in January you will find, in addition to the workers and soldiers, a large number of white individuals with four white stumps of wings on their backs. These are called nymphs and they are immature males and females that are being fed and treated in such a way that they are growing up into fully-developed sexual individuals. The nymphs reach full size at about midsummer and, after their last moult their wings expand and their colour darkens. The fully developed wings are much longer than the body, four in number and all the same size, membranous and greyish blue in colour. As these insects are destined to leave their sheltered home and face the hazards of the outside world, their skin hardens and turns black. Also, they have a pair of compound eyes, as well as two simple eyes on their heads—eyes that will only be needed on the brief wedding flight, since before and after this they live in total darkness.

From about the middle of January onwards these winged individuals can be found inside the nest. They seem to spend all their time clustered together in certain cells, where they are fed and groomed by the workers. They are kept prisoners for several weeks, for they are not allowed to leave the mound until the climatic conditions are just right for the wedding flight.

Some time in March or April the first winter rains arrive at the Cape, and then, one day, when the weather is clearing after a good rain has soaked the ground, when the air is still and the temperature rising, the long-awaited signal is given for the great event of the year to begin. We do not know who or what decides that the time is auspicious. Nor do we know how the termites, hidden in the blackness of their air-conditioned home, learn what the weather conditions are like outside. But simultaneously in all the mounds in a given area, generally about ten or eleven o'clock in the morning, a great activity begins.

The workers pierce a number of small round holes in the top of the mound, each hole being about one-eighth of an inch in diameter, so that a few square inches of the apex of the mound looks like the lid of a pepper-pot. This is the only time when the termites deliberately make openings in their bastion walls: under no other circumstances do they run the risk of allowing enemies access to their home.

Soldiers appear at the holes, with jaws wide open and antennae waving, and then a number of workers come out into the open and these are followed by the winged males and females. There is great bustle and excitement on top of the mound for a few minutes, with the insects milling around in seeming confusion. Then the princes and princesses take to flight, fluttering away from their home in a straggling swarm. When they have all gone the soldiers and workers retreat inside again, the holes are quickly closed and all is silent and still once more. Not all the winged individuals are allowed to leave at once: some are kept back to form a second, or even a third, swarm later in the season. Often the workers may be seen pulling some of the eager princes and princesses back into the mound and it seems obvious that the workers control the flight and decide how many may go and how many may be kept back.

The flying termites do not, as a rule, travel very far. They are feeble fliers and an easy prey to all kinds of insect-eating animals. Birds, frogs, lizards, praying mantes, spiders and many other enemies have a great feast when the wedding flight is on and very few indeed of the fliers that leave the nest survive for long.

The female termite, if she is not caught and killed, is the first to settle. Usually she alights on the ground and runs around for a little while, then she pauses, seems to shrug her shoulders, as it were, and all her wings drop off. There is a line of weakness near the base and it is here that the wings break off, leaving only four small

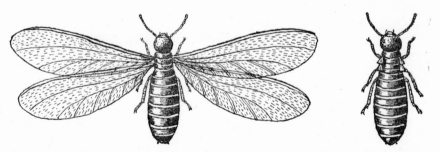

FIG. 13—Winged adult, *Amitermes atlanticus*, before and after shedding its wings

triangular stumps on her back. After shedding her wings she remains still with the tip of her abdomen raised in the air. She gives off a subtle scent that attracts the male and soon a winged male flutters down towards her and settles on the ground just behind her. Then he gives the curious shrugging movement and all his wings drop off. After this the pair move off together, tandem fashion, with the female

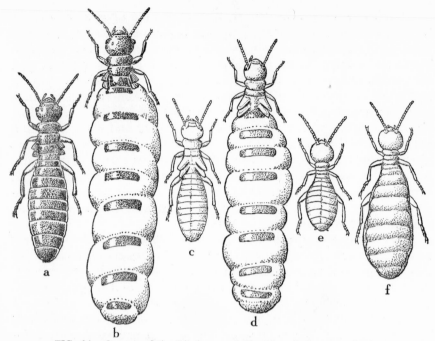

FIG. 14.—Queens of the Black-mound Termite, *Amitermes atlanticus*
a. Adult female that has just shed her wings;   b. Primary queen that develops from *a*;
c. A white nymph in the nest;   d. Secondary queen that develops from *c*;   e. A worker
about two-thirds grown;   f. Tertiary queen that develops from *e*.

leading the way and her mate keeping close behind her, tapping her tail with his antennae.

She chooses a suitable spot and the two of them dig a hole in the ground and quickly disappear.   An inch or so below the surface they construct a small cell in which they start the new colony.   She lays four or five eggs and the pair together rear from them dwarf workers, feeding their young on secretions from their own bodies, because they do not leave their cell or feed during this period.   It is a slow business and at the end of a year the young colony consists of only some half a dozen undersized workers and the king and queen. Many of them die before reaching this stage, killed by drought, cold, excessive rains, hunger, or enemies that have come upon them and devoured them.   Colonies that survive grow slowly: a mound that is four or five years old is only about the size of a man's fist: a full-sized colony may be ten years old or more.

Secondary Kings and Queens

If a queen dies or is killed, the workers immediately set about feeding up some of the nymphs in the nest so that they may be able

I. THE ANTESTIA BUG, *ANTESTIA VARIEGATA*. Below, two adults showing the variation in colour. Above, young stages and a cluster of eggs. They are feeding on one of their natural food-plants, *Psoralea* species. The small figures in the bottom right-hand corner show the natural sizes.

to take her place as secondary queens. Perhaps a dozen or more of the nymphs are selected by some means or other and are given special food, about which we know nothing, that causes their sexual organs to develop before the insects themselves are mature and they swell up and become secondary queens, slightly smaller than their mother, the primary queen, and with four small, white undeveloped wings on their backs. Their eyes are also smaller than they would have been if the nymphs had been allowed to grow up normally. Hence it is easy to tell a secondary from a primary queen: the original mother of the colony has four triangular stumps, the remnants of the wings she used on her wedding flight (the wing scales, as they are called), and two large compound eyes; the secondary queen has four white stumps of wings that have never developed properly and two small eyes.

It is difficult to understand why the workers always take nymphs that are not fully grown, that are in the antepenultimate stage of their development, for conversion into secondary kings and queens. One would have thought that it would be easier to convert full-grown individuals into reproductives to replace the dead parents, but this is not done. About half the nests of the black-mound termite that I open contain secondary reproductives; the mortaility among the primary kings and queens must, therefore, be high. There are always several pairs of secondaries, and not one only as is the case with the original king and queen.

Tertiary Kings and Queens

If there are no nymphs present in the nest when the old queen dies the colony is not necessarily doomed to extinction, because the termites have still another method of rearing sexual individuals that can take her place. The workers themselves, as stated before, are males and females that have failed to develop sexually. In a colony that has no queen and no nymphs, some of the immature workers may be fed in a special way so that their sexual organs develop and become functional and such workers are converted into tertiary kings and queens, capable of mating and laying eggs.

These tertiary reproductives are smaller than the primary and secondary and they have no eyes and no traces of wings on their backs, and are thus easily recognised. Their fertility is not high and they do not seem to be able to keep pace with the normal mortality in the colony so that the numbers dwindle and the colony slowly dies out. Also, the tertiary queens cannot lay eggs that will produce nymphs: their young are exclusively workers and soldiers, so that such a colony cannot send out winged individuals on their wedding

H

flight.   Colonies with tertiary kings and queens are rare.

There is a common idea in Africa that, if you find the queen of a termite colony and destroy her, the whole community must die out.   But this is not so: a colony that has lost its queen can still carry on by means of secondary or tertiary reproductives.

Harvester Termites

The harvester termites (*Hodotermes* and *Microhodotermes* species) are very common and widely spread throughout Africa and they are well known because of the damage they do to lawns and pasturage. About twenty different species are found in the continent and, although they differ in size and colour, they are all very much alike in their nesting and feeding habits, and they may be conveniently dealt with as a group.   They flourish best in regions of grassland with a fairly low annual rainfall and are not found on mountain tops or in areas where the rainfall is heavy.

Most of the harvesters do not build a mound above the surface of the ground.   The position of the nest is revealed by small heaps of loose soil, only an inch or so high, scattered on the ground, with a tunnel running up through the centre of each heap up which the termites bring the soil particles they remove when excavating their home beneath the ground.   The little heaps of loose soil are soon blown away by the wind or washed away by the rain and then the

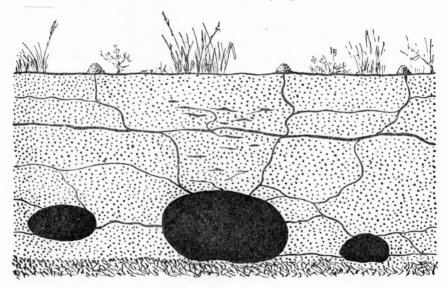

FIG. 15—Diagram of the nest of the Harvester Termite, *Hodotermes* species (After Coaton)

only indication of the underground nest consists of the entrance holes scattered about. When the termites are not working these holes are closed with plugs of mud. The nests, being deep under the ground with no indications on the surface of their presence, are very difficult to find and few people have succeeded in unearthing them, but Dr. W. G. H. Coaton of Pretoria has made a special study of these termites and the following account is based on his investigations.

Harvester termites are the only ones among which the workers have eyes and horny, brown skin. This is because the workers come out on to the surface to cut and collect the grass that forms their food. Their habit in this respect is too well known to need description. The harvesting may be done by day or at night: at the height of summer, when the days are hot, the insects work mostly in the morning and evening and during the night but in winter they come out on warm, sunny days. Besides doing considerable damage to lawns, shrubs, young trees and crops, they will attack wallpaper, books, carpets, curtains and similar articles in their interminable hunt for food. The cut-up grass and other food is carried to the entrance holes on the veld and there piled in heaps until it can be carried below.

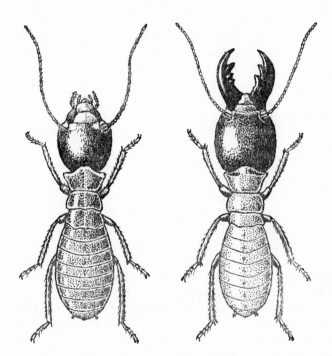

FIG. 16—Harvester Termites *Hodotermes* species. Worker on the left, soldier on the right. These termites are among the few in which the workers and soldiers have eyes.

Immediately below the ground surface the harvesting holes lead to a maze of narrow winding, branching tunnels that have small cellars along them, about three inches in diameter by a quarter of an inch high, and the termites store their food temporarily in these chambers. From these storage chambers wider tunnels lead downwards into the earth to the hives which form the actual nest of the colony and which may be from five to twenty or more feet below the surface. Surrounding the hives there are a large number of flat chambers which form the permanent storage places for the food.

The home of a vigorous colony may consist of a number of hives, up to twenty or more, scattered through the earth over a wide area and connected one with another by a network of tunnels. Each hive consists of a dome-shaped cavity, one to two feet in diameter, and the interior contains hundreds of narrow, flattened cells made of a black, brittle material of the thickness of paper. Here the termites live, surrounded by their stores of dried grass. A few of the hives in the central part of the infested area are larger than the others and, during the summer, contain eggs and immature termites, as well as the adults. The smaller hives contain only food and adult workers and soldiers, and are obviously used chiefly as storage places for food, while the large hives are the brood chambers.

The queen is not much more than an inch in length and, like the queen of the black-mound termite, can move about from one part of the nest to another: there is no royal cell as there is in the case of the fungus-growers. The winged males and females leave their nest during the summer after rain and their behaviour is similar to that already described for the black-mound termite.

The Snouted Harvester Termites

These are perhaps the commonest of all the termites found in Africa: their domed or conical mounds are a familiar sight on grass land in all parts of the country where the rainfall is not too high. There are about twenty different species of them, known as *Trinervitermes* species, but all are very similar and they may be dealt with as a group. All of them are grass eaters and feed chiefly on the grasses that are most valuable as food for stock. They may do great damage to the grazing in the areas where they are numerous.

If a mound is broken open it will be found to be like a huge sponge beneath a very hard outer crust. The interior is filled with a maze of cells and connecting passages in which the termites live and in which they store their dried grass. The base of the mound extends a foot or so into the ground and from it runways radiate in all directions under the soil, like the spokes of a wheel.

The workers collect their food only at night, making their way along the tunnels, sometimes for a considerable distance, and then coming up to the surface through narrow branch passages that are scattered for a wide area around the mound. When they have finished collecting their food for the night and have carried it all below, the

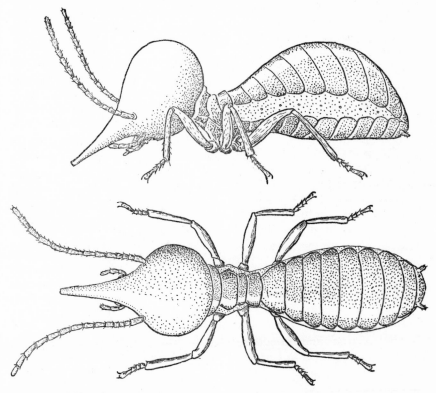

FIG. 17—Soldier of the Snouted Harvester Termite, *Trinervitemmes* species. These soldiers have brought chemical warfare to a fine art: they squirt an irritating fluid at their enemies from a large gland in their heads.

openings are plugged with soil and are no longer visible. During the day the mound and its surroundings appear to be lifeless.

A large mound in an area more or less denuded of grass may have a number of smaller mounds in the vicinity that are connected with it by underground tunnels. These are supplementary mounds used as storage places for grass collected far afield: they contain only workers and soldiers, besides the food, and no breeding takes place in them. When the rains come and grass grows again over the denuded area, the supplementary mounds may be deserted and the termites all concentrate in the main, central mound. That is why smaller mounds may often be found to be empty when they are broken open.

The snouted harvesters take their name from their soldiers. These are of several sizes but they are all alike in having heads that are of a reddish-yellow colour and drawn out in front into a pointed snout. Their jaws are reduced to useless tiny plates and they rely entirely on chemical warfare in fighting with ants and other enemies. The swollen head of the soldier consists largely of a gland in which a colourless, irritant fluid is produced and this is squirted as a sticky thread from the pore at the tip of the snout when the soldier is fighting. This can easily be seen if the mound is broken open and the soldiers that come out to defend the breach are teased. If the fluid gets on to the legs and antennae of an ant it causes that insect to writhe as though in pain, and it gives up the fight.

The workers are of the usual type and they perform all the duties of the colony except defence and reproduction. The queen, like those already described, is smallish and can move about in the nest: she is not sealed up in a royal cell but may be found in any part of the of the mound where conditions are suitable for her. Her smaller brown mate is usually to be found by her side. The wedding flight takes place in summer, after rains. Secondary and tertiary reproductives may be produced in a mound if the original pair die.

The Wood-inhabiting Termites

There are certain species of termites that do not live in the soil at all but make their homes in seasoned timber, in logs and dead branches of trees and, in some cases, in timber used in the construction of buildings and in furniture. Several species of wood-inhabiting termites are indigenous to Africa but the most important of them, from an economic point of view, is the West Indian dry-wood termite, *Cryptotermes brevis*, which has been introduced from overseas and is now well established at some of our seaports, such as Durban and Port Elizabeth.

The West Indian dry-wood termite found its way to this country about thirty years ago, probably in crates or imported articles made of wood. Because of its hidden, secretive ways, the presence of this termite is not noticed until the damage it has done is considerable. The colonies are small, even the largest consisting of only a few hundred individuals, and the only members seen outside are the winged reproductives when they leave on their wedding flight, which occurs in November and December and invariably takes place in the evening or at night.

The winged dry-wood termite is small, less than an inch across the outspread wings, and reddish brown in colour. After a brief flight the female settles on a piece of timber, almost invariably inside a building because these insects do not like timber that is exposed to the weather, sheds her wings and attracts a male who settles beside her and also sheds his wings. Then the two of them burrow into the wood and hollow out a small cell not far below the surface, sealing up the entrance hole with sawdust bound together with saliva so that there is little indication of the presence of the pair hidden below the surface.

Mating takes place after the couple are safely lodged and, after a time, the queen's ovaries begin to function and she lays a few eggs.

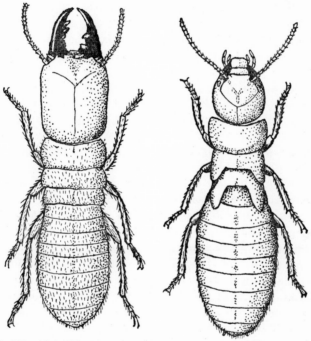

FIG. 18—The Wood-inhabiting Termite *Kalotermes capicola.* Soldier on the left, nymph on the right. There are no workers among this group of termites—the nymphs take their place.

There are no workers at all among termites of this family: the eggs all hatch out into males and females that eventually develop into winged reproductives or into soldiers. The king and queen feed the first few young but, as soon as the nymphs of the winged reproductive form are well grown they take over the work of the colony: they excavate more chambers in the wood, digest the food and feed and care for the royal couple, the young and the soldiers.

The soldiers are few in number and perform no function in the nest except that of defending it from any enemies that might intrude. The head of a soldier is black in front, enlarged and roughened, and it has a pair of stout jaws. The head is of just the right size and shape to fit closely into the narrow passages that lead from cell to cell in the wood; a soldier can therefore effectively close and guard one of these passages by putting his head into it.

Thus the inhabitants of a colony of the dry-wood termite consist of the king and queen, recognisable by their brown colour and by the swollen body of the queen, the soldiers with large black heads and white bodies, and the young winged reproductives (in various stages of growth) that will eventually leave the nest on their wedding flight, but act as workers when they are nearly full-grown.

The termites eat the wood, choosing the softer parts first and hollowing out the cells in which they live. The cells are connected one with another by narrow, circular tunnels about the thickness of the lead in a pencil. Eventually the harder portions of the wood are also eaten and little but the thin outer shell of the timber is left. Small dark coloured pellets of excrement, looking like poppy seeds, are numerous in the cells and, from time to time, the termites make small openings on the exterior of the wood and throw out these pellets. These heaps of droppings on the floor are usually the only sign that the wood is infested.

The dry-wood termite attacks almost any kind of wood and as the colonies are small, sometimes numbering only a few dozen individuals, they can infest small pieces of wood, such as wooden plugs in a wall or the three-ply backing on furniture, as well as massive timbers used in roof and floor construction. They have been found in South Africa in the blocks of parquet floors, skirting boards, flooring and ceiling boards, window frames, doors, picture rails, and so on, as well as in the pews of a church and the compositor's desks of a printing works. The colonies increase in numbers in an infested building because of the spread of the termites by their wedding flights and the damage done may be very serious after a few years.

As with the other wood-eating termites the digestion of these insects is aided by curious parasites in their intestines. If the hind gut is removed from a nymph of the dry-wood termite and the contents are examined under the microscope, an amazing number of curious protozoa will be seen. These are found only in the intestines of termites and they break down the fragments of wood into constituents that can be dealt with by the digestive juices of their host. The parasites are passed from one termite to another when they feed one another with their excrement. The higher termites do not require the assistance of these micro-organisms and few if any are found in their intestines.

There are a number of wood-inhabiting termites that are indigenous to Africa but they rarely enter buildings and are of little economic importance.

The Fungus Growers

Among the higher termites the fungus growers are serious pests and about a dozen different species of them are responsible for most of the damage done to timber in Africa. We will take, as our example of them and their work, the large fungus grower, *Macrotermes natalensis*. This species is very widely spread in the warmer parts of Africa where the rainfall is not too high, but it is not found in mountainous areas.

The mounds built by the large fungus grower may reach a height of six feet or more and they may be conical or domed or of an irregular shape with pinnacles. An old nesting site may be a grass-covered hump with a recently constructed clay mound on top. If the hard outer crust of the mound is removed, a number of passages from half an inch to three inches in diameter will be seen running down through the clay towards the nest below.

The nest cavity is usually at the base of the mound, just below the soil surface, but it may be situated higher up in the mound, above ground level. The position seems to depend upon the water table in the soil: if it is near the surface then the nest cavity is placed in the mound so that it remains dry even when the ground is water-logged. The nest cavity is more or less spherical, two or three feet in diameter, and consists of a large number of arched clay shelves on which the fungus gardens are placed and of irregular chambers in which the termites live. Many of the shelves are moist and fragile, little thicker than paper and easily broken.

The enormous queen, up to four inches in length, and her consort who is only about an inch long, are prisoners in a thick-walled royal cell situated in the heart of the nest cavity, below the fungus gardens. She is constantly attended by a number of workers licking and feeding her and carrying away the eggs as she lays them. The tunnels leading

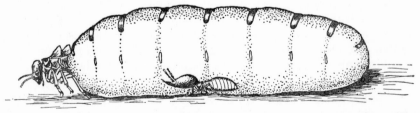

FIG. 19—The Queen of the Large Fungus-grower, *Macrotermes natalensis*, with a soldier by her side, natural size

into the royal cell are wide enough for the workers and soldiers to go in and out but are far too small for her to go through, even if she could move about, which she cannot, because of her obese abdomen.

This termite always builds covered runways when it comes out on to the surface to feed and it will carry back to the nest supplies of dry grass, dead leaves, twigs and dung, but its chief food supply consists of any dry timber it can find. If it gets into a building it builds covered runways of mud up the foundations and walls to get at the joists, flooring boards, and so on. The timber is attacked from within, leaving only a thin, outer protective skin, or devoured on the outside surface under a cover of soil particles glued together by the insects. The wood that is removed is replaced by mud so that it seems to be solid, although most of it may have been destroyed.

The food is chewed off in fine fragments and swallowed by the workers, but it is only partially digested because these termites, as already mentioned, have not got the intestinal micro-organisms to help them break down the cellulose. The faeces are collected inside the nest and moulded into spongy heaps to form the fungus gardens. Inside the cells these beds of manure look something like walnut kernels in their shells. They are reddish brown and, when the fungus grows on them, they are dotted with tiny white spheres about the size of a pin's head. These little white fungus balls form the food of the young and the royal pair.

The termites are in their limited way extremely skilful gardeners, for only the type of fungus they require is allowed to grow on their beds and all other kinds are carefully weeded out. The fungus is not allowed to develop normally and it is not known how those curious spherical bodies are produced instead of the ordinary growth. The beds are carefully tended so that there is a continuous crop to meet the needs of the colony. Sometimes after rains when the weather is warm, the termites bring up material from their fungus beds and spread it with loose soil in the shade on the surface near their nest. Numerous small, white mushrooms on slender stalks, with caps about an inch across, develop quickly from this material, produce innumerable spores in the ordinary way that are dispersed by the wind and then die. This looks remarkably like a deliberate action on the part of the insects to ensure the normal development of the fungus from time to time and to bring about its spread by means of spores—but such foresight and intelligence on the part of these lowly creatures is incredible and it is undoubtedly an instinctive action on their part. They can know nothing of the results of it. It is possible that they collect the spores to re-infect their beds, but this is merely surmise.

The common fungus grower, *Termes badius*, is perhaps the worst

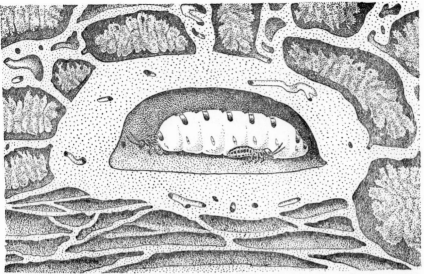

FIG. 20—Diagram showing portion of interior of the nest of the Large Fungus-grower, *Macrotermes natalensis*. The royal cell, with the huge queen and the king, is a solidly constructed prison near the centre of the nest, surrounded by cells in which the fungus gardens are situated.

pest of them all for it is the one most frequently found attacking timber in buildings and, as it is numerous and widely spread, the damage done is considerable. The mound above its nest consists at first of a low, rounded heap of soil particles loosely bound together. As the nest increases in size more heaps are added around the first one and these get worn down by the weather to form a low, grass-covered hump with heaps of recently excavated soil on it. This species does not make the conspicuous ventilation shafts that are typical of the nests of the Transvaal fungus grower, *Termes transvaalensis*. Another species that makes wide ventilation shafts from the interior of its nest to the surface of the soil is the lesser fungus grower, *Termes latericius*.

Altogether there are about a dozen species of fungus growers that attack timber in buildings, besides a number of others that restrict their attentions to dead wood on the veld. All have habits similar to those described above.

Guests and Parasites

Many strange parasites and guests are found inside the nests of termites. An account of the extraordinary beetles and flies that are found living with termites is given later in this book (pages 221, 297). In addition, there are several different species of mites that are found on the termites. A little white gamasid mite *Termitacarus cuneiformis* is quite common and these may be seen riding on the backs of the insects like miniature jockeys. They can leap nimbly from one termite to another and they seem to favour the queen as their mount, for a number may usually be found seated on her head and thorax. When the workers feed the queen or one another, the mites run down and steal a little of the food as it is passed from mouth to mouth. They seem to do little harm to their hosts.

Another kind of mite, *Cosmoglyphus kramerii*, pink in colour and belonging to the *Tyroglyphidae*, lives as a scavenger in the nest. Some times these become very numerous and may be seen clinging to the bodies of the termites in large numbers, like tiny pink ticks. These are the resting stage of the mite, known as the hypopus, when they cannot walk and are simply using the termites as a means of transport and appear to do their hosts no harm. Later, when they emerge from the hypopal stage, they drop off and run about in the nest.

A parasitic worm, a nematode, *Filaria gallinarum*, spends its young stages in harvester termites. When these infected insects are eaten by such birds as the bustard or the common domestic fowl, the worms complete their development in the intestines of the birds. The amazing assemblage of microscopic organisms found in the hind intestine of wood-eating termites has already been mentioned. It includes protozoa, spirochaetes and bacteria. The great majority of the protozoa are flagellates (*Mastigophora*) of a peculiar type and it is possible for an expert to determine the species of termite from an examination of the protozoa taken from its gut.

CLASSIFICATION

ORDER 7: *ISOPTERA*—TERMITES

Social insects living in communities composed of winged and wingless reproductive forms, together with numerous sterile males and females, workers and soldiers, of different types. Wings very similar, the fore wings being about the same size and shape as the hind wings, elongated and membranous, held flat over the back when at rest and capable of being shed by means of a zone of weakness near the base of each wing. Feet almost always four-jointed, cerci short and inconspicuous. Metamorphosis slight. Nearly 2,000 species are known from the tropical and sub-tropical parts of the world. About 400 species have been recorded from Africa.

FAMILY 1: *Mastotermitidae*
Only one living species belongs to this family, a primitive termite found in Australia. Several fossil species belong to the same family.

FAMILY 2: *Hodotermitidae*—HARVESTER TERMITES
Fontanel (the opening of the gland in the head) and simple eyes absent. First segment of thorax saddle-shaped and narrower than the head in all castes. Front wing scales (the stumps after the wings are shed) short, not overlapping the hind wing scales. These are the large termites of which the workers have eyes and may be seen collecting grass on the surface.

FAMILY 3: *Kalotermitidae*—WOOD-INHABITING TERMITES
Fontanel absent in all castes, simple eyes usually present. Pronotum (first segment of the thorax) flat, usually broader than the head in all castes: anterior wing scales large, overlapping the smaller posterior wing scales. No worker caste—the well-grown

nymphs of the reproductive caste act as workers. There are several species found in Africa, in the dead wood of trees. One foreign species, the West Indian dry-wood termite, *Cryptotermes brevis*, has become established as a pest in Durban and Port Elizabeth.

FAMILY 4: *Rhinotermitidae*

Fontanel present in all castes. Anterior wing scales large. Soldier has the pronotum flat, frontal gland almost always present. Worker has pronotum flat. About 140 species are included in this family; nearly all make their nests in the soil. They do not cultivate fungus gardens. One species, the Oriental dampwood termite, *Coptotermes formosanus*, was accidentally introduced into Simonstown and did considerable damage to timber in the dockyard area, but it seems to have been exterminated by the determined campaign carried out against it.

FAMILY 5: *Termitidae*

Fontanel present. Anterior wing scale never large. Pronotum of soldier and worker narrow, with a raised median lobe in front. The vast majority of termites belong to this large family of nearly 1,500 known species which has 122 different species in the Union of South Africa alone. They differ widely in their nesting and feeding habits: some build surface mounds, others make their nests below the surface. Certain species cultivate fungi for food, others do not. Some feed on grass only, others on dead wood and leaves, dung and decaying organic matter. The fungus growers among the *Termitidae* are the principal destroyers of wood in buildings in Africa. The termites of this family do not have the rich intestinal fauna that is found ı the lower termites and that aids their digestion.

CHAPTER VI

BOOKLICE AND THEIR ALLIES

The Silken-Tunnel Dwellers

We now come to two small, unimportant orders of inconspicuous insects that may be dealt with briefly. The *Embioptera* are a group of less than one hundred known species of fragile insects with soft, thin skin and weak powers of flight. They have no popular name and are seldom seen. As a rule, the males are winged and the females are wingless. Because the males are sometimes attracted to lights at night they are better known than their mates, which remain concealed in silken tunnels beneath the bark of trees, under stones and in other places where it is dark, damp and warm. The males look very much like miniature flying termites, usually only a quarter of an inch long, although some of the larger species reach a length of half an inch or more.

These insects are found only in the warmer regions of the world and several African species are known. They are gregarious, a number of males, females and young living together in their silken tunnel.

FIG. 21—Silken-tunnel Dwellers, *Donaconethis-abyssinica*, female on left male on right. The insects are about half an inch long.

The basal joint of each front foot is enlarged and it is said by some of the few entomologists who have studied them that the *Embioptera* spin their silk from glands lodged in these swollen joints. Certain it is that the insects, young and old, wave their front legs about when they are spinning their tunnels, but some investigators declare that the silk comes from glands in the head and that the legs are used only to place it in position. The silken tunnel is thought to protect the feeble insects from enemies and also perhaps to prevent too much loss of moisture through their thin skin. They feed on vegetation such as lichens and mosses but the males have jaws of a different type from those of the females and it is thought that they may be predacious. They are all sombre coloured, brown or yellowish brown, and the wings of the males are smoky.

Booklice and Their Allies

Very small, soft-bodied insects with long, slender antennae and no tail-feelers, or cerci, are placed together in an order of about two

thousand known species, called the *Psocoptera*, and are often spoken
of as psocids. Most householders are familiar with the tiny brown
insects that may often be seen running over books and papers, particularly if they have been stored in a damp place. These are the
booklice (*Liposcelis divinatorius*) and they feed on the paste and glue
of the book-bindings and on dried cereal products. Another species
sometimes gets into boxes where insect collections are stored and it
damages the specimens by nibbling at the dried remains—but this
insect should not be confused with the much more harmful museum
beetle (page 227).

Quite a number of different species of psocids are found in Africa
and some are very common although they escape attention because
of their small size and hidden ways. Some of them are winged, with
two pairs of delicate, membranous wings that are carried roofwise
over their backs when at rest. Others are wingless. They are to
be met with in all sorts of places—under the bark of trees, on weathered
palings and walls, in birds' nests, amid moss, in chaff and straw,
and so on. They are mostly scavengers and do little harm, as they
eat fragments of animal and vegetable matter, lichens, mosses and
fungi. Sometimes they are to be found in numbers in the nests of

FIG. 22—Psocids. A winged Psocid found on the bark of trees on the left. A Book
Louse, *Liposcelis divinatorius*, on the right.

solitary bees, feeding on the larvae that have died and on the store
of honey and pollen. Most of them are gregarious and numbers
of individuals in all stages of development may be found living together.
Some species spin thin silken webs as a cover. This group of insects
has been much neglected and little is known about even the commonest
species of them.

The second pair of jaws of these insects, the maxillae, is armed
with a stiff rod on each side, forked at the tip. The rod is known

as the pick and slides up and down in a groove. It is thought to assist in rasping small fragments off the food and it is said that this is responsible for the faint ticking sound that can sometimes be heard coming from books and papers infested by booklice. Because of this sound, these little insects share with a wood-boring beetle the name death-watch and the scientific name of the booklouse, *divinatorius*, was given to the insect because of the former belief that the ticking was a warning of the coming of death in the house.

CLASSIFICATION

ORDER 8: *EMBIOPTERA*

Small insects, only about a quarter of an inch long, that live in silken tunnels. Mouthparts are adapted for biting. The tarsi are three-jointed, the first joint of the first pair of feet being swollen and glandular. Both pair of wings alike, usually males only are winged. Cerci two-jointed and generally asymmetrical in the male. Metamorphosis slight. Only about 60 species known, from the warmer regions of the world. They live in damp situations and are gregarious.

ORDER 9: *PSOCOPTERA*

Winged or wingless insects, small, with slender antennae of nine or more joints. Mouthparts of the biting type. Wings, when present, membranous, front pair larger than hind pair, with few veins. Feet two- or three-jointed, cerci very short or absent. Metamorphosis slight. Soft-bodied insects that are mostly scavengers, of little economic importance. Not much is known about their habits and life histories.

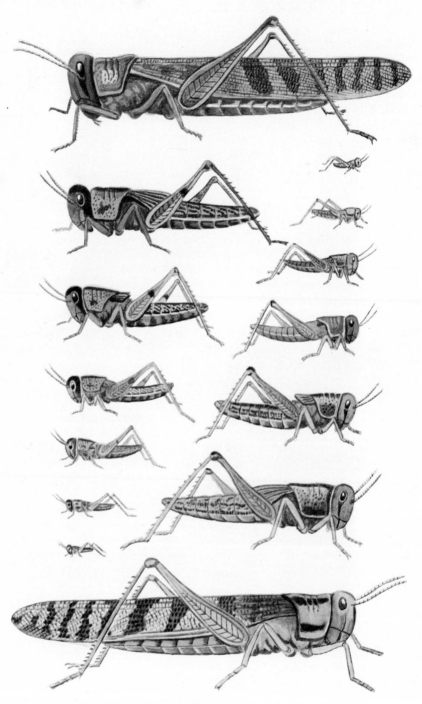

II. THE RED LOCUST, *NORMADACRIS SEPTEMFASCIATA*. Swarm phase female above. Solitary phase female below. Swarm phase hoppers on the left. Solitary phase hoppers on the right. All natural size.

CHAPTER VII

BITING LICE AND SUCKING LICE

Biting Lice

Some authors place the biting lice and the sucking lice in two separate orders but the modern tendency is to regard them as being closely enough related to justify their inclusion in one order, the *Anoplura*. This name means "unarmed tail" and apparently refers to the fact that these insects lack the jointed feelers, or cerci, on the hind end of their abdomen.

All these lice spend their whole lives on the bodies of warm-blooded animals. The biting lice are sometimes spoken of as bird lice because they are found mostly on birds, although there are some species that are common on mammals. The name of this group, *Mallophaga*, means "wool eaters" and is not very apt because the biting lice feed on feathers, hair, scurf and anything else edible which they can find on the skin of their host. They are not blood-suckers but they will feed on blood that oozes from any injury to the skin. Birds that are badly infested with these lice may have bare patches of skin where the feathers have been eaten through and fallen out. If the lice are numerous the irritation they cause is severe and may cause the bird to lose weight and condition. The dust baths that many birds are fond of taking are to help them get rid of these parasites.

The lice die within a few hours of the death of their host because they cannot live on the cold body nor can they survive in the open. They probably migrate from one animal to another only when the animals are in contact, in their sleeping places, in nests, and so on. Their life histories are very simple. The small oval eggs are glued separately to the bases of the feathers or hairs on the host's body and these hatch in a few days into young that resemble their parents. They have the same habits and eat the same food and, after moulting a few times, are mature when a few weeks old.

Perhaps the most interesting feature about the biting lice is the fact that closely-related animals have on them parasites that are closely related one to another. For example, the biting lice found on different species of ducks are all very much alike and form a group that is different from the group of lice found on pigeons; similarly with hawks, waders, dassies, carnivores, and so on. The case of the lice on dassies is a striking one and of particular interest in Africa.

As is well known, dassies, or hyraxes, or conies, as they are called in the Bible, form a small group of peculiar mammals that are placed in a family all by themselves. Although they look something like rabbits, they are more closely related to elephants and hoofed mammals than to rodents. The classification of these little animals

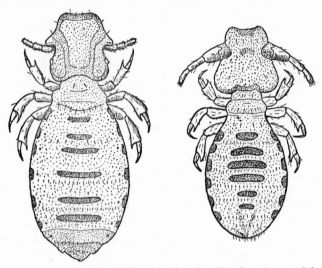

FIG. 23—One of the several kinds of Biting Lice found on Dassies. *Procaviphilus serraticus*, female on left, male on right.

is difficult and the specialists who deal with them are not agreed on the subject: dassies are all so much alike that it is not easy to decide whether they should all be placed in one genus or whether they should be divided into two or three genera. Similarly with the species: the common dassie of the Union of South Africa is known to science as *Procavia capensis*, but there are slight differences in specimens collected in various parts of the country and these have been described and named as seven separate sub-species, each being given triple names to distinguish them. For example, the dassie found at the Cape is known as *Procavia capensis capensis*, that from East Griqualand as *Procavia capensis chiversi*, that from Natal as *Procavia capensis natalensis*, and so on. The questions at once arise, are these just unimportant variations of one and the same species, or are they sub-species, or are they truly distinct species? It is by no means easy to answer questions such as these, and similar problems have arisen with the dassies found in other parts of Africa. Nowadays the entomologists who have made a special study of lice are able to step in and throw some light on this vexed question.

Dassies are lousy animals, in the literal sense. No less than nine different species of lice, including the biting and sucking types, have been found on one dassie. Sometimes the lice are very numerous and rarely if ever is an animal found without any lice on it. Hunting through the dried skins of dassies in museums has yielded a rich harvest of dead lice, so that quite a lot has been learned about them and their distribution. One particular type of biting lice, known as *Procavicola* (the dweller on the dassie) is abundant on dassies in the Union and it has been found that each of the seven sub-species of dassies has its own particular species of *Procavicola*. For example, dassies collected in the Cape Peninsula have the louse, *Procavicola vicinus*, on them and this louse has not been found elsewhere in the Union; the East Griqualand dassies have *Procavicola subparvus* on them, and so on. From this it is argued that those so-called sub-species of dassies are really separate and true species: it is believed that these animals have been isolated in their mountain homes for so long that, not only have they evolved into separate species themselves but even their lice have had time to become differentiated in each of the geographical areas. So, says the entomologist, show me the lice and I will tell you the species of dassie and what part of the country it came from.

The same argument holds with the division of dassies into three groups, rock dassies, tree dassies and a mixed group known as *Heterohyrax*. The studies of their lice indicate that rock dassies are distinct enough from tree dassies to be included in separate genera, but that the *Heterohyrax* group is not a natural one and should be split up, some going to rock dassies and the remainder to tree dassies.

When more is known about the lice on different types of birds and mammals, and their distribution, doubtless much more light will be thrown on some of the difficult problems of classification.

Sucking Lice

The sucking lice are small, flat-bodied insects that suck blood and they are found only on mammals. They are known to science as the *Siphunculata;* in many works they are referred to as the *Anoplura*, the biting lice being regarded as a separate order, the *Mallophaga*. The lice found on human beings belong to two species, *Pediculus humanus* and *Phthirus pubis*. The former of these exists in two forms, the head louse and the body louse, but they are regarded as biological races and not as separate species because they interbreed and the differences in their form are indistinct. The lice belonging to this family, the *Pediculidae*, are the only ones with eyes: all the rest are blind. The body louse, the head louse and the crab louse are the only ones found on human beings and they are not found on any other animals.

All the sucking lice are parasites that spend their whole time on the skin of their host and live exclusively on blood. About two hundred and fifty different species are known in the world and they are found on all kinds of land mammals except carnivores (excluding the dog family) and marsupials. As with the biting lice, the relation of the sucking louse to its host is very close, one species of louse living on one host or, in some cases, on a few species of hosts that are closely related to one another. Lice from one animal are reluctant to feed upon the blood of a different species.

It has even been asserted that lice from different races of man differ from one another in colour, those from dark races tending

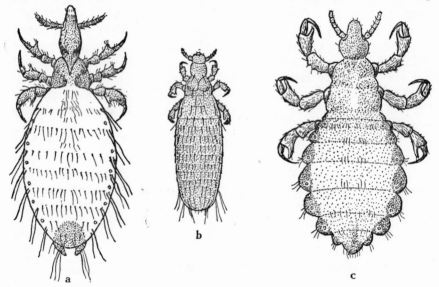

FIG. 24—Sucking Lice
(a) From wildebeest, *Linognathus gnu*, female;
(b) From field mice in Zululand, *Polyplax cummingsi*, female;
(c) From buffalo, *Haematopinus* species, male;
The largest is about an eighth of an inch long.

to blackness whilst those from white people are paler in colour. There is some truth in this statement and it has been found that the colour of a louse is influenced by its surroundings in early life: a louse from a man with black skin and hair is usually darker in colour than one from a fair-skinned host.

Because of its great importance as a conveyor of disease, the life history of the body louse has been carefully studied. Devoted entomologists have carried these disgusting insects in pill-boxes, with silk gauze on the bottom, next to their skin, beneath their socks or strapped to their fore-arms. As the lice cannot live for any length of time away from the body of their host, they have to be kept in this way and allowed to feed on blood regularly, in order to study them.

The egg of the louse is large when compared with the size of the insect that laid it, yellowish white, and flattened at the front end with a characteristic cap on it. It is fastened to a fibre on the underclothes, next to the skin, in the case of the body louse and to the root of a hair in the case of the head louse. The egg hatches in about a week when kept at about the same temperature as that of the human body; it fails to hatch at temperatures below about 75 degrees Fahrenheit.

The cap of the egg is porous and the young larva inside sucks in air and blows itself up so that it is able to force off the lid and

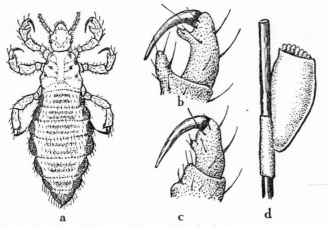

a   c   d

FIG. 25—The Body Louse of Human Beings, *Pediculus humanus*
    (*a*) Adult male: the female's abdomen has a forked tip;
    (*b*) Front foot of male, to show "thumb";
    (*c*) Front foot of female;
    (*d*) Egg of a louse, or "nit", attached to a hair.

emerge. The larva is like its parents and feeds on blood. During the ten days or so it takes to reach maturity it casts its skin three times. The female starts to lay eggs about four days after she reaches full size and she lays at the rate of three to five a day until she has deposited between one hundred and two hundred eggs, after which she dies. Her length of life as an adult is about a month.

Lice are conveyed from one human being to another almost exclusively by contact, either directly from one person to another or through infested clothing and bedding. These insects are of the utmost importance because of the part they play in the spread of such diseases as typhus, trench fever and relapsing fever. It has been said that lice have played a much more important part in the history of the world than all the great militarists put together; that they, in the past, have had more to do with the winning of wars and battles than the generals and admirals, because diseases carried by the lice have killed far more of the soldiers than all the efforts of their enemies. Fortunately, the discovery of D.D.T. and the high susceptibility of lice to this insecticide have removed most of their terrors and have made it comparatively easy to rid whole populations of these dangerous parasites.

A number of different kinds of sucking lice are found on domestic and wild mammals, but little is known about their life histories.

CLASSIFICATION

ORDER 10: *ANOPLURA*—BITING AND SUCKING LICE

Small, flattened, wingless insects living as parasites on birds and mammals. Antennae short, three- to five-jointed. Eyes reduced or absent. Mouthparts highly modified and adapted either for biting or piercing. Thoracic segments more or less fused together. Legs short, tarsi one- or two-jointed, with claws adapted for clinging to host. Abdomen without cerci. Metamorphosis slight.

SUB-ORDER 1: *MALLOPHAGA*—BITING LICE

Parasites, mainly of birds, but sometimes found on mammals. Eyes reduced. Mouthparts modified for biting. First segment of thorax separate but second and third more or less joined. Tarsi one- or two-jointed, with single or paired claws. About 2,000 species are known from all parts of the world.

SUB-ORDER 2: *SIPHUNCULATA* (sometimes *Anoplura*)—SUCKING LICE

Parasites of mammals. Eyes reduced or absent. Mouthparts highly modified for piercing and sucking, withdrawn into head when not in use. Segments of thorax fused. Tarsi one-jointed with only one claw. About 250 species of sucking lice are known.

CHAPTER VIII

MAY-FLIES
The Ephemeroptera

People living near lakes, streams and rivers are familiar with may-flies because of the sudden appearance of large numbers of these delicate insects at certain times of the year and their equally rapid disappearance. Many adult may-flies emerge in the evening and are dead by the next morning, their mating and egg-laying having been completed in this brief period. Some species can, however, live for several days as adults although all are short-lived because they cannot feed. The mouthparts of the adult are degenerate and its alimentary canal is filled with nothing but air which gives it buoyancy but is certainly not sustaining. Because of their very short life as adults may-flies have been given the name *Ephemeroptera*, which means "winged creatures of but a day".

May-flies have two pairs of wings, the first pair larger than the hind pair, distinguishing them from stone-flies, which have hind wings bigger than the front ones. There are some may-flies that have lost the second pair of wings altogether. Usually there are three long, slender feelers on the tail, but some species have only two. All of them spend their immature stages in water, some taking six to nine months to reach full size, others longer. Anglers know these insects well for they form an important part of the food of trout and many of the artificial flies used by fishermen are made to resemble may-flies as closely as possible. They are known as duns and spinners and each kind has its own special name. Even in South Africa, where few small insects have popular names, various kinds of may-flies are known to fly-fishermen by such names as red border wing, yellow dun, Worcester dark blue, September brown, blue-winged orange, bronze spinner, and many others. It has been suggested that, as may-flies is not a very appropriate name for the group as a whole, seeing that May is certainly not the month when most of them appear, they should be called day-flies because of the brief duration of their lives.

The Life History of a May-fly

The September brown may-fly, *Adenophlebia peringueyella*, appears, as its name implies, in the spring, in September and October, along the banks of stony mountain streams in the south-west Cape.

77

Very similar and closely allied species are found further north. The
adult has a brown body, mottled with pale yellow on the abdomen,
and about half an inch long. Its three slender tails are a little longer
than the body and the outspread wings are just over an inch across.

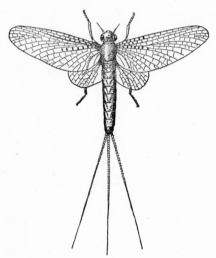

The female is slightly larger than the
male and he has a pair of claspers
on the end of his abdomen that
she lacks.

The adults of this species are
rather long-lived for may-flies, as
it has been found that specimens
reared in captivity live for ten or
eleven days, although, like the rest
of their kind, they cannot take any
food and their stomachs are filled
only with air. Mating takes place
after the graceful aerial dance above
the water, and soon after this the
female lays her eggs. They are very
small—one hundred of them placed
end to end would not measure one
inch—oval in shape and covered
with small pits. The female drops

FIG. 26—The September Brown May-fly, *Adeno-*
phlebia peringueyella, adult female. It is a little
more than an inch across the outspread wings.

them in batches as she dips down and just touches the surface of the
water with the tip of her abdomen.

The eggs sink to the bottom and lie on the sand amongst the
stones for three weeks before they hatch. The newly-hatched larva
is white and very small, only about one-fiftieth of an inch long, and
it is exactly like the nymph shown in figure 27, only it has no gills
at this stage in its career and no traces of wings on its back. It creeps
about on the bottom of the stream, generally keeping under stones
for protection, but it can swim fairly well in still water, or with the
current, by a jerky motion of its body. Its food seems to consist
chiefly of any dead and decaying animal and vegetable matter which
it can pick up on the bottom. In an aquarium it thrives and grows
if given a little mud from time to time from the bottom of a pond:
it swallows the mud and finds nourishment in the organic fragments
contained in it.

At first it gets all the oxygen it needs by absorption through
its thin skin but, as it grows bigger, it needs an increased supply and
seven pairs of gills appear along the sides of its abdomen. These
gills are what are known as tracheal gills because they do not contain
blood-vessels, as the gills of a fish do, but tracheae, or air-tubes,

PLATE 13

(*a*) A mound of the Black-mound Termite, *Amitermes atlanticus*. The coin is half-a-crown and shows the comparative size.

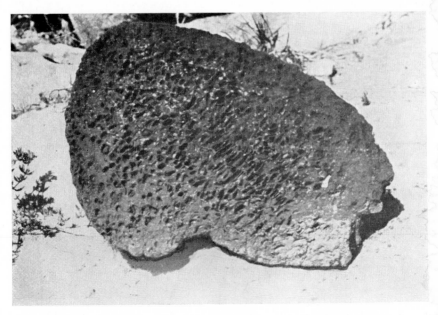

(*b*) A mound of the Black-mound Termite sawn in half to show internal structure

PLATE 14

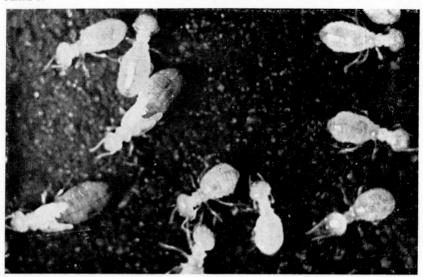

(a) Young termites inside an artificial nest. They are white because they are fed only on digested food by the adult workers.

(b) A fungus garden of *Macrotermes natalensis*. The termites eat the little white spherical nodules. About natural size.

and the air dissolved in the water passes through the thin skin of the gills into the respiratory system of the insect. Often the gills may be seen moving rapidly, with a quivering motion. This does not help the insect to swim but serves to keep a current of fresh water flowing over the gills to renew the air-supply.

The insect casts its skin several times in the course of its growth: it is said that some may-flies moult twenty-three times and more, but the exact number is not known in the case of the September brown. By the autumn the nymph is about two-thirds grown and the buds of the future wings can be clearly seen on its back. It is fully grown by July and the earliest adults may emerge towards the end of this month, although the majority do not come out until a few weeks later.

The change from a life in the water to a life in the air is fraught with great danger for the may-fly, as it has to leave the shelter of the stony bottom of the stream and make its way up to the surface, and any hungry fish that sees it will at once snap it up. The change is made, therefore, with remarkable speed. The full-grown nymph of the September brown usually creeps out of the water on to a stone or tree-root or other object that projects above the surface. If it cannot find a suitable resting place, it will simply swim up to the surface and change to an adult there, supported only by the surface tension. A split appears in the skin of the back and the winged insect struggles out and flies away in a few seconds.

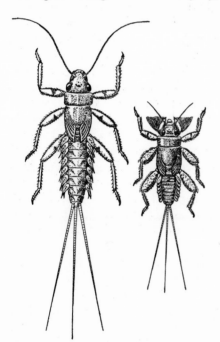

FIG. 27—May-fly nymphs.
On the left, nymph of *Adenophlebia peringueyella.*
On the right, nymph of *Tricorythus discolor.*
The body of the larger of the two is about an inch long.

At this stage the may-fly is known as a sub-imago and it differs from the adult, or imago, in that it is duller in colour and still has a thin coat which must be shed. This final moult from the sub-imago to the imago is unique and found only among may-flies. After resting for a brief period, the sub-imago creeps out of this last thin skin and flies away on the final stage of its career. The duns of the angler are may-flies in the sub-imago stage, whilst the spinners are the imagos.

J

Other May-flies

May-flies have only been studied in detail in Africa in the Cape Province and Natal, and about seventy different species are known from these two areas. There are doubtless many more species that await discovery in other parts of the continent. The immature stages are to be found in almost every type of stream and the different forms are well adapted to the conditions under which they live. Some

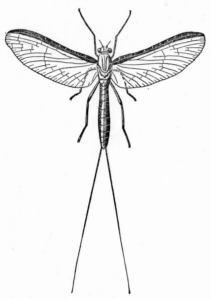

species are burrowers and live in tunnels they dig for themselves in muddy banks and these have strong forelegs. Others, like the Worcester dark blue, *Tricorythus discolor*, are adapted for life in swift-flowing streams and have flattened bodies and strong legs for clinging to stones. These nymphs do not swim much but run rapidly over and under the stones. In the case of the Worcester dark blue, the nymph has long bristles on each mandible that project on either side like a handsome moustache, serving, apparently, to catch any tiny creatures or fragments of other food that are swept into them by the current. Some nymphs living in swift water do not come to the surface to emerge as adults: they cling to a stone a

FIG. 28.—The Red Border-wing, a common two-winged may-fly, *Cloeon lacunosum*. Its body, without the tails, is little more than a quarter of an inch long.

few inches below the surface, their skin splits and the adults shoot to the surface enclosed in a bubble of air which bursts and projects them, quite dry, into the atmosphere. They fly away immediately to the bank, where they rest until they cast their last skins.

Some of the smaller kinds (*Baetis* species) are very abundant in clear, strong-flowing streams and they form an important part of the food of trout. The nymphs are agile swimmers, as they have rows of stiff bristles on their tails which together form an efficient paddle. The adults may be recognised by the possession of two tails only, instead of the usual three. The females generally creep just below the surface of the water in order to lay their masses of tiny eggs. Along some of the trout streams in Britain it is thought worthwhile to put boards and slabs of concrete in the water, sloped and anchored in such a way that the females are attracted to them as attractive places for oviposition. The aim is to increase the number of nymphs in the river so as to provide more food for the trout.

The adults of most may-flies emerge by day but some species hatch at night and are attracted to lights. Usually the insects may be seen on the wing from about sunset to dusk, sometimes dancing in clouds like gnats. Also like gnats, these swarms consist mainly of males; females that are ready to mate visit the swarm, pick up a partner and then the couple drop out.

Although the adult may-flies are short-lived, some dying after only a few hours although others may live for a week, the nymphs live longer. Some of the smallest species, under very favourable conditions, may grow up in a little over a month, others take four months, others nine months and some of the largest of the burrowers may take nearly two years to reach full size.

As a general rule, the females lay their eggs by dapping on the water—that is to say, by dipping down in flight and just touching the surface with the tip of the abdomen as the eggs are dropped. In some cases each egg has a bundle of tiny threads attached to it which spread out in the water and serve to anchor the egg to weeds or other objects below the surface. The females of a few species, such as the common two-winged may-fly, *Cloeon lacunosum*, retain their eggs in their body until they are ready to hatch and the young nymphs emerge as soon as the eggs fall into the water. These are, naturally, the may-flies which have a comparatively long life of several days in the adult state. The females hide for a few days after mating, while their eggs develop inside their bodies, then they fly back to the water, fall on to it and the larvae emerge from the eggs as soon as they are laid. The females die as soon as the oviposition is finished.

CLASSIFICATION

ORDER 11: *EPHEMEROPTERA*—MAY-FLIES

Soft-bodied insects with short, threadlike antennae. Mouthparts of adults vestigial so that they cannot feed. Wings membranous, held vertically upwards when at rest, the hind pair much smaller than the front wings (hind wings are absent altogether in some species). Abdomen terminated by long cerci, generally three in number, but two only in the case of some species. There is an additional moult between the sub-imago and the imago stages that is not found in any other insects. Immature stages spent in water, respiration by tracheal gills. Metamorphosis slight.

CHAPTER IX

DRAGON-FLIES
The Odonata

Dragon-flies are among the handsomest and most striking of all insects because of their size, their swift flight and their beauty and brilliance of coloration. With their large, well developed eyes, they are perhaps the keenest sighted of all insects and, relying mainly on vision in their pursuit of prey and other activities, their antennae are reduced to small, threadlike organs. This group of insects, of which about three thousand different species are known in the world, falls naturally into two sub-orders. The larger and more stoutly built dragon-flies belong to the sub-order *Anisoptera* (insects with

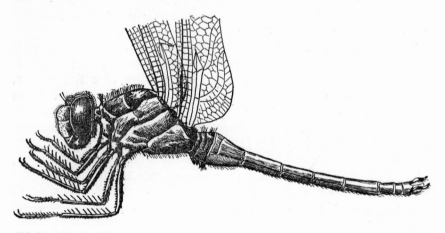

FIG. 29—The Sky-blue Dragon-fly, *Orthetrum caffrum*, male, showing the distortion of the thorax that brings the legs forward and throws the wings backward. The swelling at the base of the abdomen where the curious mating organ is lodged, and the claspers at the tip of his abdomen are also shown.

unequal wings). It is very easy to recognise them by their swift flight and by the fact that their wings, when at rest, are held stiffly outspread at right angles to the body. The hind wings are larger than the front pair. The damsel-flies belong to the sub-order *Zygoptera* (insects with yoked wings); they are smaller and have slender bodies. All four wings are of the same size. When they settle, they hold their wings folded vertically above their backs. Both these groups are very well represented in Africa.

The name *Odonata* means "toothed" and seems to refer to the sharp teeth on the mandibles of these voracious insects. The shape of the thorax is peculiar in all dragon-flies, as an adaptation to their highly specialised mode of life. The three segments are elongated from above downwards and are sloped backwards so that the legs are all brought forward near the mouth and the wings are carried somewhat further back than is the case with most insects. Because of the position of its legs, a dragon-fly can scarcely walk at all—it can only cling; but they are armed with stiff bristles and together they form a basket-like trap in which the insect captures its prey as it darts through the air.

Damsel-flies

Damsel-flies are smaller and more slender and weaker than their robust relatives, the true dragon-flies. Their narrow, delicate wings are not suited for a swift, darting flight and these insects spend much more of their time resting on reeds and bushes beside the water in which they spent their immature stages. Most of them are brightly coloured, metallic green, or azure blue or blood-red, or a combination of these. Often the males are of quite a different colour from the females.

As our example of this group we may take the common conspicuous damsel-fly, *Chlorolestes conspicua*, that is found in the south-west Cape. Closely related species with similar habits are found in other parts of the country. This insect is about two inches long, with a dark brown body and narrow yellow stripes at the sides, the male being of the same colour but slightly smaller.

The adults may be seen on the wing in the second half of summer, making short flights along the banks of a mountain stream and

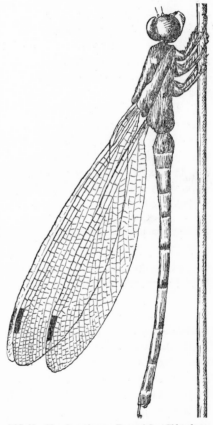

FIG. 30—The Conspicuous Damsel-fly, *Chlorolestes conspicua*, female

returning again and again to the same perch. The mating takes place in the extraordinary manner that is characteristic of all dragon-flies and is found in no other insects. The male has a pair of claspers on the tip of his abdomen by means of which he seizes the female round the neck, immediately behind the head. The pair may be seen flying over the water linked tandem fashion, with the male always in front, holding his partner's head securely in his claspers. After a time they settle and the female then bends her abdomen forward, bringing it right under the male until the tip reaches the underside of the second segment of the male's abdomen. Here his copulatory organ is lodged and the male cells are transferred to his mate during this act.

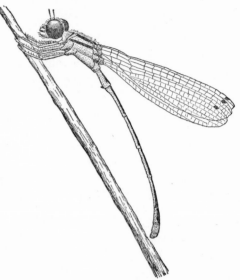

Fig. 31—The conspicuous Damsel-fly, *Chlorolestes conspicua*, male

The reproductive organs of the male are of the usual type found in insects and he has a genital opening at the tip of his tail. But, in addition, he has the peculiar special apparatus on the second segment of his abdomen, which includes a receptacle for his sperms and an elaborate arrangement for transmitting them to the female. Just before he seizes her in his claspers he turns the tip of his own abdomen forward and injects the contents of his testes into the receptacle and then, later on, second-hand as it were, he passes them on to his mate. It is not known how or why dragonflies have evolved this unique method of mating.

The ovipositor of the female is armed with two pairs of slender, sharp saws. With these she makes small slits in the tender green shoots of trees or bushes overhanging the water and deposits her oval white eggs, one in each slit. The punctures are made one below the other, about an eighth of an inch apart and generally she lays five or six eggs in a row, before leaving to lay another batch of eggs in another twig later on. The tissues of the twig swell slightly round each hole and small gall-like knobs are formed on the twig, marking the spots where the eggs have been inserted.

The tiny larva drops into the water as soon as it hatches and spends all its life there until it is ready to change into a winged adult. When fully grown it is nearly an inch and a half long, brown, and mottled with darker and lighter patches. It has a pair of prominent round compound eyes, two slender antennae and the buds of wings on its back. At the end of its tail there are three flattened tracheal gills, paddle-shaped, with a dark band across the middle of each.

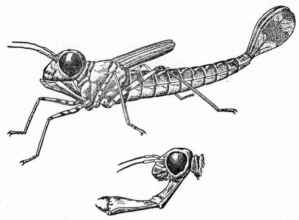

FIG. 32—The Nymph of the Conspicuous Damsel-fly, *Chlorolestes conspicua*. It is about one and a half inches long. Below is shown the head with the mask extended.

It is an active insect, swimming and running about amid the stones on the bottom of the stream, hunting for the may-fly nymphs and other small water creatures that form its prey.

On the underside of its head it has the curious organ known as the mask, characteristic of all dragon-fly nymphs and not found in any other insects. This mask is so called because, when not in use, it is held so that the lower part of the head is hidden by it. It is the lower lip, or labium, elongated and jointed and armed with a pair of pincers at the tip, wonderfully adapted to form a very efficient weapon for the capture of prey. When the nymph sights any small creature that might serve as food it stalks its victim until it is near enough to shoot out that lower lip with remarkable speed, grip the prey in the pincers and then, folding the lip back again, bring its captive within reach of its jaws.

When the nymph is fully grown it creeps out of the water, up a reed or other plant, and there it fixes itself firmly by means of its claws. Then the skin splits and the adult damsel-fly slowly and laboriously pulls itself out of the nymphal skin. When its head, thorax, legs and wings are free, it hangs head downwards, held in position only by its abdomen still in the old skin. Then, after its skin has hardened sufficiently, it jerks itself upright and grips the stem above by its feet and finally drags its abdomen free and creeps up the stem a little way, leaving the empty husk still clinging to the stem below it. When its wings have expanded and hardened, it flies away, a living flash of light, to enter on the last stage of its career. The mask and the tracheal gills are discarded with the nymphal skin since these organs are no longer of any use to the winged creature of the air.

A large number of different species of damsel-flies have been described and named from Africa. We still have a great deal to learn about their life histories but some of them (*Lestes* species) seem to be well adapted to live in regions where the rainy season is short and uncertain and where droughts are long. The eggs of these damsel-flies lie dormant and protected in slits in stems and only hatch after good rains. The nymphs grow with astonishing rapidity, reaching full size in a few weeks, so that they are ready to change into adults before the stream or pool dries up.

The nymphs of some species of damsel-flies are almost transparent and are difficult to see as they swim about in the water. Others are greenish and mottled and are well hidden among the water-weeds they choose as their hunting ground. Still others are brown and mottled and live partially covered and concealed by the mud on the bottom.

Dragon-flies

Dragon-flies, in the restricted sense, are the strongly built, swift-flying, larger members of the order. They include some of the most beautiful and most conspicuous of our insects. Most of them are very wary and exceedingly difficult to catch. Unfortunately the brilliant colours fade when the insects are killed and pinned in collections and the dried specimens do not reveal anything like the full beauty of the living insect. In some parts the gaily coloured giants of the order are feared and regarded as dangerous, but they are all completely harmless to man and are not possessed of any sting or other weapon by which they can do any damage. Most of the species are widely distributed, some being found from the Mediterranean down to the Cape, and quite a number are found throughout the whole continent south of the Sahara.

The sky-blue dragon-fly, *Orthetrum caffrum*, is common in East Africa as far north as Abyssinia and is also abundant in South Africa as far south as the Cape of Good Hope. About two inches long the male is blue, with a bloom on him something like that of a ripe plum; his mate is of about the same size and usually of a reddish tinge, but without the bloom. They mate in the manner already described for damsel-flies, but in their case the whole act is often completed on the wing: she bends her abdomen right forward until

PLATE 15

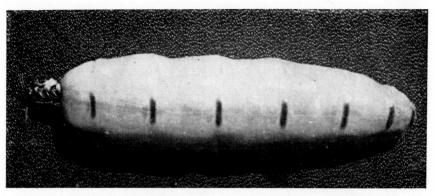

(a) The Queen of *Macrotermes natalensis*. She is about four inches long.

(b) A termite mound in Northern Rhodesia

PLATE 16

(*a*) Primary King and Queen, *Amitermes atlanticus*, in an artificial nest, with workers and winged adults

(*b*) Workers and Tertiary Queen of *Amitermes atlanticus* inside an artificial nest

the tip reaches the peculiar apparatus on the underside of his second abdominal segment and the transfer of male cells is made whilst the pair are in full flight.

The female lays her eggs by "dapping" on the surface of the water, in the same manner as already described in the may-fly. Her oval

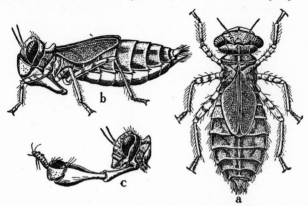

FIG. 33—The Nymph of the Sky-blue Dragon-fly, *Orthetrum caffrum*. It is about an inch and a quarter long.
(*a*) Viewed from above;
(*b*) Viewed from the side, showing how the mask covers the lower part of the head;
(*c*) Head with mask extended to capture prey.

white eggs are washed off the tip of her abdomen and sink to the bottom where they rest in the mud until they hatch. The nymph is like that of the damsel-fly, only more stoutly built, rounded on the back and more or less flattened on the underside; and it has not got the three paddle-shaped tracheal gills that are characteristic of the damsel-flies. It breathes in a different manner.

Usually the dragon-fly nymph creeps about over the bottom or amid the water-weeds and its brown or yellow colouring, mottled with darker brown, helps to conceal it. It can, however, move faster when disturbed and, if watched whilst doing so, it will be seen to move its legs with a rowing action, although the legs are too slender to serve as efficient swimming organs. The speed attained is obviously due to some other form of locomotion. If a nymph is put in a saucer of water and a few drops of ink are dropped into the water just behind the insect, the ink will be seen to swirl and eddy in a current that issues from the hind end of the nymph, even whilst the insect is quite motionless. If the water is only just deep enough to cover the insect a tiny fountain of water may be thrown up above the surface and it will be seen that this comes from its tail-end.

If the nymph is put in a narrow glass tube of water and held up to the light and examined through a hand-lens, a bulky organ

K

can be seen through the translucent body-wall in the hind half of the abdomen. This organ is the greatly enlarged rectum and, by its regular pulsation, it pumps water in and out constantly. When the nymph wishes to move quickly through the water, it squirts the water from its rectum with some force and the jet drives it forward—so these little insects were making use of jet-propulsion long before man thought of it.

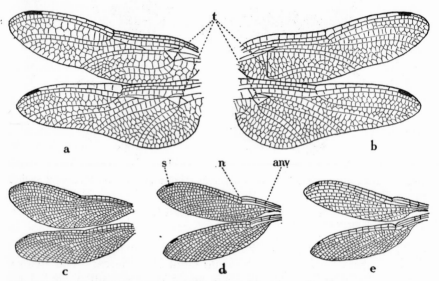

FIG. 34—The Classification of Dragon-flies is based largely on the wings.
(*a*) and (*b*): *Anisoptera*, unequal-winged dragon-flies;
(*c*), (*d*) and (*e*): *Zygoptera*, equal-winged damsel-flies;
(*a*): Family 1, *Aeschnidae*, large dragon-flies with the triangles (t) on the fore- and hind-wings similar or nearly so;
(*b*): Family 2, *Libellulidae*, moderate sized dragon-flies with the triangles dissimilar on the two pairs of wings;
(*c*): Family 3, *Libellaginidae*, damsel-flies with the base of the wings not very narrow and several ante-nodal veins (anv.) between the base of the wing and the node (n);
(*d*): Family 4, *Lestidae*, damsel-flies with wings narrow at the base, only two ante-nodal veins and a large stigma (s) covering two or more cells;
(*e*): Family 5, *Agrionidae*, damsel-flies with wings narrow at the base, only two ante-nodal veins and a small stigma covering only one cell or less.

Besides making use of its rectum as a means of getting about quickly, the dragon-fly nymph also uses this part of its body as its chief respiratory organ. Inside the rectum, along its muscular wall, there are folds which are richly supplied with tracheae and the constant renewal of the water that bathes them supplies the insect with all the air it needs. Because of its rectal gills, the dragon-fly nymph does not need the external paddle-shaped gills, so it has only three points on the tip of its abdomen.

The mask is similar to that of the damsel-fly nymph, only the pincers on it are much wider and the general form of the trap is more that of a scoop, with stiff bristles along the inside edge to prevent the escape of small prey. The nymph does not chase its victims. It remains motionless or creeps about slowly, waiting patiently for some small creature to approach close enough for the mask to shoot out with extraordinary speed and capture it. It only uses the jet-propulsion to move quickly in an emergency. The full-grown nymph creeps out of the water and casts its skin in the manner already described.

African Dragon-flies

Although a large number of different species of dragon-flies and damsel-flies have been described and named from Africa, little is known about their life histories. The immature stages of them all are spent in water, generally in pools, lakes and slow-flowing streams with muddy bottoms. The nymphs of damsel-flies are slender and jerky and swift in their movements and some of them may be found in fast-flowing clear streams where they prey upon small crustaceans and may-fly nymphs. The dragon-fly nymphs are much more sluggish and are usually found in stagnant water, particularly in shallow weedy ponds with muddy bottoms.

The eggs of damsel-flies and of some dragon-flies are laid in slits made in stems of plants over-hanging the water. The females of most dragon-flies simply drop their eggs in the water while flying over the surface, but some of them alight on reeds and other water-plants and creep below the surface in order to lay their eggs. The eggs of some species are laid in strings of jelly and attached to sub-merged twigs.

The nymphs cast their skin eleven to fifteen times in the course of their development. Some of them reach full size in a few weeks whilst others take a year or longer to grow up. They are remarkable in that they have large compound eyes whereas the larvae of most other insects have only a few simple eyes or none at all. All are predacious and are armed with the curious mask or elongated lower lip, for the capture of their prey.

The adult females of many species are differently coloured from the males: in some cases the females occur in two or three different colour forms and it is not easy to associate the sexes unless they are seen flying in tandem while mating.

CLASSIFICATION
ORDER 12: *ODONATA*—DRAGON-FLIES AND DAMSEL-FLIES
Predacious insects with biting mouthparts and two pairs of membranous wings, each wing with a complex network of veins and usually with a stigma, or dark spot, near

the tip. Eyes very large and prominent, antennae short and threadlike. Abdomen usually long and slender, male with a peculiar mating organ on underside of second and third abdominal segments. Nymphs live in water and capture prey by means of a highly modified labium known as the mask. Breathe by means of tracheal gills in rectum or in three flat plates on tip of abdomen.

SUB-ORDER 1—*ANISOPTERA*—DRAGON-FLIES IN THE RESTRICTED SENSE

Wings held out flat on either side of the body in repose: hind wing always broader near the base than the fore-wing. Eyes not separated by a space greater than their own diameter. Nymphs breathe by means of rectal gills.

FAMILY 1: *Aeschnidae*

Large dragon-flies with the triangles in the fore- and hind-wings similar or nearly so (see figure 34a). This family includes some of the largest and swiftest of all our dragon-flies.

FAMILY 2: *Libellulidae*

Triangles dissimilar in the two pairs of wings (see figure 34b). This family includes some of our commonest dragon-flies. Some of them are brilliantly coloured and some have wings blotched with black and yellow. Many are widely spread, some occurring from the Mediterranean to the Cape. Some of them, such as *Sympetrum fonscolombei*, are known to be migratory and to fly long distances in search of new breeding places.

SUB-ORDER 2: *ZYGOPTERA*—DAMSEL-FLIES

Wings held closed over abdomen in repose. Fore- and hind-wings very similar, with narrow bases. Eyes separated by space greater than their diameter. Nymphs with caudal gills.

FAMILY 3: *Libellaginidae*

Base of wings not very narrow. Several veins between base of wing and node (see figure 34c).

FAMILY 4: *Lestidae*

Wings narrow at base. Only two veins between base of wing and node (see figure 34d). Stigma (black spot on wing) large, covering two or more cells.

FAMILY 5: *Agrionidae*

Wings narrow at base. Only two veins between base of wing and node. Stigma small, covering only one cell or less (see figure 34e). This is the largest family of damsel-flies and includes most of our species.

CHAPTER X

THRIPS

The Thysanoptera

The tiny insects known as thrips seldom attract any attention because of their size and their sober colours. Few of them exceed one-eighth of an inch in length and nearly all are black, brown or yellow. They are common enough on flowers, especially those of the daisy type, and most of them feed on the juices of plants, piercing the tissues with their peculiar mouthparts and sucking up the sap. Some of them are predacious and feed upon aphides and their own kind. Usually they have two pairs of narrow wings fringed all round with long hairs. The name of the order, *Thysanoptera*, means "fringed wings" and refers to this characteristic feathery outline of the wings. The feet are peculiar in that each has a curious bladder at the tip, which can be withdrawn when not in use; but if the insect is walking over a smooth surface, such as a leaf, the bladders on its feet can be protruded and enable it to cling securely. Thrips are sometimes spoken of as the *Physopoda*, a name which means "bladder-footed."

The Life History of a Thrips

A common and widely spread thrips which is a pest is the onion thrips, *Thrips tabaci*. The full-grown insect is only about one twentieth of an inch in length and varies from yellow to light brown in colour. Among other plants, it feeds on onions and if it becomes numerous whitish-silvery patches appear on the leaves as a result of the damage caused by the insects. These patches spread, particularly in dry weather, and eventually the leaves curl up and wither. The insect is difficult to see, not only because of its size but also because it hides beneath the leaf-bases and amid the dead leaves, but the harm it does to the crop is evident enough.

The microscopic kidney-shaped eggs are inserted by the female in minute slits in the leaves and they hatch in about a week. The young larva is like its parents, but white, with bright red eyes and without wings. It feeds on the sap of the leaves and casts its skin four times before it is fully grown. After the second moult, wing-pads appear on the back and the insect assumes what is known as the prepupal stage. It can move about, but it does not feed and usually it remains hidden. Then it casts its skin again and becomes a pupa with long wing-pads and with its antennae bent back over its head.

It does not feed and moves very little in this stage, which closely resembles, in a simpler form, the chrysalis of higher insects. Finally it casts its skin for the fourth and last time and becomes an adult.

The greenhouse thrips, *Heliothrips haemorrhoidalis*, is a well-known pest in Europe and America and it has also found its way to South

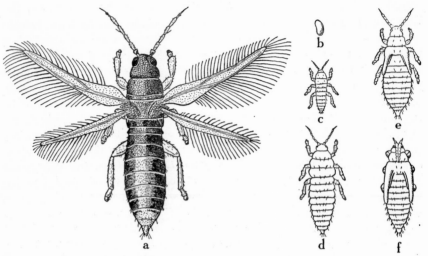

FIG. 35—The Greenhouse Thrips, *Heliothrips haemorrhoidalis*, greatly enlarged
(*a*) Adult; (*c*) First-stage larva; (*e*) Prepupa;
(*b*) Egg; (*d*) Second-stage nymph; (*f*) Pupa.
The adult is black and only about one twenty-fifth of an inch in length.

Africa where it is now well established and, in some years, does very serious damage to young pine trees. It is thought to have come originally from tropical America. Although a greenhouse pest in cooler countries, it flourishes out of doors here and attacks many different kinds of plants. In the pine plantations the female lays her eggs within the tissues of the pine-needles, from ten to twenty in number, and these hatch in about ten days. The tiny white young feed in colonies on the surface of the needles and cause them to turn from a healthy green to a mottled yellow colour, with black spots of the insects' excreta. The larval stages last for two or three weeks, during which period the insects moult twice, changing to a prepupa at the last moult. The prepupal stage lasts only for a few hours and then it changes to a pupa. About five days later the winged adult emerges, only about one twenty-fifth of an inch in length, black, and with white legs. The insect breeds continuously throughout the year and there are some twelve generations annually, so it is not surprising that, weather conditions being favourable, it can multiply very rapidly and do great harm to the trees by destroying the foliage.

African Thrips

This group of insects is very well represented here and quite a number of species have already been described and named. Some of them are pests and do harm to the blossoms of fruit trees, to grasses and grain and to fruit. One kind, by feeding on young oranges, round the stem, causes white rings to appear on the rind before the fruit is half grown. On hot, still days the adults can fly from tree to tree and so the trouble spreads. If a thrips is watched through a hand lens it can be seen to curl up its abdomen just before taking to flight. This action is apparently performed in order to straighten the hairy fringe on its wings by using its hairy abdomen as a comb.

The males of some species are rare and parthenogenesis, or development from unfertilised eggs, is known to occur among thrips. When disturbed, some species crawl away in a leisurely fashion, others are able to leap, but few of them take to wing readily. Occasionally, on sultry days, certain kinds may invade the house from the flowers in the garden and they may then be mistaken for lice as they rest on the walls and curtains, although a close examination will reveal the presence of wings.

CLASSIFICATION

ORDER 13: *THYSANOPTERA*—THRIPS

Small or minute slender-bodied insects with short antennae of six to nine joints and curious asymmetrical mouthparts that form a cone beneath the head. Tarsi one- or two-jointed, each with a terminal bladder than can be protruded or withdrawn. Wings, when present, very narrow and armed with a fringe of long hairs. Metamorphosis includes a simple, primitive pupal stage.

CHAPTER XI
PLANT BUGS AND THEIR KIN
The Hemiptera
We now reach one of the largest of all orders of insects and, from an economic point of view, the one that is undoubtedly by far the most important. The members of this order vary very widely indeed in size, shape, habits and life histories, but they all have mouthparts that are adapted for piercing and sucking. They live entirely on liquids, such as the sap of plants or the blood of other living creatures, and they have no mandibles for chewing. Many of them are wingless and the wings of the others are so varied in structure that it is impossible to give a general definition of them. The name of the order, *Hemiptera*, means "half-winged" and refers only to the type of wings found among some of the plant bugs. This enormous group of insects includes stink bugs, twig wilters, aphids, scale insects, white flies, cicadas, bed bugs, water bugs and a host of others.

Shield Bugs
Shield bugs form a large family of well over four thousand known species and they receive their popular name from the shape of their flattened bodies. Many of them are brightly coloured, some are well known pests of crops and garden plants and all have the power of emitting an unpleasant smell that serves as a protection from enemies.

As our example of this important group we may take the Antestia bug which is very widely spread in Africa, being a serious enemy of coffee-growers in East Africa and of fruit-growers in the Cape Province. It is a rather pretty insect, about three-eighths of an inch long, usually yellow marked with dark brown and red, but the colouring is variable and specimens may be found that are green, marked with red and blue. If roughly handled it gives off a strong "buggy" odour that comes from a fluid produced in special glands lodged on the underside of the abdomen and that open by a pair of slits just behind the bases of the hind legs. Its scientific name is *Antestia variegata*.

Many of the shield bugs might at first sight be mistaken for beetles, but a glance at the underside of the head should serve to distinguish them. Beetles are armed with biting jaws, but the bugs all have a slender, tubular beak which is carried folded back against the underside of the body when not in use, between the bases of the legs. The beak or proboscis consists of a grooved sheath, the labium, in which four slender lancets are lodged—these lancets correspond

94

PLATE 17

These photographs show secondary kings and queens of *Amitermes atlanticus* in an artificial nest

PLATE 18

(*a*) Nymphs and a winged adult, *Amitermes atlanticus*

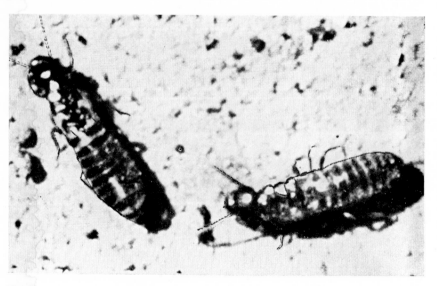

(*b*) A young King and Queen, *Amitermes atlanticus*, immediately after they have shed their wings, hunting for a suitable spot in which to make their home, she leading the way

to the mandibles and maxillae of other insects, highly modified to serve as piercing and sucking organs—and the food passes up the capillary tube formed by the four lancets, assisted by a pumping action of the pharynx. The grooved sheath does not enter the puncture made by the lancets: it serves only as a protective covering and guide for the lancets.

The Antestia bug and its relatives can also be readily distinguished from beetles by the nature of their wings. The hind wings are membranous and resemble those of beetles, but the fore wings are quite different from those of other insects. The front half of each of the first pair of wings is hard and horny, but the hind portion is soft and membranous—hence the name, *Hemiptera*.

The female Antestia bug is slightly larger and more robust than the male, but otherwise she is like him in coloration and markings. She lays her eggs on the twigs and leaves of the food plant in clusters of from ten to fourteen. They are about one-sixteenth of an inch long, pearly white when first deposited and shaped like short, stout barrels, with a clearly marked circular lid on top of each. In about a week the eggs darken to a slate colour and they hatch in from ten to fourteen days. The young bug emerges from the egg by pushing off the lid and is black and similar to its parents, but wingless.

For about twenty-four hours the little creatures remain clustered round the empty egg shells, but after this they move off and scatter in search of food. The young bug feeds on the sap of the plant for about twelve days and then rests and moults to the second stage. The colour is now somewhat changed, for the second stage nymph is gaily spotted with yellow and black. It feeds again for a fortnight and then casts its skin for the second time and the first signs of its future wings appear on its back. In all, the skin is cast five times and after the fifth moult the adult stage is reached. The female deposits several batches of eggs before her ovaries are exhausted and she dies. The whole life cycle from egg to the death of the adult, extends over about one hundred days and there are three generations a year, as the development during the winter is slower than in the summer.

The Antestia bug is left alone by insect-eating animals because of its unpleasant smell, but it has one tiny enemy that destroys a large number of its eggs. This is a tiny black parasitic wasp that may infest as many as ninety per cent. of the eggs in some seasons, causing them to turn black, the parasite's offspring emerging from them instead of the young bugs.

Antestia feeds on several different kinds of veld plants including taaibos (*Rhus* species), some composites and species of *Psoralea*. When the fruit or coffee berries are ripening, the bugs find their way

L

into the orchards and plantations and attack the fruit. The punctures made by the bugs cause the fruits to become misshapen: as they ripen, the area round each puncture fails to develop and depressions are produced that mark the sites of the punctures. Just below the skin hard little lumps form and the value of the fruit is greatly depreciated. Quinces and pears are particularly liable to this type of damage; when stone fruits are attacked, gum oozes from the punctures and the fruit becomes misshapen and "furry". Many of the fruits drop prematurely. Furthermore, the tiny holes made by the bugs undoubtedly serve as means of entry for various disease-causing organisms.

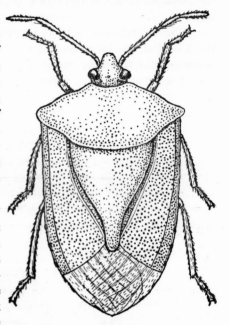

Another common and widely spread shield bug is the green stink bug, *Nezara viridula*, which is often seen in vegetable gardens and may do much damage to tomatoes and other plants. There are a number of other species that the gardener and farmer will come across and they can all be recognised as shield bugs by the shape

FIG. 36—The Green Shield Bug, *Nezara viridula*, showing the characteristic shape of all shield bugs.

of their bodies and the nature of their wings. The Bagrada stink bug, *Bagrada hilaris*, is one of the most troublesome of all our shield bugs. Not quite a quarter of an inch long, black with a few bright orange or yellow spots, it attacks all kinds of plants belonging to the cabbage family, and when numerous, may completely destroy the young plants. The female lays her small, oval, cream-coloured eggs in the soil and these hatch out into little black bugs that go through the same stages as those described for the Antestia bug.

The large pale green shield bug, *Eucosternum delegorguei*, is found in large numbers at the end of the rainy season in some parts of Africa. The young stages of this bug are unknown at present but the adults, about an inch long, are strong fliers and they gather in swarms on certain kinds of bushes and trees. Although they give off a strong buggy odour that is disgusting to Europeans, the natives collect and cook and eat them, regarding them as great delicacies.

Twig-Wilters

The dull brown bugs, about an inch long, that suck the sap of plants and cause tender twigs to wilt are well known to all gardeners. The odoriferous glands that secrete the stinking fluid are particularly well developed in members of this family, which are also known as stink bugs. The slits through which the liquid is poured can be seen with the naked eye on the underside of the body of the adult, near the bases of the hind legs. They are surrounded by a slightly raised, roughened border which is called the evaporating surface as the liquid is retained on it so that it evaporates slowly. The immature

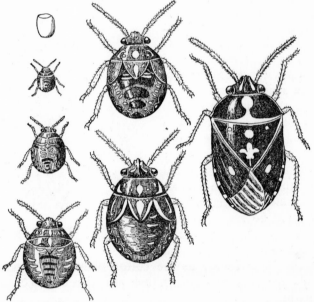

FIG. 37—The Bagrada Bug, *Bagrada hilaris,* showing the stages of development from egg to adult. The adult is about a quarter of an inch long, black with orange spots.

stages have the slits on their backs and they also can be seen with the naked eye. The change of position of the glands is apparently necessary because the bug acquires two pairs of wings when it casts its skin for the last time and, if the glands were still on the back, their openings would be covered by the wings and the smell from them would not be so widely or freely diffused.

The female twig-wilter, *Holopterna vulga,* lays her oval brown eggs in a row, generally fixing them along a twig of the food plant. They are about as large as cabbage seeds and hatch in a fortnight. Each has a lid at one end and, in order to force its way out, the young bug is armed with a sharp T-shaped egg-piercer on top of its head.

After it has burst open the lid of the egg the youngster takes a rest when it is halfway out of the shell. It casts its skin in this position and so leaves the egg-piercer behind in the empty egg-shell. This T-shaped instrument can be seen if the eggshell is examined through a good hand lens. All the stink bugs have this special means of breaking out of the egg.

Many species of this large family of bugs (*Coreidae*) attack culti- vated plants. They are mostly dull coloured and more elongated than the shield bugs, although there are some that are brightly coloured. We have several kinds of red bugs in Africa that are closely related to the twig-wilters, although they are put in a family by themselves (*Pyrrhocoridae*). These bugs are important because they include such important pests as the cotton-stainer bugs, so called because they pierce the bolls of cotton and stain the fibre. They are easily recognised by their strongly contrasting colours of red and black: the males are smaller than the females and mated cou- ples may often be seen, walking about tail to tail. Several species of red bugs feed habitually on

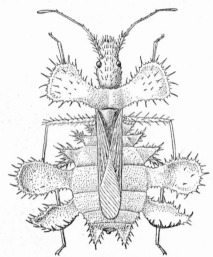

FIG. 36—The Spiny Brown Coreid, *Pephricus capicola.* It is about half an inch long.

plants of the same family as the cotton plant, and therefore, when cotton is planted, they quickly turn their attention to this crop and may do great harm.

The lace bugs (*Tingidae*) are pretty little bugs that feed on the sap of various kinds of plants and are sometimes numerous enough to do harm. There is nothing remarkable about these insects when they are young, but the mature bugs have curious flattened projections on their thorax and abdomen, armed with long spines and the result is they have a characteristic lace-like appearance that gives them their popular name.

Pond-Skaters

Pond-skaters (*Hydrometridae*) are common everywhere and may be seen skimming over the surface of almost any pool of water. They are slender, dark-brown bugs about half an inch in length, wonderfully well adapted for their life as skaters on the water. The underside of the body is clothed in a coat of dense white hairs that give the insect a silvery appearance, in sharp contrast with the dark upper side. These hairs prevent the bug from getting wet. Even though it is pushed under the water with a piece of stick, it bobs up again immediately, quite dry.

At first sight the pond-skater seems to have only four legs, but it actually has six, like the rest of its kind. The first pair of legs are short and are usually carried tucked away beneath the front of the body. They are so placed as to form efficient grasping organs by means of which the bug can hold any dead or dying insect floating on the water. It is a timid little creature and does not hunt its prey but contents itself with the juices of insects that have been drowned, or are struggling on the surface and cannot defend themselves. When the skater finds a dead insect it seizes the body in its front legs, brings its beak forward and thrusts the four lancets deep into the tissues.

The bug's middle and hind legs are long and thin and, although they do not seem to be modified in any particular way to support the insect on water, they enable it to skim swiftly over the surface, held up only by surface tension. Its body does not touch the water. On rare occasions, when hard pressed, the bug will dive beneath the surface for a time, but its movements are awkward and it soon rises to the surface again. There are a number of different species of these 'water-measurers' found in Africa. Most of them are winged so that they can fly away in search of fresh abodes when the water of a pool dries up. But there are a few kinds that are wingless and certain other species in which two, or even three, different types are found: certain individuals may have fully developed wings, while others have only half-wings and still others are wingless, all these individuals belonging to the same species.

The female lays a number of tiny, oval eggs, enclosed in jelly and attached to submerged plants. The eggs hatch into tiny black youngsters that run about over the surface among the bigger skaters, looking like animated blackdots. Their habits and their food are exactly the same as those of their parents.

Pond-skaters have some very interesting relatives that are the only insects found living far out on the open ocean. They are very much like the common pond-skaters in appearance, only smaller, being little more than a quarter of an inch in length when fully grown. These marine skaters are known as *Halobates* and they are found in the warmer parts of the Pacific, Indian and Atlantic Oceans, certain species having been recorded from off the east coast of Africa. In calm weather these sea skaters skim over the surface and feed on the juices of any dead creatures they can find. When the weather is rough they dive beneath the surface and cling to floating sea-weed or drift-wood. All the known species of *Halobates*, some fifteen or so, are wingless and they spend their whole life on the surface of the sea.

Assassin Bugs

This is a large family of more than two thousand known species and the members of it may readily be recognised by their short, curved beaks. Most of them feed on the blood of insects and other small creatures, but some of them attack higher animals, including man himself. Only a few of them feed on the juices of plants. The strong, three-jointed beak is armed with four sharp lancets and many of these assassin bugs are able to inflict a painful wound if they are handled carelessly. Most of them are dull coloured, brown or black, and may be found lurking under stones and fallen logs and amid decaying vegetation where they hunt for their prey. Some have slender bodies and long legs and look much like daddy-long-legs flies. Others have the front legs adapted for seizing prey and might be mistaken for small

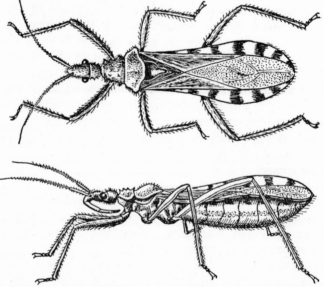

FIG. 39—An Assassin Bug. It is little more than half an inch long.

praying mantes, but the curved beak below the head reveals the fact that they are assassin bugs. A few small species are marked with black and white in such a way that they closely resemble the ants among which they run and upon which they prey. Very little indeed is known about the life histories and habits of the numerous assassin bugs found in Africa.

Bed Bugs

This is a small family of wingless bugs that are parasites on the higher animals and feed on their blood. The common bed bug, *Cimex lectularius*, is cosmopolitan and very widely spread in Africa. A second very similar species, *Cimex rotundatus*, is also found here and has the same objectionable habits. They are prevalent in dirty, over-crowded dwellings, hiding by day in any convenient cracks in

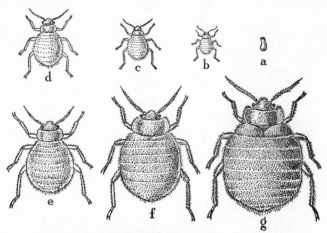

FIG. 40—The Development of the Bed Bug, *Cimex lectularius*
(*a*) Egg;   (*c*) First-stage nymph;   (*e*) Third-stage nymph;
(*b*) Larva;   (*d*) Second-stage nymph;   (*f*) Fourth-stage nymph;
                                                                (*g*) Adult female.

the furniture or walls and coming out at night to feed on the sleeping inhabitants. Some people feel severe irritation as a result of their bites while others scarcely notice any effects at all. Because of their bloodsucking habits, these bugs might be capable of transmitting certain diseases from sick to healthy persons, but so far there has been no conclusive evidence of their doing so.

The female lays her eggs in cracks in bedsteads and other objects and they hatch in about eight days. The young bugs are like their parents and feed only on blood. They cast their skin six times before they are fully grown, taking from six to eight weeks to reach full size. They are capable of withstanding long periods of starvation, in which case the life cycle takes much longer.

Other members of this family, very like the common bed bug, are known as parasites on different kinds of birds and bats.

Giant Water Bugs

The giant water bugs (*Belostomatidae*) include among their number some of the largest of all insects. Certain species found in

Africa are more than four inches in length and they are formidable insects that attack tadpoles and small fish. The lancets in the strong, curved beak are capable of inflicting a painful wound if one of these bugs is held in the hand. They can fly quite well and move from one sheet of water to another at night and are sometimes attracted to lights. Their favourite haunts are the muddy bottoms of weedy pools, where they lurk, well concealed by their dull colours, in wait for their prey. They can swim very well because their hind legs are flattened and fringed with stiff hairs so that they form efficient swimming organs.

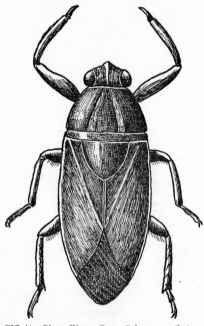

FIG. 41—Giant Water Bug, *Belostoma niloticum*. It is about three inches long.

They have two appendages on the tip of the abdomen that can be withdrawn or extended at will: each is grooved and, when they are closely applied one to the other, form a tube down which air can be drawn when the tip is thrust above the surface of the water. The back of the abdomen is hollowed out so that a space is enclosed between it and the wings and this forms a reservoir for air, so that the insect can remain for a long time beneath the surface. In some species of giant bugs the eggs are carried by the male, glued to the upper surface of his first pair of wings. They are placed here by the female and it is said that often she has to hold him by force whilst she is imposing them upon him. He carries them about with him until they hatch and often the young bugs prey upon one another for their first meal before leaving the paternal back.

Water Scorpions

The water scorpions (*Nepidae*) are aquatic bugs that have the front pair of legs adapted for seizing their prey much in the same way as the fore-legs of praying mantes, some assassin bugs and Mantispa (page 134) are adapted. The slender brown water scorpions (*Ranatra* species) are quite common although they are not often seen because they spend their time creeping slowly about amid water-weeds and on the muddy bottoms of shallow pools, where they hunt for the may-

PLATE 19

(a) An artificial nest for termites. It consists of circular cells, one and a quarter inches in diameter, cut in cork lino. The left half of the tray contains humus and decayed wood. The nest stands on four screws in containers of D.D.T. powder to prevent the escape of the insects and attack by ants.

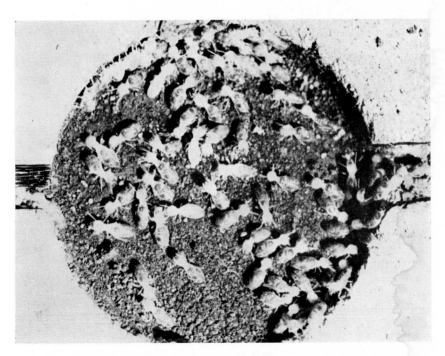

(b) One of the cells in an artificial nest containing workers of the blackmound termite, *Amitermes atlanticus*

PLATE 20

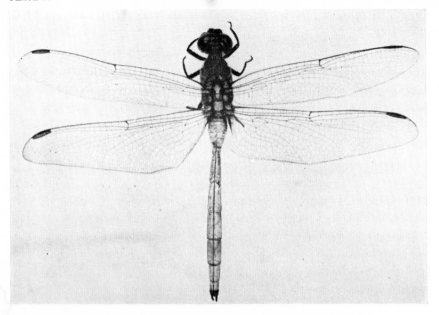

(a) THE SKY-BLUE DRAGON-FLY, *Orthetrum caffrum*, male

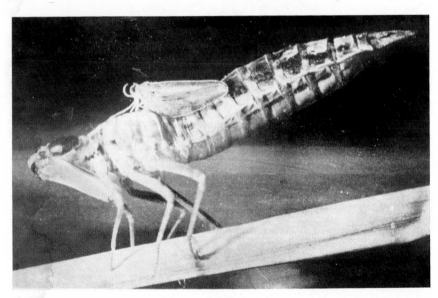

(b) The empty husk of the nymph of a large dragon-fly (Aeschna species). The husk remains clinging to the reed for some time after the insect has left. The white threads on the back are the tracheae cast off with the skin.

fly and dragon-fly nymphs, crustaceans and small tadpoles upon which they feed.

The beak of the water scorpion is short, curved and strong, well able to pierce the body of its victim and to suck the blood. The first segment of the thorax is elongated, as well as the coxa, or basal joint of the front legs, so that its grasping legs have a long reach for seizing the prey. It is a sluggish, slow-moving creature and always lies in wait until a victim comes near enough for those legs to shoot out and grip it.

No antennae can be seen on the head because they are hidden in special cavities on the underside of the head: it is the same with the

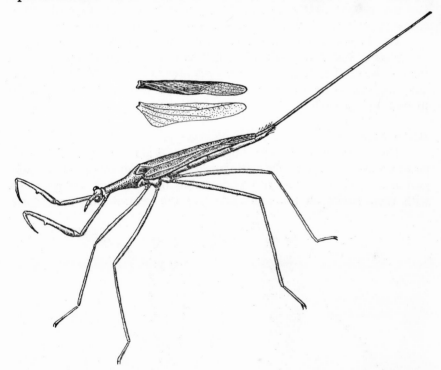

FIG. 42—A Water Scorpion, *Ranatra grandicollis*, wings shown above. All natural size.

giant water bugs and the water boatmen and this is obviously an adaptation for a life under water. These aquatic bugs with hidden antennae are placed in a group by themselves called the *Cryptocerata*, or 'hidden-horned'. The female water scorpion lays her eggs in slits she cuts in the stems of water plants by means of her sharp toothed ovipositor. Each egg has a pair of threads or filaments on it that protrude from the hole in the stem and it is thought that these filaments

M

help the embryo inside the egg to obtain air from the water. The young are like their parents.

The long, slender thread on the tail is the respiratory tube and consists of two grooved appendages, or cerci, locked together by stiff bristles along the edges of the groove. In order to breathe, the insect simply brings the tip of the tube to the surface. The wings are of the usual type but they are small and narrow and it is surprising that the long, ungainly insect is able to fly at all, but it does migrate from one pool to another during the night. Often the resting stage of small red water mites may be seen clinging to the legs and respiratory tube of the water scorpion, but they do not seem to do any harm to their host and use it only as a means of getting about. After a time the mites cast their skin and become free swimming and leave the insect.

The broad water scorpions, *Nepa* species, have similar habits to *Ranatra*, but their bodies are flat and broad and their breathing tube is short. The female lays her eggs in chains in the water, the eggs adhering one to the other by means of seven slender threads attached to one end of each.

Water Boatmen

The common little water bugs known as water boatmen fall into two families that are easily distinguished from each other. The back-swimmers (*Notonectidae*) are remarkable in that they always swim with their backs on the underside and the ventral side uppermost.

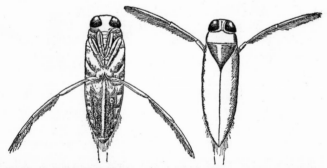

FIG. 43—The Back Swimmer, *Anisops varia.* Underside on left, upper side (underneath when swimming) on right. The insect is about a quarter of an inch long, bluish white on back with bright orange triangle at base of wings.

The back is strongly ridged so that it is shaped like the bottom of a boat and it is smooth and shiny and snow-white in some species. The under surface of the abdomen (the upper side of the swimming insect) is dark coloured and has four rows of hairs along it, a double row down the middle and a row down each side. These hairs, overlapping on each side, enclose air so that the bug is able to breathe while below the surface.

The front and middle legs are carried tucked away against the sides so that they offer little resistance when the insect is swimming, but its hind legs are long and fringed with stiff bristles and project from the sides just like a pair of oars. It swims with a vigorous rowing motion of the hind legs and it 'feathers' its oars on the return stroke because the bristles fold back along the legs and offer less resistance. When it dives it carries a layer of air between its wings and its back and this gives it the silvery appearance. It can leap from the surface of the water and take to wing.

About fifty different species of back-swimmers have been recorded from Africa but doubtless many more still await description and names. They are common in shallow, stagnant water and are predacious insects, feeding on any small creatures they can capture. The males have stridulatory combs on their front legs by means of which they can produce a chirping sound. The females of some species lay their eggs in slits they make in the stems of water-plants, while the females of other species lay their eggs on the surface of submerged stems and other objects. The nymphs live in water and have habits similar to those of their parents. There are five nymphal stages before the adult form is reached.

The water boatmen (*Corixidae*) differ from the back-swimmers in having a flat back, not keel-shaped, and they swim right side

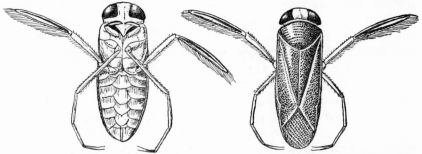

FIG. 44—The Water Boatman, *Sigara meridionalis*. Underside on left, upper side on right. It is about a quarter of an inch long, swims right way up and is brown in colour.

up. They are small insects, brown in colour, with short front and middle legs and long, fringed hind legs that are used as oars. The beak is short and unjointed. These bugs are common in shallow pools with muddy bottoms: they are not found in deep water, or in the open water of a large lake. It is still uncertain what these insects feed on. According to some entomologists they feed on small creatures such as mosquito larvae, but others assert that they feed on the juices of waterweeds. Little is known about their life history, but the females of some species are known to attach their tiny eggs to the leaves and stems of water plants.

Cicadas

Perhaps the most characteristic sound of a hot, drowsy day in Africa is the shrill call of the cicadas. Only the male cicadas sing: the females are voiceless. If one of these insects is captured it is easy to determine the sex by an examination of the underside. The female has a sharp ovipositor at the tip of the abdomen while the male lacks this: he has two semi-circular plates at the base of the abdomen, just behind the hind legs. These are the covers of his sound-producing organ.

This organ, which is so characteristic of the cicada family, consists of a cavity on either side of the abdomen in which the drums, or timbals, the folded membranes and the mirrors are lodged. The timbals are tightly stretched membranes like miniature drums, with strong muscles attached to them. By the contraction and expansion of these muscles the timbals are made to vibrate and so the sound is produced, much in the same way as a sound can be produced by pressing the bottom of a tin vessel in and out.

The folded membranes on each side simply act as sounding boards and increase the volume of the sound. The mirror seems to function as an ear. Each of the sound-producing organs is covered by a semi-circular plate, as mentioned above. If one of these is lifted with the point of a pin the mirror can be seen at the back of the cavity as a small, white, round, shining plate. The timbal is at the side of the cavity and not so easily seen, while the folded membrane is in front of the mirror and also not readily detected.

By raising or lowering the opercula (the semi-circular plates), while it is calling, the cicada can increase or diminish the sound. This action also has a ventriloquial effect, making it difficult for the human listener to locate the exact spot whence the sound is coming. The elaborate sound-producing organ is lacking in the female, but she has a pair of mirrors at the base of her abdomen that serve as her ears.

Usually two or three cicadas will be found close together on a tree, with their beaks embedded in the branch, feeding on the sap. One or more of them will be males, singing tirelessly, while the silent members of the group will be females. It is thought that the loud song serves as an assembly call, and it may also have a stimulating effect on the mating instinct.

The cicada has four membranous wings, stiff and flat and held roofwise over the body. The front wings do not have the front portion hard and horny, as do the shield bugs and others already described and, therefore, the cicadas and the other members of the order still to be mentioned are placed in a separate division known as the *Homoptera*—insects with uniform wings. It has two large compound eyes, with three small simple eyes between them. The antennae are short, black and threadlike. Its mouthparts are of the true bug type, consisting of a grooved beak in which are lodged four slender lancets for piercing the tissues of plants and sucking the sap. Throughout its life the cicada is a sap-sucker.

The female lays her eggs in slits she makes in the bark of trees. Nobody has yet studied the life history of any of our cicadas in detail but it would seem, from observations made overseas, that the eggs take about six weeks to hatch. The young cicada is like its parents but is more stoutly built and has two curious front legs, with greatly enlarged spiny thighs and shanks that serve as digging implements. The little creature drops to the ground and at once burrows beneath the surface. It spends the whole of its immature life tunnelling through the soil in search of tender young roots upon the sap of which it feeds.

In the United States the cicada, popularly known as the seventeen-year locust, is very well known. In some years these insects appear in immense numbers. By studying the intervals between the appearance of the various broods it has been found that this cicada takes thirteen years to reach maturity in the southern states and seventeen years in the colder north. We do not know how long the different species of cicadas found in Africa take to reach maturity. There may be some that are as long-lived as the American periodical cicada, but disconnected observations made here from time to time indicate that some of our cicadas spend only two or three years underground.

When the nymph is fully grown it burrows its way upwards to the surface and out into the light and air. It climbs a few inches up some nearby tree-trunk, digs its claws in and clings there motionless for some time. Then its skin splits down the back and the adult cicada struggles out of the nymphal skin, slowly and laboriously. After its wings have expanded and dried it is ready to fly away and spend a few brief weeks revelling in the sunshine and singing its shrill, monotonous song.

There are well over one thousand different species of cicadas known in the world, chiefly from the warmer regions. As far as is known, all have a life history similar to that just described. Sometimes, under circumstances not understood, the immature cicada constructs a curious chimney or cone of earthen particles glued together by saliva. The chimney projects four inches or so above the surface of the ground and is hollow inside and closed at the top. The cicada lives inside this for some weeks before breaking a hole at the base and emerging. It is not known why some individuals build these chimneys and others do not.

Frog-hoppers

Small, spittle-like masses of white foam may often be seen on the twigs and leaves of different kinds of plants. These are the dwelling places of immature plant bugs known as frog-hoppers (*Cercopidae*) because, when they are adult, they look something like small frogs and they can leap well. If a patch of the cuckoo-spit, as it is called, is swept aside with a match-stick the owner of the bubbly home will be found inside. It is a stout, soft-bodied insect, usually green in colour, but some species have dark markings on them. It moves sluggishly and is very ill at ease when forcibly removed from its watery home, and it soon dies if it is exposed to the hot sunshine and allowed to get dry. If the insect is watched closely as it creeps up the stem it will be seen that its tail is telescopic and can be extended or withdrawn at the creature's will.

The frog-hopper feeds on the sap of the plant. The sap is a weak solution of sugars and salts and the insect has to imbibe a great deal of it in order to get sufficient nourishment; its watery excretion, therefore, is copious. Along each side of its abdomen there is a membranous flap which is folded under the belly and these flaps meet in the mid-line to enclose a space between them and the underside of the abdomen. The insect's spiracles are lodged inside this chamber, which opens to the exterior at the back, near the anus, by a valve. Glands that give off a waxy secretion open near this valve. When the liquid from the food is excreted it is mixed with the secretion from the glands. By working its telescopic tail in and out, the frog-hopper forces air through the valve, together with the liquid, and so the innumerable small bubbles are blown that form its foamy home. This is spread round and over the insect by its tail and serves as a protection from the hot rays of the sun, besides affording concealment from its enemies. The tiny bubbles do not burst in a few seconds because they are strengthened by the waxy secretion: they last for quite a time and, as they are being constantly added to by the frog-hopper inside, the foam provides a cool shelter for the insect as long as it is feeding and growing.

Eventually, when it is fully grown, it leaves the foam and casts its skin for the last time. The wing-buds on its back expand into a pair of stiff wings that are held roofwise over its back, with a pair of delicate, membranous wings folded beneath them. Most frog-hoppers are small—only about a quarter or three-eighths of an inch in length and dull in colour—but some are brightly coloured with red, yellow and black. The members of this family can be recognised by their shape, by their leaping powers and by the one or two prominent spines and cluster of shorter spines at the apex of the tibiae of the hind legs.

Tree-hoppers

These quaint little bugs (*Membracidae*) are easily recognised by the shape of the first segment of the thorax which is prolonged over the back and often bears horn-like projections that give the insects

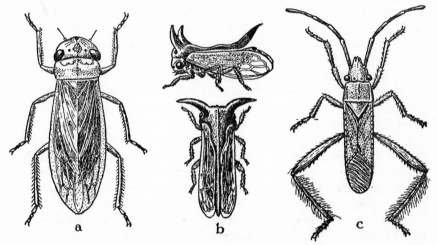

FIG. 45—(a) A Jassid Bug, *Bythoscopus cedaranus;* (b) A Treehopper (Membracid) *Lobocentrus suffulta;* (c) A Lygaeid Bug.

a bizarre appearance. They are small, few of them being more than a quarter of an inch long when fully grown and they are mostly brown or black. As far as is known, the female lays her eggs in slits cut in twigs of trees and shrubs. The young, usually black, are gregarious and feed in a group on the sap of the plant and they are eagerly attended by ants for the sake of the sweet excretion. The ants stroke the young tree-hoppers with their antennae and the latter respond by exuding their liquid excrement from their anal tube which can be thrust out or withdrawn.

Leaf-hoppers

Excepting the aphides, the agile little leaf-hoppers (*Jassidae*) are probably the most abundant of all the plant bugs, although they do not attract much attention because of their small size and protective coloration. Some of them are of considerable economic importance because they attack crops and have been proved to be the agents that spread certain diseases among the plants, much in the same way as mosquitoes spread malaria among men. The large green jassid, *Bythoscopus cedaranus*, for example, transmits the disease known as 'froghopper' among wattles, a disease that causes the new growth to be stunted and deformed with many small unhealthy twigs bunched together to give the appearance often spoken of as 'witch's broom'. Despite its name this insect is only about one eighth of an inch long. By feeding on the sap of an infected tree and then flying to a healthy one and feeding on that it transmits the virus of the disease.

Similarly the maize leaf-hopper, *Balclutha mbila*, is now known to be the chief agent in the spread of mosaic disease of maize and sugar-cane. This is a virus disease that causes the leaves to be mottled and stunts the whole plant. The adult insect is only about one-sixteenth of an inch long, slender, purplish black in colour, with a yellow line down the middle of its back. Like the rest of its kind, it can leap vigorously and fly well. The female inserts her tiny white eggs into slits she makes in the leaf. These hatch in about a fortnight into white nymphs with black eyes and they puncture the leaves and feed on the sap like their parents. The nymphs moult five times and are fully grown in about a month. There are several generations a year and, if the weather conditions are favourable, they may increase greatly in numbers and do considerable harm by robbing the plants of sap and by spreading the virus of the disease among them.

Leaf-hoppers may be recognised by their delicate, slender form and by the double row of spines along the hind tibiae. The first segment of the thorax is not prolonged backwards as it is in the tree-hoppers.

Lantern Flies

Some of the larger members of this family (*Fulgoridae*) are hand-some insects with brightly coloured wings and might easily be mistaken for butterflies or moths, but an examination of their antennae and the jointed beak beneath the head will reveal their true character as plant bugs. Many of them have the front of the head elongated as a hollow, horn-like projection and it was once thought that this part of the body was luminous—hence the name of lantern flies. Certain species secrete long threads of white wax from the hind end of the abdomen and these trail behind them as they fly. The young forms are also often covered with long, curled waxy filaments that make them very conspicuous as they feed in a group on the sap of a twig or leaf.

The adults of some species occur in two quite different colours. For example, some may be green and others red and it is said that when the insects congregate together, as they often do, they arrange

PLATE 21

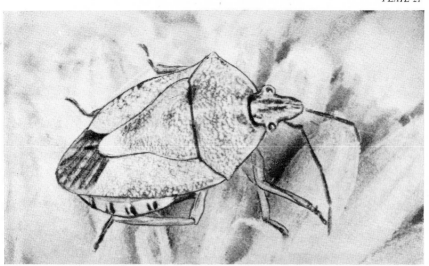

(*a*) THE SPECKLED BROWN SHIELD BUG

(*b*) THE ANTESTIA BUG, *Antestia variegata*, photograph of adult

PLATE 22

(*a*) THE BROWN TWIG-WILTER, *Holopterna vulga*, female

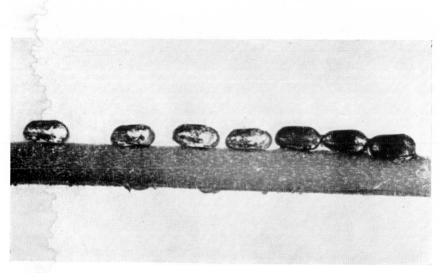

(*b*) A row of eggs of the Brown Twig-Wilter on a twig. Each egg is about one twelfth of an inch long.

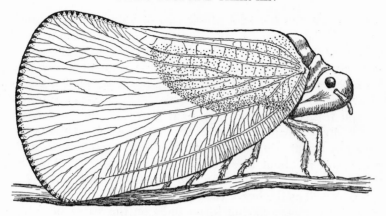

FIG. 46—A Lantern Fly, *Flata semanga*

themselves with the red individuals below and the green ones above, so that they look like a spike of red flowers with green buds above. The larger, showy members of this group are mainly tropical but there are many smaller, inconspicuous species that are found in more temperate regions. They have been little studied in Africa.

Jumping Plant Lice

The jumping plant lice, or psyllids (*Psyllidae*), are small insects about the size of aphids and they look something like tiny cicadas. As an example of the group, we may take the common citrus psyllid,

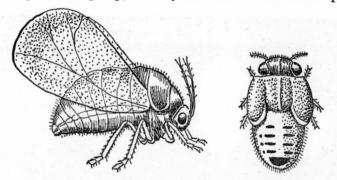

FIG. 47—A Jumping Louse, or Psyllid, from a wild fig tree. Adult on left, young stage on right. The adult is about one eight of an inch long.

Spanioza erythreae, which is found on orange trees and some native trees from Abyssinia in the north right down to the Cape. The adult is only about one-twelfth of an inch long, green at first but darkening almost to black as it grows older, with four transparent wings held roofwise over its back when at rest.

N

The female lays her eggs at the tips of young shoots, usually on the edges of tender young leaves, and they hatch in about a week into sluggish nymphs that can creep slowly about but that soon settle down to feed, after which they scarcely move at all unless they are overcrowded. Clustered on the underside of the young leaf the insects look very much like small scale insects. Where each nymph settles a small pit forms in the leaf and, as it grows, so the pit increases in size. A badly infested leaf becomes stunted, discoloured and deformed. The nymphs moult five times in the course of their growth and they reach full size in about three weeks to a month. The hind legs of the adults are rather stouter than the two front pairs and the adults can jump as well as fly, hence their popular name.

Another common psyllid forms galls on the leaves of stinkwood trees whilst yet another is found on wild figs.

White Flies

The insects known as white flies (*Aleyrodidae*) are small, with four wings dusted with a characteristic mealy white powder and measuring only about an eighth of an inch across the outspread wings. They attack plants in greenhouses as well as pot-plants and tomatoes, beans, pumpkins, oranges, and others. A severe attack will cause the leaves to turn yellow and eventually to dry up and drop off.

The female lays her oval white eggs on the tender young leaves, generally in a semi-circle and attached by short stalks. These hatch

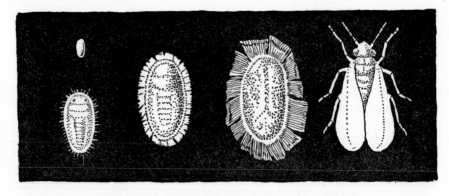

FIG 48—The Development of the White Fly of the Castor Oil Plant, *Aleurodes ricini*. Egg and young stages on left, full grown nymph in middle, adult on right. The adult is about one eighth of an inch long.

into oval, flattened young that can creep about but, after they have attached themselves to the leaf by their beak, their legs become degenerate after the first moult and they can no longer move: they look very much like small scale insects. The nymph moults three times and then enters upon what is known as the pupal stage. During the first part of this stage of its career it feeds, but after a time it becomes quiescent and the adult wings and legs develop, enclosed in sheaths, so that the insect is now very like the pupa of one of the higher insects, hidden within its old skin. Finally a T-shaped slit appears in the back and the adult emerges. The adult is a rather sluggish insect and lives for only a few days. Often the males are rare in some generations and parthenogenesis, or the development of unfertilised eggs, is known to occur.

Aphids

Plant lice, or aphids (*Aphididae*), are familiar to every farmer and gardener because of the harm these little insects do to many different kinds of cultivated plants. Although they are among the feeblest and most defenceless of all insects, and although they have many natural enemies, they not only manage to survive but they may be exceedingly abundant. Their strength lies in their amazing fecundity. A female aphis may begin to produce young when she is only a week old and

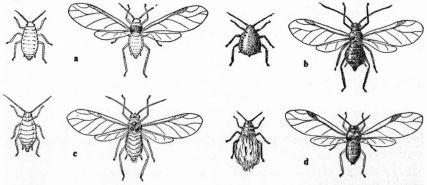

FIG. 49—Aphids: (*a*) the maize aphis, *Aphis maidis*; (*b*) the black peach aphis, *Anuraphis persicaeniger*; (*c*) the green grain aphis, *Toxoptera graminum*; (*d*) the woolly aphis, *Eriosoma lanigera*. Females only, wingless form on left, winged individual on right.

may give birth to two or three offspring every day until she has a family of one hundred or more. It has been estimated that the descendants of a single plant louse, if all survived, would at the end of a year reach the colossal total of 210 raised to the 15th power, a truly astronomical number.

Yet there are plant lice in Africa of which the males have never been found. In other words, the countless hordes of tiny insects on peas and beans, roses, peach trees, cabbages and so on, are all fatherless. Let us take the common pea aphis *Aphis leguminosae*, as an example. Very common and widely spread on various kinds of leguminous plants, such as peas, beans and ground-nuts, it is of great economic importance not only because of the damage it does by sucking the sap of the plants, but also because it spreads a serious disease among ground-nuts called rosette disease.

When the plant lice feeding on the underside of the leaves get over-crowded, some of them proceed to grow wings and are able to fly. It is these winged individuals, flying from sick to healthy plants, that carry the virus with them. The female aphis does not lay eggs. Her eggs mature one at a time in her ovaries and they hatch inside her body. She deposits her young singly at short intervals, generally at the rate of two or three a day if weather conditions are favourable. Anybody sufficiently interested can witness this interesting event at almost any time with the aid of a good hand lens. The tiny newly-hatched aphis, only about one-fiftieth of an inch in length and pale green in colour, is slowly extruded by the mother, head first with its legs folded along its sides. As soon as it drops on to the plant behind its mother it gets on its feet and creeps away, while the mother goes on unconcernedly feeding and takes no heed at all of her new-born youngster.

The young aphis soon begins to feed and its colour darkens rapidly until it is almost black. It grows quickly and casts its skin four times before it reaches the adult stage, about a week after its birth. The total length of its life-span is little more than a month. It has two tubes projecting on its back, like a pair of horns on the rear end of the body. At one time it was thought that the sweet liquid called honey-dew was given off from these cornicles, as they are called, but it is now known that they are the exit tubes of glands that secrete a waxy fluid. This secretion helps to keep the insect dry when rain or dew falls and it may also help to repel natural enemies. The honey-dew that is so eagerly sought after by ants is simply the sap of the plant after it has passed through the alimentary canal of the aphis. Sugars, salts and proteins are absorbed as food by the insect but the passage of the sap through its body is so rapid and so copious that there is still enough nourishment left in the liquid that is excreted from the vent to make it attractive to ants. Here again the observer can easily see what goes on if he watches some aphids under a good hand lens. An ant visiting the plant lice runs among them, tapping each one with its feelers. If the louse is ready to excrete it lifts its tail in response to the ant's invitation and a drop of clear liquid appears at its vent which is greedily lapped up by the ant before it passes on to another of its "cows".

At first all the plant lice in a colony on a leaf, mother and daughters, are wingless and they live amicably and peacefully side by side. But as the numbers increase the leaf begins to wither and curl because of the numerous tiny beaks robbing it of sap. Over-crowding and the diminishing food supply cause some of the young aphids to change their form as they grow up. They are more slender than the others and four wing-buds appear on their backs. At the last moult these wing-buds expand into four gauzy, transparent wings with dark veins. This amazing change of form brought about by means quite unknown, enables the winged individuals to leave the over-crowded colony and to fly to other plants to start new colonies going. Sometimes on a warm, still day the air is filled with these flying aphids seeking new homes for themselves. The offspring of the winged lice are wingless, until increasing numbers and pressure of population cause more winged individuals to appear.

So it goes on throughout the year in this country, generation after generation of virgin females giving rise to countless numbers of young like themselves, without the intervention of any males at all. There may be forty, fifty or more generations a year, all fatherless, all pro-duced parthenogenetically. Although several different species of aphids of economic importance have been studied by entomologists in South Africa, no males or eggs have ever been discovered, so far as I am aware. In the cooler parts of the world, such as Europe, breeding among the aphids goes on the same as here during the summer months, but when winter is approaching there is a remarkable change that does not take place in our warmer climate. Males as well as females appear among the offspring in late autumn in Europe. Usually the males are winged but the females are wingless. The males die after mating and the females each lay a single egg, large for the size of the insects and thick shelled. These eggs are generally placed in cracks and crevices of the bark. The aphids are killed off by the onset of cold weather but the eggs survive the winter and give rise to females only in the following spring. These are the virgins that carry on the pest throughout the summer until the arrival of shorter days and cool weather cause the males to appear once more.

This is the cycle recorded from Europe and the United States and Canada, but it does not, so far as is known, occur in Africa. Besides temperature, the number of daylight hours seems to control the appearance of males. It has been found by experiment in England that no males are produced and no eggs are laid in autumn if the aphids are kept in a greenhouse exposed to artificial light at night. On the other hand, if they are shut up in the dark after a daily exposure of only eight hours to the light during June, at the height of summer, males and eggs are produced. It would be interesting to repeat this experiment in Africa to see if males and eggs would appear here as a result of exposure to longer hours of darkness.

There are a large number of species common in this country, found on all kinds of plants. All are small soft-bodied and feeble and all are sap-suckers. It is not easy to determine one species from another because they are much alike, and they are variable in colour: the winged forms differ from the wingless individuals and, in some cases the aphids feeding on one plant differ from individuals of the same species feeding on another kind of plant. Microscopic characters are used in determining the species, such as the arrangement of the sense organs on the antennae and the length and shape of the cornicles and the tip of the abdomen. The species that are of economic importance and that are widely distributed include the cotton aphis, *Aphis gossypii*, dark in colour and found on fruit trees and garden plants as well as cotton: the maize aphis, *Aphis maidis*, dark green and a pest of grain crops, particularly maize and kafir corn: the sugar-cane aphis, *Aphis sacchari:* the powdery cabbage aphis, *Brevicoryne brassicae:* the black peach aphis, *Anuraphis persicae-niger:* the woolly aphis, *Eriosoma lanigera:* the wheat louse, *Toxoptera graminum:* the vine phylloxera, *Phylloxera vitifoliae*, and many others.

As a counter-balance to their prodigious powers of increase, aphids have many natural enemies, including ladybirds (page 224), hover flies (page 284), lacewing flies (page 130) and parasitic wasps (page 318).

Scale Insects

Scale insects (*Coccidae*) are such insignificant-looking insects, mere specks adhering to fruit, leaves and twigs, that it is difficult to believe they are capable of much harm, yet they include among their number some of the worst pests with which the fruit-grower and gardener have to contend. Over three hundred different species of scale insects are known from South Africa alone, the only part of the continent where this family has been studied in detail, and of these about sixty have been introduced from overseas.

One of the commonest and most troublesome of the scale insects is the red scale, *Aonidiella aurantii*. It is not a native of Africa and it is not known how or when it was first imported, but it was a long time ago—perhaps a century or more—and probably on imported fruit trees. It is widely spread throughout the world to-day and is of extreme economic importance because of the damage it does and the difficulty of controlling it. These little sap-suckers attack all parts of the tree: fruit, leaves, twigs and branches. The leaves that are badly infested turn yellow, die and drop off. This may be followed by the dying back of the twig. Later on the branches become thickly encrusted with the scale and they also may be killed. If the pest is

OUTSTANDING BOOKS AT ONLY A FRACTION OF THE NORMAL PUBLISHED PRICES!

Join **A Foyles Book Club**

You Buy Books published at 10/6, 12/6, 15/-, 21/- for ONLY 4/-

not controlled it is capable of causing the death of a well-grown tree in three or four years.

A close examination of the scales on an orange, or on an infected twig, will show that the insects range in size from tiny dots to fully grown females that are about the size of the letter 'o' in this print. Two types may be seen among the scales: there are circular ones and smaller

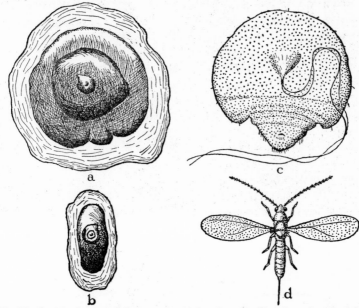

FIG. 50—The Red Scale, *Aonidiella aurantii:* (*a*) female scale; (*b*) male scale; (*c*) adult female removed from scale; (*d*) adult male.

ones that are oval. The larger, round individuals are full-grown females, while the oval scales cover the males.

The adult female is a very degenerate insect because of her easy mode of life and because it is not necessary for her to move about. Her body consists of a flattened bag with a long, threadlike beak on the underside that is thrust deep into the plant upon which she is feeding. The round, hard scale that covers and protects her body consists of her cast-off skins, together with a hardened exudation that forms the outer rim of the scale. If the insect is examined through a hand-lens, a sort of nipple can be seen protruding slightly from the middle of the scale. This is the skin that the insect cast when she moulted for the first time. This nipple projects from a slightly raised area, like a miniature watch-glass, and this is the second cast skin. The scale insect moults only twice, therefore the portion of the scale outside the central area consists of the hardened exudation given off after the insect is mature.

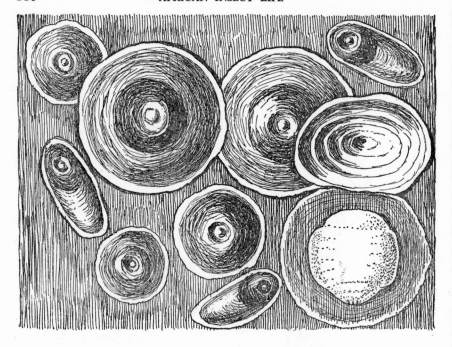

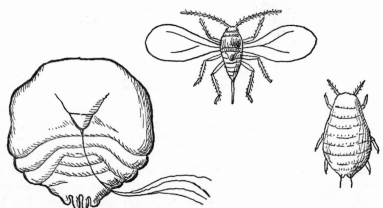

FIG. 51—The Pernicious Scale, *Aspidiotus perniciosus*. Above, scales enlarged, showing immature and mature female scales (one raised to show insect beneath) and three male scales. Below, female on left viewed from beneath, male in the middle, larva on right.

If a needle point is pushed beneath the scale and it is lifted up, it will be found that the body of the female comes away with the scale. There are certain other scale insects found in this country, such as the pernicious scale, which resemble the red scale but, in the case of these insects, if the scale is lifted up, the body of the female is left behind on the plant. The edge of the scale is turned in under the body

PLATE 23

(a) Eggs and newly-hatched larva of the Brown Twig-Wilter. On the left a larva can be seen in the act of emerging from an egg.

(b) PYRRHOCORID BUG, *Cenaeus carnifex*. Female on left, male on right. They are about three-quarters of an inch long, red and black in colour.

PLATE 24

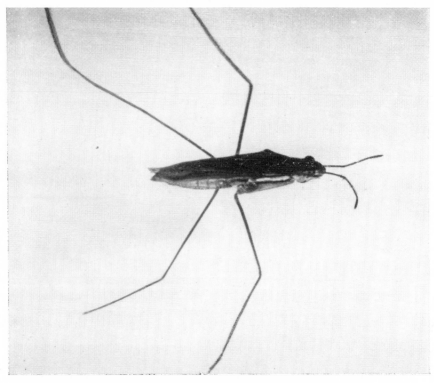

(*a*) **A POND SKATER**, *Gerris diversa*

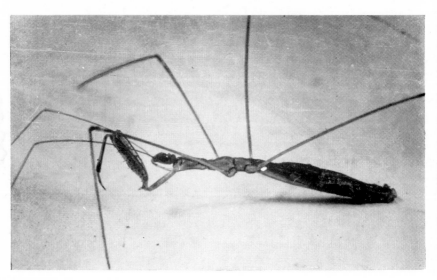

(*b*) AN ASSASSIN BUG

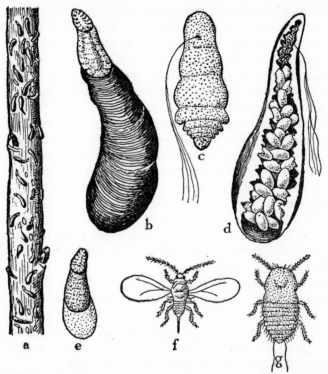

FIG. 52—The Mussel Scale, *Lepidosaphes pinnaeformis:* (*a*) twig with scales, natural size; (*b*) female scale; (*c*) female insect removed from scale; (*d*) female scale seen from underside, containing eggs; (*e*) male scale; (*f*) male insect; (*g*) newly hatched larva.

of the red scale, completely enclosing it except for a circular opening on the underside, which is why the whole insect comes away when the scale is lifted.

It is still not known how the scale insect manages to thrust its long and very slender beak so deeply into the tissues of the plant. The beak consists of four very thin black threads, much finer than a human hair and much longer than the insect's body. It is thought that the ring of muscles at the insect's mouth holds these four lancets just behind the tip, so that the points can be pushed a little way into the plant. Then the hold is shifted a little way further back and the lancets are thrust a little deeper in, and so it goes on until the whole beak is inserted—a lengthy process that needs to be carried out only once in the insect's lifetime, since it never moves again after it has once settled down and fixed itself in position.

The male scale insect is quite unlike the female. If you lift up a number of the smaller oval scales you will find that some of them are empty, but under others you may come across a tiny little fly, so small

o

that you can only make out the details of its structure with the aid of a hand-lens. It has a pink body, two gauzy wings, well developed eyes, long feelers and six legs, but it has no mouthparts and it cannot feed as an adult. Its life as an adult lasts only for two or three days at the most and its sole function is to creep out from under its protective scale when the weather conditions are favourable, to seek out a female and to mate with her and then to die.

The female red scale does not lay eggs. She retains her eggs inside her body until they hatch and she gives birth to her young at the rate of about one a day over a period of about three months. The number of young and the rate at which they are produced varies according to the climatic conditions, more young being produced over a shorter period during the summer than in the winter. The newly-hatched insect is a tiny yellow creature, about one-hundredth of an inch in length. It has six legs and a pair of feelers, but is quite blind. It creeps out from under its mother's scale and wanders about on the plant until it finds a suitable spot where it can insert its beak and settle down for the rest of its life. If a wind is blowing at the time, it may get blown away to another plant—this seems to be the principal way in which scale insects are spread from plant to plant. The tiny young scales, crawling restlessly about on the tree, may also creep on to larger insects, such as beetles, flies and bees, and on to the feet of birds, and in this way they may be carried far afield.

When the young scale insect settles down and starts to feed it grows a hard skin on its back, the beginning of the scale. In from two to three weeks it casts its first skin and this forms the nipple on the back. At this stage there is no visible difference between a male and a female. The second stage lasts for about six weeks, after which the female moults for the second and last time. The male changes into a chrysalis at this stage and about ten days later the adult emerges. The whole life history of the red scale takes three or four months.

Of the many other hard-scale insects found in this country, the following may be briefly mentioned. The pernicious scale, *Aspidiotus perniciosus*, was introduced into South Africa nearly fifty years ago and its discovery in the Transvaal caused alarm because this is one of the most harmful of all scale pests. Strict measures of control have, however, prevented its spread. It infests various kinds of fruit trees as well as oak, poplar, willow, rose and pepper trees. The scale of the young female is black with a central grey dot: the adult female scale is grey with a central black area and dot. Infested twigs and fruits often show red discoloration round the insects. The aloe red scale, *Furcaspis capensis*, is a large, striking scale found only on aloes, dark red in colour, with much smaller oval scales covering the males.

The mussel scale, *Lepidosaphes pinnaeformis*, may be recognised by its shape and its bluish-brown colour. It is found on citrus and other plants.

The soft scales differ from the hard, or armoured, scales in not being covered by a definite scale: they are protected only by their own thickened skin. The best known and commonest of these is perhaps the black scale, *Saissetia oleae*, very widely spread in Africa

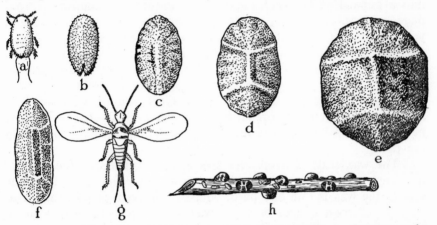

FIG. 53.—The Black Scale, *Saissetia oleae*: (*a*) newly hatched larva; (*b*) young scale; (*c*) second stage scale; (*d*) immature female; (*e*) adult female scale; (*f*) male scale; (*g*) male insect; (*h*) scales on twig, natural size.

and other parts of the world and found on citrus, olives, oleander and a wide range of other plants. The harm done by this pest on fruit trees is not so much due to the loss of sap as to the unsightly growth of sooty mould fungus caused by the presence of the insects. Soft scales give off a good deal of the sweet excretion known as honey-dew and this, if not removed by ants, forms a favourable medium on which the fungus can grow. Fruit and twigs infested by black scale are often blackened by the sooty mould growing around and over them.

The female black scale is rounded, dark brown or black with a distinct H-mark on her back. She may be as much as one-fifth of an inch in length but many are smaller. She grows slowly and takes about nine months to reach full size and then she starts laying her numerous tiny eggs, about forty a day, up to two thousand or more in number before she dies. Her oviposition lasts for about two months, the tiny young creeping out from under her body as they hatch. The newly-hatched scale is barely visible to the naked eye, oval, flat and brown, with two small black eyes, long antennae and six legs. It creeps about until it finds a suitable place to settle down, on a leaf or tender twig. After moulting twice it reaches the adult stage in about three months and at first it is flat and pale brown but, as it grows older, its back becomes arched and it darkens in colour.

The male black scale is rare, sometimes absent altogether, and the eggs of the females develop parthenogenetically. When present, the male scale is similar to the female until after the first moult, then it becomes oval and elongated, flat and pale brown. At the end of the second stage it forms a glassy covering to itself under which it changes into a pupa. Finally, when about three months old, the tiny winged male emerges. He is only about one twenty-fifth of an inch in length, yellow in colour and he lives but for two or three days.

Numbers of black scales on a plant may often be found with small round holes in them. These have been destroyed by small parasitic wasps (page 321). Many years ago these parasites were sent from South Africa to California, to help to fight the black scale there, where it is a serious pest in citrus orchards. The parasites flourished in their new home and have played an important part in helping to control the pest.

The wax scales (*Ceroplastes* species) are soft scales, the females of which secrete a waxy covering over their bodies. In some species the wax is thin and hard, whilst in others it is soft, thick and watery. Certain species of white wax scales are common on thorn trees, others on wild figs, avocado pears and Syringa trees.

The margarodes scales are perhaps the most remarkable of all the members of this family. They are adapted for a life underground and both sexes have strong legs and claws suitable for digging in the soil. They feed on the sap of the roots of various kinds of plants. The females go through a curious resting stage enclosed in a yellow glassy case, in which they may remain for a long time during a period of drought. After rain the females emerge from their cases and look like mealy bugs. The brassy-looking cases of some margarodes are rather large, a third of an inch in diameter or more, and these are sometimes strung on thread as beads, but few people have any idea what these strange ornaments are.

Mealy Bugs

Mealy bugs are small insects, the largest being only about one-eighth of an inch long, pink or purplish in colour but appearing to be white because their bodies are covered with a waxy powder. Along each side of the body there are projections that consist of bundles of waxy threads. Over thirty different species are known from South Africa alone, several of which have been introduced from overseas, and they include serious pests of citrus, pine-apples, vines, pears, guavas, sugar-cane and many other cultivated plants.

The citrus mealy bug, *Pseudococcus citri*, may be taken as a typical example of the group. It is widely spread and often does serious harm in citrus orchards, particularly to navel oranges. It infests the young fruits in the spring and may cause many of them to drop. Later in the season the bugs migrate to the navel end of the fruit where they find shelter. They secrete fluffy masses of white waxen threads that may fill the cavity and they produce much honey-dew on which sooty mould develops. The honey-dew also attracts ants which feed on it and at the same time protect the bugs from ladybirds that would otherwise destroy them and keep them in check.

The female mealy bug, when ready to lay her eggs, produces a mass of fine waxen threads, like cotton wool, at the hind end of her body and in this she deposits her numerous, tiny yellow eggs, up to one thousand or more in number. The egg-laying extends over two or three weeks and, by the time it is completed, the bug shrivels up and dies. The eggs hatch in ten to thirty days, according to the weather conditions, into tiny yellow young that creep out of the sheltering mass of threads and seek out a suitable spot on a fruit or leaf where they can settle down and feed. Many of them get blown or carried away at this stage to other trees.

During the first stage of their career the young males and females

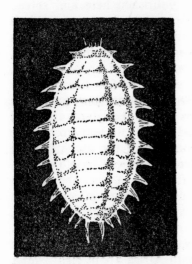 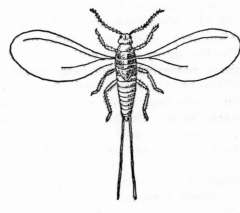

FIG. 54—The Citrus Mealy Bug, *Pseudococcus citri*, female on left, male on right. She is about one eight of an inch long.

are alike. After the first moult, however, they are quite different. The female does not change her form but casts her skin four times in the course of her growth, reaching the adult stage in about two months during summer, but taking much longer in winter. The male makes a cocoon for himself when he is three or four weeks old and inside this he changes into a pupa. Two or three weeks later the winged adult emerges, very similar to the males of all this family, a feeble little creature that cannot feed and that lives only for three or four days. There are three generations a year and the bugs can be found on the trees at all times of the year.

Cochineal insects are mealy bugs that were formerly cultivated for the sake of the colouring matter obtained from them and that are of importance to-day because of the part they play in the control of prickly pears. They are natives of America but some species have spread to other parts of the world with their food-plants. Two or three species are found on prickly pears in Africa and are easily recognised by the fluffy masses of white waxen threads beneath which the insects shelter. If they are crushed a rich purple colour is seen.

In 1938 a species of cochineal, *Dactylopius opuntiae*, was deliberately introduced into South Africa by the Department of Agriculture, to be used in the fight against the pest prickly pears that covered so much fertile land in the Eastern Province and rendered it useless for farming. Although a native of America, this cochineal came from Australia where it has proved useful, with other insects, in destroying the prickly pears. It has flourished here and spread and it has played an important part in helping to control certain kinds of prickly pears. Unfortunately, it also attacks spineless prickly pears that are grown for fodder, although, like the other cochineal insects, it will not infest any plants other than those of the prickly pear family. The life history of the cochineal is very similar to that described for the citrus mealy bug, but, in the case of *Dactylopius opuntiae*, the female retains her eggs inside her body until they hatch. Ladybirds that feed on the insects, a fungous disease, hail and heavy rain and frost in the winter have prevented the increase and spread of the cochineal that was hoped for, and they have not, therefore, proved so effective in killing off the pest prickly pears in South Africa as was the case in Queensland. Nevertheless, they have done good work in conjunction with the cactoblastis moth (page 159) and the prickly pear beetle, *Lagochirus funestus*.

The Australian bug, *Icerya purchasi*, is allied to the mealy bugs and was accidentally introduced into South Africa about eighty years ago. It became a very serious pest of citrus trees, roses, acacias and other plants, but was eventually controlled by the introduction of the Australian ladybird, *Rodolia cardinalis* (page 226). This was the first and perhaps the most famous example in the history of agricultural science of what is known as biological control—that is to say, the control of a pest by the introduction and encouragement of its natural enemies.

The fully grown Australian bug is about half an inch long, with a fluted white bag making up the greater part of its body. Because of this characteristic bag made of waxen threads the insect is known in America as the cottony-cushion scale. All the bugs are females. Only a very few males have ever been found and all these were reported from other parts of the world—none from South Africa. The actual body of the female is the flattened yellow disc at the front end. She is attached to the twig only by her slender beak which is deeply embedded in the woody tissues. The yellow colour of her body is more or less hidden by the white waxy material that oozes from glands in her body and forms a powdery coating.

If the white bag is torn open it will be found to contain two hundred or so oval pink eggs that look like little coral beads in their soft bed of waxy down. The eggs are all unfertilised and they hatch parthenogenetically in about fourteen days.

The newly hatched bug is about the size of a pin's head, pink in colour, with six black legs, a pair of black feelers and two well-developed eyes. After it has settled down to feed and has sunk its beak into the twig it never moves again. The wax glands in its skin begin to secrete the powdery covering and slowly the little insect assumes the adult form.

CLASSIFICATION

ORDER 14: *HEMIPTERA*—PLANT BUGS

Mouthparts piercing and suctorial, consisting of a grooved sheath, the labium, in which four slender stylets, the mandibles and maxillae, are lodged. A very large and important group of insects, including many thousands of species, of a great diversity of form and size.

SUB-ORDER 1: *HETEROPTERA*—The LARGER PLANT BUGS

Wings, when present, two pairs: first pair stiff and horny in basal half, membranous apically, overlapping when at rest, second pair membranous. Tarsi usually three-jointed. Metamorphosis incomplete.

FAMILY 1: *Pentatomidae*—SHIELD BUGS

First segment of the thorax and the scutellum (the triangular projection behind the first segment) large, scutellum reaching base of membranous portion of wings, sometimes completely covering the back. Antennae inserted on lower side of head, usually five-jointed. Beak four-jointed. These bugs may be recognised by their shape, more or less like a shield. They are all sap-suckers and some are brightly coloured.

FAMILY 2: *Coreidae*—TWIG-WILTERS

Antennae four-jointed, inserted on upper part of the head. Tarsi three-jointed. Mostly dull-coloured bugs, narrower and more oblong than the *Pentatomidae*. Many have strange dilations on their antennae and legs, the function of which is unknown. All are sap-suckers and, like the shield bugs, all have the power of emitting an unpleasant odour.

FAMILY 3: *Lygaeidae*

Antennae inserted below middle of the eyes. Tarsi three-jointed. Ocelli, or simple eyes, present. These bugs resemble the twig-wilters in general form but are smaller, softer and often brightly coloured. All are sap-suckers.

FAMILY 4: *Pyrrhocoridae*—COTTON STAINERS

This family differs from the *Lygaeidae* only in that its members do not have simple eyes. Most are red and black. A few are predacious, feeding on other insects, but the majority are sap-suckers.

FAMILY 5: *Tingidae*—LACE BUGS

Small, flattened insects of a great variety of strange forms with the sides of the body produced into flattened outgrowths adorned with spines. In many of them the prothorax and first pair of wings are lacelike in appearance. The tarsi are two-jointed.

FAMILY 6: *Hydrometridae*—POND SKATERS

Aquatic bugs, running nimbly on the surface of the water. Clothed on the underside with a silvery coat of hairs. First pair of wings without the membranous apex. Antennae four-jointed.

FAMILY 7: *Reduviidae*—ASSASSIN BUGS

Beak short, usually three-jointed, curved so that it does not lie flat along the underside of the head when not in use. Antennae slender. Tarsi three-jointed. Most, if not all, are predacious, feeding on other insects or on the blood of higher animals. Some are found in houses and feed on human blood.

FAMILY 8: *Cimicidae*—BED-BUGS

Flattened insects, wingless, with beak lying in a ventral groove. Tarsi three-jointed. All are parasites of mammals and birds and they include the well-known bed-bug.

FAMILY 9: *Belostomatidae*—GIANT WATER BUGS

Antennae four-jointed, hidden in pockets on underside of head. Hind legs adapted for swimming, with flattened tibiae fringed with hairs. Abdomen with two retractile appendages that form the respiratory tube. Beak short and curved. Large, rapacious, aquatic bugs that feed on small fish, tadpoles, young frogs and insects.

FAMILY 10: *Nepidae*—WATER SCORPIONS

Antennae three-jointed, hidden beneath head. Front pair of legs prehensile, hind legs not adapted for swimming. Tarsi one-jointed. Abdomen with a breathing tube at tip. Aquatic bugs that creep about on bottom and amid water-weeds and feed on other aquatic insects, small tadpoles, etc.

FAMILY 11: *Notonectidae*—BACK-SWIMMERS

Body convex dorsally, boat-shaped. Insects swim on their back. Beak three- or four-jointed. Antennae four-jointed, hidden beneath head. Tarsi two-jointed, hind pair without claws.

FAMILY 12: *Corixidae*—WATER BOATMEN

Body flattened, beak short, concealed and apparently unjointed. Antennae three- or four-jointed, hidden. Front legs short and without claws on tarsi: hind tarsi also clawless. Small aquatic bugs that swim right side up, mostly brown in colour.

SUB-ORDER 2: *HOMOPTERA*

This is a very large and mixed division of the *Hemiptera*. The *Homoptera*, as the name implies, have wings (when present) that are alike; the front wings are not divided into a horny and membranous portion—they are wholly membranous, like the hind wings. The members of this sub-order vary in size from the large cicadas and lantern flies down to the tiny scale insects.

PLATE 25

(*b*) A newly-emerged CICADA, female

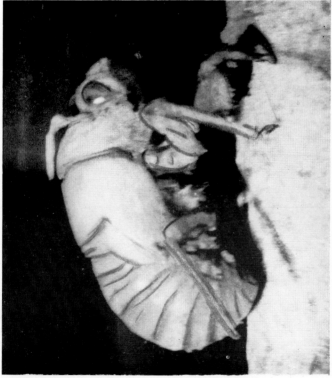

(*a*) The empty nymphal skin from which the above Cicada emerged, just as she left it clinging to the tree trunk

PLATE 26

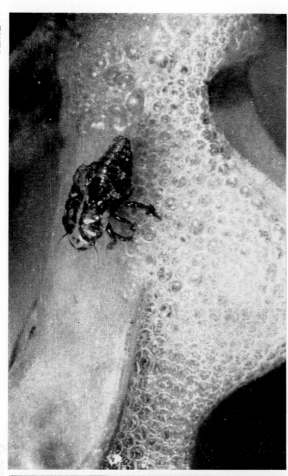

(a) A young FROGHOPPER outside its home of "cuckoo-spit"

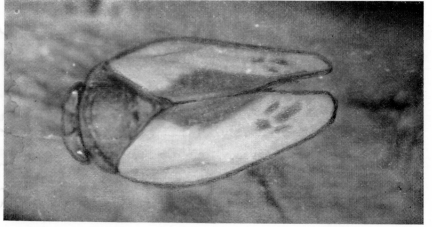

(b) Adult FROGHOPPER

FAMILY 13: *Cicadidae*—CICADAS

Usually large insects with four membranous wings and three ocelli. Front femora thickened and armed with strong spines. Males with peculiar sound-producing apparatus on either side of base of abdomen. Immature stages spent underground, feeding on sap of roots.

FAMILY 14: *Cercopidae*—FROG-HOPPERS

Smallish bugs with only two ocelli or none. Tibiae of hind legs armed with one or two stout spines and a cluster of smaller spines at apex. Immature stages generally spent in frothy foam made by the insects as a shelter and place of concealment, often called cuckoo-spit. Adults agile jumpers.

FAMILY 15: *Membracidae*—TREE-HOPPERS

Smallish bugs with back of thorax prolonged down the back, often with grotesque horns and projections. Young usually gregarious and eagerly visited by ants. Adults can leap and are mostly brown or black.

FAMILY 16: *Jassidae*—LEAF-HOPPERS

Small bugs with delicate bodies and wings. Two ocelli. Back of thorax never prolonged backwards. Hind tibiae armed with double row of bristles. Numerous species common in grass and other herbage.

FAMILY 17: *Fulgoridae*—LANTERN FLIES

Includes some large species with showy wings that look like moths. Many have front of head drawn out into prominent hollow projection. Some species produce long white waxen threads that trail behind them: immature stages of many species also produce flocculent white wax.

FAMILY 18: *Psyllidae*—JUMPING PLANT LICE

Small insects, about size of aphides and look like tiny cicadas. Tarsi two-jointed. Antennae ten-jointed. Adults can jump as well as fly.

FAMILY 19: *Aleyrodidae*—WHITE FLIES

Small insects with powdery wings, usually white. Antennae seven-jointed. Tarsi two-jointed. The young look like flattened scale insects. Both sexes pass through a rudimentary pupal stage.

FAMILY 20: *Aphididae*—PLANT LICE

Wings transparent, only found in males and migrant females, Tarsi two-jointed. Antennae three- to six-jointed. A pair of cornicles usually present on fifth segment of abdomen.

FAMILY 21: *Coccidae*—SCALE INSECTS AND MEALY BUGS

Tarsi one-jointed with a single claw. Females usually degenerate, wingless, obscurely segmented, legs and antennae vestigial. Males small, with only front pair of wings, mouthparts degenerate therefore cannot feed in adult state.

(Some small and unimportant families have been omitted from the above summary.)

P

CHAPTER XII

ANT LIONS AND THEIR KIN

The Neuroptera

This interesting group of insects includes ant lions, lacewings, alder flies and some smaller members that have no popular name. The adults have two pairs of gauzy, net-veined wings, both pairs alike and held roofwise over the body when at rest. The scientific name, *Neuroptera*, refers to the network of so-called veins or nerves on the wings and means "nerve-winged." They are mostly slender, soft-bodied insects that are weak fliers. Some are large and showy and might easily be mistaken for dragon-flies, whilst others are medium sized or small. The larvae of them all are predacious and feed on other insects. All the members of this order have a true pupal stage, often enclosed in a silken cocoon spun by the larva.

Alder Flies

Alder flies have been little studied in Africa. Less than a dozen species are known from the whole sub-continent south of the Sahara

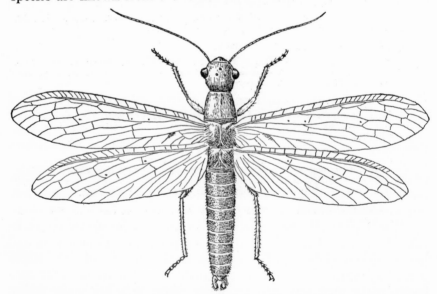

FIG. 55—The Cape Alder Fly, *Taeniochauloides ochraceopennis*, male: the outspread wings measure about two and a quarter inches across.

and these have been found haunting the mountain streams of the south-west Cape and the Drakensberg. Doubtless many more await discovery in other mountainous regions.

128

The common Cape alder fly, *Taeniochauliodes ochraceopennis*, is one of the largest of them, measuring between two and three inches across the outspread wings. It is found along the mountain streams of the south-west Cape at an altitude of two thousand feet or more. The adult insect is brown with transparent wings that are tinged with grey or brown and dotted with darker brown along the veins. The

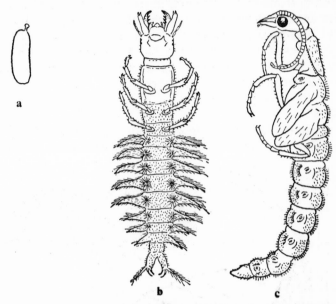

FIG 56—(*a*) Egg of Cape Alder Fly; (*b*) larva of Peringuey's Alder Fly; (*c*) pupa of Peringuey's Alder Fly, *Chloroniella peringueyi*. The larva and pupa are about one and half inches long. (After Barnard.)

flies may be found during the summer months in shady kloofs where they settle on the bushes beside the stream or on rocks jutting out of the water. When at rest, the wings are folded more or less round the body and, when disturbed, the insects fly swiftly and erratically but soon settle again.

The female lays her numerous brown eggs in masses on rocks near the water. Each egg is about one twelfth of an inch long and has a curious club-shaped projection at the upper end: the whole mass may measure nearly an inch in diameter. The larvae, when they hatch, make their way into the water where they live under stones and amid the plant growth, hunting for the aquatic insects and crustaceans upon which they feed. The full-grown larva is about an inch and a quarter long and armed with a pair of powerful jaws with which it attempts to bite fiercely if it is handled. It has six legs and eight hairy, pointed projections along each side of its abdomen. At its tail end there are a pair of double hooks by means of which it clings to submerged objects in order to prevent itself from being washed away by the swift current. If disturbed, it curls up, but soon uncurls again and creeps under a stone or anchors itself by its abdominal hooks.

When ready to change into a pupa the larva creeps out of the water and burrows into sphagnum moss beside the stream. The pupa is about an inch long, yellow, with the antennae, compound eyes, legs and wing-buds of the adult clearly evident. Just before the fly emerges the pupa wriggles its way to the surface of the moss. The adults may be found on the wing during the summer months and are commonest in January and February.

Lacewings

The pretty little green insects with eyes of a yellow, metallic lustre, popularly known as lacewings, or golden-eyes, may be found

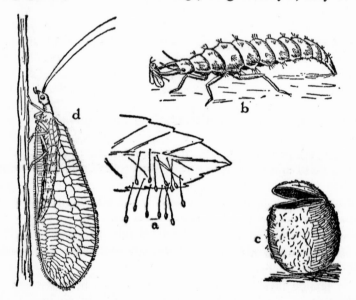

FIG 57.—A Lacewing, *Chrysopa* species: (*a*) eggs; (*b*) larva; (*c*) cocoon; (*d*) adult. The adult is about one inch across the outspread wings.

on plants that are infested with aphides. There are a number of different species but they all look very much alike and they are mostly about half an inch long. Some give off an unpleasant smell when handled, from a pair of glands on their thorax, and they are sometimes spoken of as stink flies.

The eggs of the lacewings (*Chrysopa* species) are remarkable objects and easily recognised. Each one is mounted on top of a slender stalk and looks rather like a miniature balloon on the end of a string. The female generally chooses the underside of a leaf on a plant that is infested with aphides and, when she is laying, she touches the leaf with the tip of her abdomen and ejects a drop of sticky fluid from the glands associated with her ovaries. Then she raises the tip of her abdomen and the gummy substance is drawn out in a thread which rapidly hardens in the air. On top of this she deposits her egg. The eggs are, as a rule, placed in a group and they look like a tuft of clubbed hairs projecting from the surface of the leaf.

Mounted on their stalks, the eggs are less liable to be found by enemies that might eat them and also the young insects, which are fiercely cannibalistic, cannot get at one another so easily when they first hatch; there is, therefore, more chance for them to survive than if the eggs were simply laid on the leaf, side by side, as is the case with most insects.

The larva is six-legged, active and armed with a pair of sharp jaws by means of which it pierces and sucks the juices of the aphides. Some species have the habit of covering themselves with the empty skins of their victims, others fix fragments of bark, dead leaves and other material on to the hooked hairs on their backs, but many kinds do not trouble to conceal themselves in any way. The larva of a lacewing might be mistaken for the larva of a ladybird (page 225), which they resemble, but they can be recognised by the curious trumpet-shaped appendage between the claws on each foot: this is so small it needs a good hand-lens to see it, and its function is quite unknown.

When the larva is fully grown it seeks out a sheltered spot and there it spins a spherical silken cocoon inside which it pupates. Two or three weeks later the adult insect emerges.

Some male lacewings have scent glands and they attract their mates by sitting passively on a twig and emitting the odour that guides the females to them.

Ant Lions

Ant lions are extraordinary insects with remarkable life histories. They are common and widely spread throughout the continent of Africa. The adults are rather like dragon-flies in general appearance but they may be recognised by their antennae. The antennae of an ant lion are conspicuous and clubbed at the tip, like those of a butterfly, whereas the antennae of a dragon-fly are small, threadlike and scarcely visible. Furthermore, ant lions are feeble, clumsy fliers when compared with dragon-flies and they fly mostly in the evening and at night.

The conical pit of the typical ant lion is familiar to everybody in this country who takes the least interest in natural history. It is found in dry, sandy soil, an inch or so in diameter and of a similar

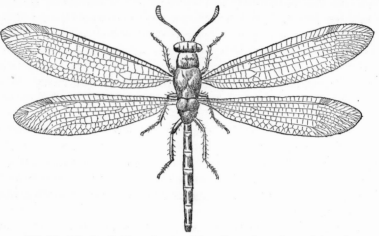

FIG. 58—The Small Clearwing Ant Lion, *Cueta lanceolata*, adult male

depth, and a drab, squat creature, dull brown in colour and armed with a pair of sharp, curved jaws is found at the bottom of the pit, buried in the sand. If an unwary ant or other insect walks over the edge of the pit and begins to slip down the crumbling sides, the head of the ant lion at once appears at the bottom of the pit. With a jerky motion of its head the owner of the pit throws sand up at the struggling ant, causing it to slip further and further down the side towards the bottom. As soon as the ant is within reach of the murderous jaws it is seized and dragged below the surface, where its body is sucked dry of juices and the empty skin is discarded.

Although the ant lion larva is such a voracious feeder, it has no mouth. Either the mouth is permanently sealed with a membrane that grows over it, or the upper and lower edges are so closely joined that it is impossible for the insect to open its mouth. The two sickle-like jaws have a narrow groove along the inner edge and the long, slender maxilla on each side fits over the groove to form a channel along which the juices of the victim pass into the pharynx (figure 60). All the members of this order have sucking jaws of this type.

Owing to the nature of the soil in which it is made, the pit is often destroyed, by wind, rain, or the feet of passing animals. Such destruction does not incommode the larva to any great extent for a new home is quickly excavated. The insect moves round in a small circle, with its body just beneath the surface of the sand, and it always creeps backwards, tail first. As it moves round and round in circles of decreasing diameter, it throws the sand to one side by jerking its head. In this way the conical pit is slowly sunk until, when it is deep enough, the larva conceals itself at the bottom to wait for its next victim. If the site chosen proves to be an unprofitable spot, with captures too few and far between, the ant-lion deserts the pit and digs a new one somewhere else. This removal and digging of a new pit usually takes place at night.

The stomach of the ant-lion is blind, it does not connect with the intestine at the rear end. Owing to the nature of its food there is little waste matter and this is dealt with by the malpighian tubes. There are eight of these malpighian tubes and six of them are extraordinary in that they are connected with the hind intestine and they are put to a strange use. When the larva is fully grown it buries itself two or three inches deep in the sand and makes an oval cell for itself. Then it spins a spherical cocoon of silk, the material coming from those six malpighian tubes and oozing from its anus. As the silk is sticky when it is first emitted, the grains of sand stick to it and so the larva constructs a compact, secure shelter in which it can change into a pupa. The pupa is short and stout and it is astonishing that such a long, slender, four-winged adult can emerge from it.

The large and rather showy adults, such as the spotted-wing ant lion, *Palpares speciosus*, with yellow wings blotched with brown

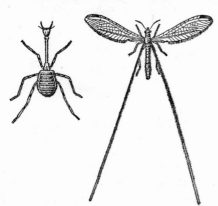

and a body about three inches long, and the smaller ant lions with transparent wings, such as *Cueta lanceolata*, are common and their larvae are typical pit-dwellers. The larvae all have a large head with curved, toothed jaws, four or five simple eyes on each side of the head at the base of the jaws, a small thorax and six short legs, and a flattened, rounded abdomen armed with bristles. They are ugly, ungainly creatures, but they can burrow in the soil with remarkable speed; often their trails can be

FIG. 59—The Thread-wing Ant Lion, *Pterocroce storeyi*, long-necked larva on left, adult male on right. The larva is about one third inch long and the adult's threadlike hind wings are about one and a quarter inches long.

seen as slight raised ridges on the sand, winding in all directions as the insects walked backwards in search of a suitable site for their home.

The thread-wing ant lions are highly specialised and are placed in a family by themselves. They are common in some of the drier parts of the country and these striking and beautiful insects, flying with a curious up and down motion, with their long, threadlike hind wings trailing behind them, may sometimes be seen around lights in the evening, particularly when rain is threatening. As far as their life history is known, the female lays her eggs in the fine, dry dust just inside the entrance of caves, or beneath over-hanging rocks, or on the dirty floors of buildings that are little used.

The larva has a long, narrow "neck" and it covers itself with dust so that it is hard to detect. It has the typical curved, sucking jaws and feeds on psocids, small spiders, mites and any other creatures it can capture. It makes a cocoon of silk and sand grains when it is fully grown and the pupa is easily recognised because the long, slender hind wings are coiled like watch-springs along the sides.

The long-horned ant lions are also placed in a family by themselves (*Ascalaphidae*). The adults are more active fliers than the true ant lions and they may be seen in the evening hawking for their prey to and fro, like dragon-flies. When they settle they usually adopt a characteristic attitude, with the abdomen held up at right angles to the thorax and the wings folded down away from the body, as shown in the photograph.

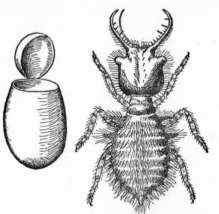

The female of one of the commonest of the Ascalaphids *Proctarrelabris capensis*, lays her oval white eggs in an irregular group on a rock, generally on the underside of a projecting ledge so that they are protected from the weather and the direct rays of the sun. These may be found at mid-summer and the newly-

Fig. 60—A newly-hatched larva of the Long-horned Ant Lion, *Proctarrelabris capensis*, with the empty egg-shell. The egg is about one sixteenth inch long and pure white.

hatched black young remain clustered round the empty shells for a day or so after they emerge. They sit quite still, with their jaws held wide open and, if you bring an aphis or other small insect into contact with these jaws, they snap shut. Unfortunately it is difficult to rear these little creatures in captivity: I have tried several times and succeeded in keeping them alive for a time by feeding them on young termites, but they soon become restless and wander about until they die. In the natural state it seems that they hunt beneath stones and amid dead vegetation for their prey. They do not construct pits.

The mantispas are relatives of the ant lions that are placed in

PLATE 27

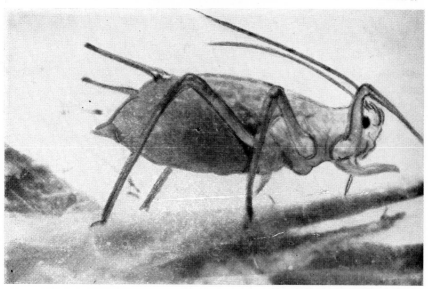

(*a*) A female APHIS, greatly enlarged, showing the pair of cornicles on her back

(*b*) GREEN APHIDS on a rose twig. They are all females and produce living young without prior fertilisation.

PLATE 28

(*a*) **THE AUSTRALIAN BUG,** *Icerya purchasi*, adult females on twig

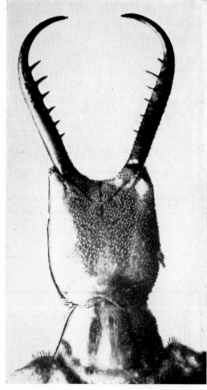

(*b*) Larva of small Clearwing Ant Lion, *Cueta lanceolata*

(*b*) Head of larva of large Spotted-Wing Ant Lion, *Palpares speciosus*

yet another family by themselves (*Mantispidae*). The adults look like small praying mantes because their front legs are modified for capturing and grasping prey, with a row of sharp spines along the outer edge of the femur, and a tibia that closes down on the femur like the jaws of a trap. There are a number of different species found in Africa but little is known about their habits and life history. According to observations made overseas, the female lays a large number of small eggs that are mounted on stalks like those of the lacewing.

The newly hatched larva of the mantispa is very small and slender, with six legs, and it looks very much like a tiny white louse. It runs about actively and is capable of enduring a long fast: it may even hibernate for several weeks without food if conditions are unfavourable. In order to survive it must find the egg-cocoon of a spider. If it succeeds in finding a spider's bag of eggs, the larva burrows through the silken envelope and takes up its abode amid the ball of eggs inside. Here it waits patiently until the eggs hatch and then, for the first time since its birth, it begins to feed. It devours the young spiders inside the cocoon and is soon surrounded by the shrivelled skins of its victims. The larva grows rapidly and in a few days it is a bloated yellow maggot that can scarcely move. When fully grown it spins a neat spherical cocoon of silk, with the dried remains of the young spiders stuck all over the outside.

Practically nothing is known about the habits of the adult. The nature of the front legs indicates that it is predacious and feeds on small insects which it captures by stalking, because it cannot run quickly and it is a feeble flier. Apparently it waits on flowers for small flies, bees and beetles to come close whilst hunting for nectar.

CLASSIFICATION

ORDER 15: *NEUROPTERA*—ALDER FLIES, LACEWINGS, ANT LIONS

Small to rather large soft-bodied insects, with mouthparts adapted for biting. Two pairs of membranous wings, usually alike, held roofwise over body when at rest. Larvae carnivorous with biting mouthparts adapted for sucking. Pupae with legs and wings free, not bound down to rest of body as in butterflies and moths.

SUB-ORDER 1: *Megaloptera*—ALDER FLIES AND SNAKE FLIES
Primitive Neuroptera with two pairs of similar wings. They are divided into three families.

FAMILY 1: *Corydalidae*—LARGE ALDER FLIES
The outspread wings measure from two to four inches across. Larvae are all aquatic, with eight pairs of gills on the abdomen, predacious.

FAMILY 2: *Sialidae*—SMALL ALDER FLIES
The outspread wings measure less than two inches across. The larvae are all aquatic and predacious, with seven pairs of gills on the abdomen.

FAMILY 3: *Raphidiidae*—SNAKE FLIES
These insects are terrestrial, the larvae generally found amid rank vegetation, under bark and in dead leaves, where they hunt their prey. The adults are remarkable for their elongated prothorax which, together with the narrow head, give the insect

Q

something of a snakelike appearance. The membranous wings each have a dark spot on the front border near the tip.

SUB-ORDER 2: *Planipennia*—LACEWINGS AND ANT LIONS

This sub-order includes the majority of the Neuroptera. The larvae of them all have the grooved mandibles with slender maxillae closing the grooves to enable the insects to suck the juices of their prey. All, as far as is known, have a blind stomach and some of the malpighian tubes attached at the hind end to the intestine and they serve as spinning organs at the time of pupation. All are predacious.

FAMILY 4: *Hemerobiidae*—BROWN LACEWINGS

Small, delicate insects with slender antennae and no ocelli. The eggs are not stalked. Larvae feed on aphides and other small insects. Adults are small, sombre-coloured lacewings.

FAMILY 5: *Chrysopidae*—GREEN LACEWINGS

A large number of species characterised by their green colour, their golden eyes and their delicate membranous wings. Eggs are laid on stalks and the larvae predacious.

FAMILY 6: *Nemopteridae*—THREAD-WING ANT LIONS

Adults with elongated, ribbonlike hind wings. Larvae live in dust and are characterised by their long, narrow 'neck'. Slender hind wings coiled like watch-springs in the pupal stage.

FAMILY 7: *Mymeleonidae*—ANT LIONS

These are the typical ant lions. Adults resemble dragonflies in appearance but may be recognised by clubbed antennae. Most of the larvae dig conical pits in soil, but there are a few species that hide under stones, the bark of trees, etc.

FAMILY 8: *Ascalaphidae*—LONG-HORNED ANT LIONS

Adults with long, clubbed antennae: active fliers, mostly nocturnal in their habits. Larvae hunt in debris and under stones and the bark of trees for their prey.

FAMILY 9: *Mantispidae*

Adults with front legs adapted for capturing and holding prey and much like those of the praying mantis. Small insects. Larvae are, as far as is known, parasitic in egg-cocoons of spiders.

(Two or three small and unimportant families have been omitted from the above summary.)

CHAPTER XIII

SCORPION FLIES

The Mecoptera

This is a small and unimportant order that includes only about two hundred known species from all parts of the world. The popular name, scorpion flies, is applied to this group because the males of some of them hold the tip of the abdomen curled up over the back and they look something like miniature winged scorpions. They are slender, moderate or small-sized insects with two pairs of narrow, membranous wings and long threadlike antennae. At first glance the adults look like crane flies, or daddy-long-legs, but they can be readily distinguished by their four wings: crane flies have only one pair of wings, and short antennae. The front of the head is prolonged to form a curious beak with the mandibles at the tip. The scientific name, *Mecoptera*, means "long-winged".

African Scorpion Flies

In shady places, among bushes along the side of a stream or on the edge of a forest, brown four-winged flies, an inch or more

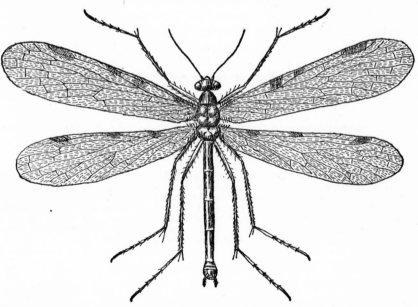

FIG. 61—A South African Scorpion Fly *Bittacus nebulosus*, male. It is about two inches across the expanded wings and brown in colour.

137

across the outspread wings, may sometimes be found resting amid the rank vegetation. They have long legs, a slender body and a characteristic beak on the front of the head. Their resting attitude is peculiar in that they hang on mainly by their front legs, with the middle and hind legs stretched out behind. These are the scorpion flies known to science as *Bittacus* species, several of which have been recorded from Africa, but very little indeed is known about their habits and life histories.

Judging from observations made in other parts of the world, these insects are all carnivorous. The adults capture any small insects they can overcome, gripping them in their prehensile feet, or tarsi, and nibbling at their victims much in the same way as praying mantes do. The female lays her eggs in a damp spot, in the soil or in moss and the larvae that develop from them closely resemble caterpillars. The larva of the scorpion fly has six true legs on the three segments behind the head and eight pairs of abdominal legs on the following eight segments. A caterpillar never has more than five pairs of abdominal legs; and in addition a caterpillar has only four to six simple eyes on each side of its head, while the scorpion fly larva has a group of twenty or more simple eyes on each side. Finally, the antennae of the scorpion fly larva are prominent and four-jointed, whereas those of a caterpillar are small and difficult to see.

The scorpion fly larva feeds on any small victims it can capture. When it is fully grown it buries itself in the soil and changes into a pupa, with the legs, buds of wings and compound eyes of the adult clearly visible. It can move about if disturbed because its legs are not bound down to its sides as they are in the pupa of a moth or butterfly. When the adult is about to emerge the pupa works its way to the surface.

CLASSIFICATION

Order 16: *MECOPTERA*—Scorpion Flies

A small, unimportant order of slender or moderate-sized insects with two pairs of narrow, membranous wings. Antennae long and threadlike. Head usually produced into a narrow beak with the biting mouthparts at the tip. Legs long and slender. Larvae resemble caterpillars but have, as a rule, eight pairs of abdominal legs, prominent four-jointed antennae, and a group of twenty or more simple eyes on each side of the head. The insects are carnivorous. Only a dozen or so species have been recorded from Africa and very little is known about their habits and life histories.

CHAPTER XIV

CADDIS FLIES

The Trichoptera

Caddis flies are small to moderate-sized insects, dull coloured and with their bodies and wings densely clothed with hair. They look very much like moths and might easily be mistaken for them, particularly as many caddis flies fly in the evening and some are attracted to lights. Moths are, however, clothed in scales and their mouthparts are modified to form a long, coiled proboscis for sucking nectar. Caddis flies have no such proboscis and their mandibles are reduced to useless vestiges so that they cannot chew solid food: they can, therefore, only lap up liquids such as nectar from shallow flowers, or sap from a wound in the stem of a plant. The adults may be found in the herbage along the sides of lakes and streams and most of them fly feebly for a short distance when disturbed before settling again. Some of them are strong fliers. The immature stages are spent in water. The scientific name of the order, *Trichoptera*, means "hairy-wings".

African Caddis Flies

About one hundred different species of caddis flies have been described from various parts of Africa, most of them from the mountain streams of the south-west Cape. There are undoubtedly many more that still await discovery. The adults vary in size from species with a wing expanse of about one and a half inches, down to small flies that measure only a quarter of an inch across the outspread wings.

The large Cape caddis fly, *Dyschimus thrymmifer*, may be taken as our example of the group. The adult measures about one and a quarter inches across the outspread wings and its body is dark brown, clothed in blackish hairs. The wings are very hairy, mottled with different shades of brown. When at rest the insect folds its wings at a low angle over the abdomen. It may be found during the summer months resting on bushes and trees along the banks of mountain streams at an altitude of a thousand feet or more. Being a nocturnal insect, it is sluggish during the day and only flies if it is disturbed and soon comes to rest again. It is, therefore, seldom seen unless sought for.

The eggs of this species have not so far been found but it is probable

139

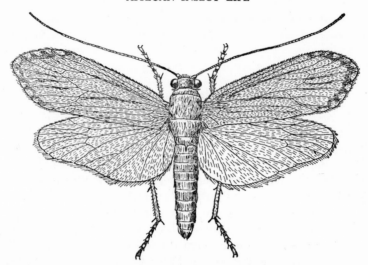

FIG. 62—The large Cape Caddis Fly, *Dyschimus thrymmifer*. It is about one and a quarter
     inches across the outspread wings and brown in colour.

that the female, like the rest of her kind, lays her small eggs in masses
in the water or on overhanging trees and bushes, and that they are
enclosed in a kind of mucilage that swells rapidly when wetted. The
larva, or caddis worm, resembles a caterpillar with six rather long
legs and it constructs a case in which to protect its soft body from
the many predacious enemies in the water. Different species of caddis
worms use various materials for their cases and the kind we are dealing
with constructs its home out of bits of dead stick, leaves and other
vegetable debris, bound together by silk that the insect produces from
its specialized salivary glands and that issues as a thread from the
spinneret below its mouth. It feeds on water plants and on any
edible vegetable or animal debris that comes its way.

The full-grown larva is about three quarters of an inch long.
Its head and the first two segments of its thorax are brown and the
skin is thick and tough because this is the part of its body the insect
sticks out when it is dragging its case along. The rest of its body
is thin-skinned and white. The first pair of legs are stout and strong,
and the second pair are the longest and are slender, whilst the third
pair are much shorter. At the hind end of its abdomen it has a pair
of strong hooks which enable it to hold securely to the silken lining
inside the case. If you try to pull a caddis worm out of its case you
will find that it hangs on so tightly by those hooks that you are liable
to tear its body apart before it will let go. But you can usually get
it out without injuring it by poking a thin grass stalk or pin in at
the back of the case. Then, if you put the naked worm into a jar

of water and supply it with beads, or bits of coloured paper or wool, or tiny shells, it will build itself an elegant case out of the materials supplied. In the case of caddis worms that live in running water, the jar must be placed under a tap with a trickle of water coming from it, otherwise the insect will die from lack of oxygen.

On the larva's back there are slender white threads, mostly in groups of three. These are its gills. The insect renews the water inside the case by undulating its body, thus causing a slow current to flow in at the front end and out at the smaller opening at the back. The first segment of its abdomen has three swellings on it, one at each side and one on the back, and these hold it in place inside the tube whilst allowing the water to flow past.

When the larva is ready to change into a pupa it first of all anchors its case securely by silken threads in a crevice between stones or amid some heavy debris on the bottom of the stream. Then it closes the front and back entrances to its case by spinning silk across them and by fastening sand grains on to the silk, but these barriers to keep out enemies are sievelike so that water can still flow through them and bring air to the pupa inside.

The compound eyes, the long antennae, the four wings and the six legs can be clearly seen in the pupa; they are not bound down to the sides as is the case with the pupa of a moth or butterfly. The

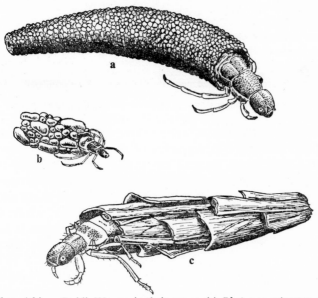

FIG. 63—Three African Caddis Worms, in their cases: (a) *Rhoizema spinosum*, case about one inch long; (b) *Sinion hageni*, case about one third inch long; (c) *Dyschimus thrymmifer*, case nearly one inch long.

pupa also has gills on its abdomen similar to those of the larva so that it may breathe under the water. On its head it has two prominent, long, sharp mandibles which are used only once in its life. When the adult is ready to emerge the pupa becomes very active and cuts an opening in the top of the case by means of its mandibles. Then it wriggles out into the water and either crawls or swims to the surface. Arrived there, the skin splits, and the adult emerges very quickly, casting off the mandibles and the gills which it no longer needs.

Caddis worms utilise various materials in constructing their cases. Some make tubular homes out of slender bits of stick bound together in a bundle, side by side. Certain tiny species make neat little bivalve cases out of green algae and silk. Others build ovoid or cylindrical cases of sand grains. Some are content to use only their own silk as their protective covering and they make tubular homes, shaped like miniature elephant tusks, or tiny flask-shaped cases, or small bivalve cases that look very much like caraway seeds. Finally, there are species that do not make a definite case but build a rough network of silken threads amid the stones and debris and live in this, several individuals often living together in one such home. Some, if not all, of the species that live in the rough silken tunnels are carnivorous and feed on mayfly larvae and other small aquatic creatures.

CLASSIFICATION

ORDER 17: *TRICHOPTERA*—CADDIS FLIES

Small to moderate-sized mothlike insects with long, slender antennae. Mandibles vestigial or absent and there is no proboscis for sucking as is found in the Lepidoptera. Wings membranous and more or less densely hairy and held roofwise over body when at rest. Tarsi five-jointed. Larvae aquatic, more or less caterpillar-like and usually living in cases: two hooks at end of abdomen for holding on inside case. Pupae with legs and wings free, not bound down to body as in lepidopterous pupae.

PLATE 29

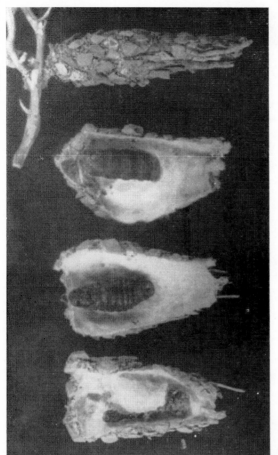

(a) THE STONY BAGWORM. Case on right, cases on left cut open to show (1) inner case, (2) caterpillar, (3) female pupa.

(b) The above-ground tunnel of the Common Cape Ghost Moth. It is made of silk, encrusted with excrement and fragments of grass. The coin (half-a-crown) shows relative size.

PLATE 30

(a) THE LONG-HORNED ANT LION, *Proctarrelabris capensis*, male in characteristic resting attitude

(b) THE LARGE SPOTTED-WING ANT LION, *Palpares speciosus*, female

CHAPTER XV

MOTHS

The Lepidoptera

The most familiar and most easily recognised of all insects are moths and butterflies. Because of their beauty they are also the most popular with collectors. Many of them are of great economic importance because they are serious pests of crops and various stored products. For these reasons this large group of insects has been more intensively studied than any other and is the best known. There are nearly 100,000 different species that have so far been named and described all over the world.

Moths and butterflies have two pairs of membranous wings that are covered with flattened scales, arranged something like tiles on a roof. They give the colouring and patterns to the wings and are easily rubbed off; hence specimens are quickly damaged if they are carelessly handled. Because of the scaly covering these insects are known as the *Lepidoptera*, or scaly-winged insects. Butterflies are generally distinguished from moths by their habit of flying by day and by the fact that their antennae are swollen or clubbed at the tip—hence the name *Rhopalocera*, insects with clubbed horns, often applied to them. Moths, on the other hand, mostly fly at night and have varied antennae, long or short, feathered or plain, swollen in the middle or of the same thickness throughout, and so on, and they are often classified under the name *Heterocera*, insects with varied antennae.

This distinction between butterflies and moths is, however, not a very good one from a scientific point of view, and entomologists to-day regard butterflies as forming two only of the thirty-odd families into which the whole order is divided: perhaps the highest of the families, but not sufficiently distinct from moths to form a separate sub-order. The Lepidoptera are divided into two sub-orders, but these are not moths and butterflies: the first sub-order, called the *Jugatae*, includes only two families of primitive moths, while the second sub-order, the *Frenatae*, includes all the rest, the higher moths and the butterflies.

When a moth is in flight the two wings on each side need to be coupled together so that they beat up and down as one, but when the insect is at rest it folds its wings one over the other. The coupling apparatus must, therefore, be something that readily locks or unlocks

R

the wings. Among the primitive moths we find a small lobe on the hind margin of each front wing (see Fig. 64): this is called a *jugum* (yoke) and it clips over the undersurface of the hind wing when the moth is flying but is easily slipped off when the insect folds its wings. The higher moths lack this jugum on the front wings and in its stead they have one or more stiff, curved bristles on the front margin of each hind wing. This coupling apparatus is known as a *frenulum*: the bristles lock into a tuft of stiff hairs on the hind margin of the front wing when the insect is flying. Thus the two families of primitive moths with a jugum on each front wing are known as the *Jugatae*, while the higher members of the order with a frenulum on each hind wing are the *Frenatae*.

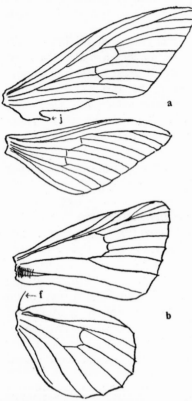

The classification of moths and butterflies is largely based on the number and arrangement of the veins on the wings. Among primitive moths the veins on the front and hind wings are similar, twelve in each, and they are, therefore, spoken of in some textbooks on entomology as the *Homoneura*, insects with similar veins on each wing. The higher moths and butterflies, on the other hand, have more veins in the front wings than in the hind wings and they are somewhat differently arranged and, in consequence, are called the *Heteroneura*,

FIG. 64—Wings of moths, with scales removed, to show venation: (*a*) Wings of the silver-spotted ghost moth, *Leto venus*, showing jugum and similarity of veins in fore and hind wings; (*b*) Wings of a geometrid moth, *Semiothisa interrupta*, showing frenulum and dissimilarity of veins in fore and hind wings.

insects with dissimilar veins. The *Homoneura* are the same as the *Jugatae*, and the *Heteroneura* the same as the *Frenatae*.

Finally, the mouthparts and the genitalia of the primitive moths are different from those of the higher members of the group. The genitalia are the parts of the body associated with mating and they are complicated and difficult to describe. They are, however, of great importance in the classification of insects and any student who wishes to take up seriously the study of butterflies and moths must master the details by consulting such a work as *The Moths of South Africa* by Dr. A. J. T. Janse of the Transvaal Museum, Pretoria.

Primitive Moths
There are certain small moths, only half an inch or less across the expanded wings, that have bright, metallic colours and long, slender antennae and that fly by day. They are usually found near damp spots on the outskirts of woods, where sunlight and shade mingle,

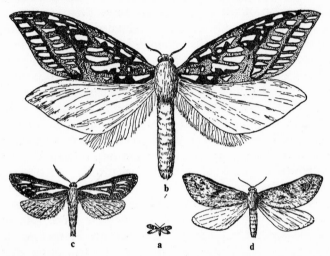

FIG. 65—Primitive Moths: (*a*) the only Micropterygid moth so far found in Africa, *Agrionympha psiliaema:* only two specimens have been caught, both in Natal; (*b*) the silver-spotted ghost moth, *Leto venus*; (*c*) the common Cape ghost moth, *Gorgopis cochlias*; (*d*) the yellow-spotted ghost moth, *Antihepialus antarcticus*. All slightly smaller than natural size.

and they seldom attract any attention because of their small size and their short erratic flight from one patch of shade to another. These little moths are of great interest because they are regarded as the most primitive of them all and form a connecting link between caddis flies and the higher moths.

Most butterflies and moths have no jaws or only tiny, useless vestiges of jaws, but they have a long tubular tongue by means of which they can sip nectar from the flowers. The primitive moths have no tongue for sucking, but some of them have jaws for biting and they feed on pollen instead of nectar. There are about eighty different species of these moths known in the world, mostly from temperate lands in the northern hemisphere, and they are placed in a family by themselves called the *Micropterygidae*.

So far only one species of this interesting family has been found in South Africa and only two specimens have been captured, both by Dr. A. J. T. Janse in Natal. This is a tiny moth only one third of an inch across the expanded wings, "coppery-golden-bronze with a purplish reflection" and silvery spots. The tiny caterpillars of moths of this family found in other parts of the world feed on mosses, and it is probable that the Natal species does the same. The caterpillar has not yet been discovered but, when it is, it should be interesting because it should have eight pairs of legs on its abdomen, instead of the five pairs usual among caterpillars of the higher families—another indication of the primitive nature of these moths.

The only other family of moths included in the *Jugatae* are the ghost moths, or swift moths, *Hepialidae*, and these are very well represented in Africa, over one hundred and seventy different species of them having already been described from South Africa alone. They have short antennae and are rapid fliers—hence their name of swift moths; most of them are sombrely coloured, usually of a pale shade of brown, and they look like the ghosts of moths as they flit swiftly past in the twilight. Their mouthparts are very small and useless and the moths do not feed at all in the adult state.

The caterpillars of most of our ghost moths feed on grass roots. The female moths simply drop their numerous small eggs casually on the ground as they flit just above the grass and the newly-hatched caterpillars burrow into the soil to get at their food. As they grow bigger certain species make silken tubes above the surface of the soil, among the grass stems, and they fix their droppings on the sides of this tube. Some male ghost moths give off a scent and it is said that, in these cases, it is the females that seek out the males at mating time, and not *vice versa* as is usually the case.

The most beautiful and most striking of all our ghost moths is the silver-spotted ghost moth (*Leto venus*). Between five and six inches across the outspread wings, it has orange-coloured front wings spotted with silver, pink hind wings and a scarlet abdomen. It is found only in the Knysna Forest. The female lays her eggs in the soft soil at the base of a keurboom (*Virgilia capensis*) which is the only known food plant of this insect. The caterpillars burrow into the tree and, like most wood-borers, they take a long time to reach maturity: possibly two, three or more years. They pupate inside their burrows and the adult moths emerge in February or March and, being unable to feed, are short-lived.

Clothes Moths and Their Kin

Most householders are familiar with the damage done by clothes moths but few are able to recognise the actual moths that are responsible. There are three species that are common and widely spread in this country, the common clothes moth (*Tineola bisselliella*), the case-bearing clothes moth (*Trichophaga tapetiella*) and the old-fashioned clothes moth (*Tinea pellionella*). All three are small yellowish or grayish moths with narrow, fringed wings, and they are not more than half an inch across the expanded wings. The common clothes moth is of a pale yellowish colour without any markings on its wings and the small, narrow insect, little more than a quarter of an inch long, easily escapes the notice of the housewife when it is at rest inside a cupboard. The female lays her tiny eggs on woollen goods and furs, but not on cotton or linen fabrics. The damage is caused by the little white caterpillars with dark heads that spin delicate silken tubes over the material and feed on the wool and fur. They pupate inside thin white cocoons on the material.

The case-bearing clothes moth may be recognised by its black and white front wings. The caterpillar feeds on wool, fur and any other dead, dry animal matter it can find. It makes a neat silken case inside which it lives and which it carries about with it: as this case generally has dust particles and fragments of the food sticking to it, it is not at all conspicuous. The old-fashioned clothes moth is gray, speckled with indistinct darker spots on the front wings. The caterpillar also makes a silken case in which it lives and it

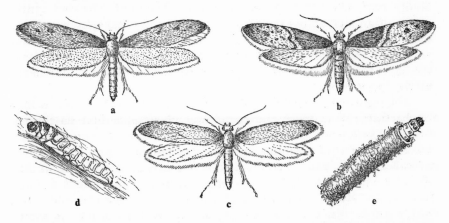

FIG. 66—Clothes Moths: (*a*) the old-fashioned clothes moth, *Tinea pellionella*; (*b*) the case-bearing clothes moth, *Trichophaga tapetiella*; (*c*) the common clothes moth, *Tineola bisselliella*; (*d*) the caterpillar of the common clothes moth; (*e*) caterpillar of the case-bearing clothes moth.

may often be found on the wall of a room, creeping slowly upwards to find a suitable spot where it can fix its abode and turn into a pupa.

The diamond back moth (*Plutella maculipennis*) is a well known pest of cabbages that has been spread all over the world by man's commerce. It is very common in Africa on plants of the cabbage

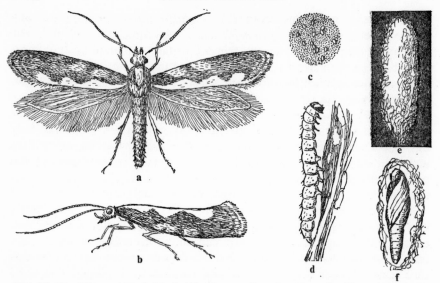

FIG. 67—The Diamond Back Moth, *Plutella maculipennis:* (*a*) moth; (*b*) moth in resting attitude; (*c*) eggs on cabbage leaf; (*d*) caterpillar; (*e*) cocoon on cabbage leaf; (*f*) pupa inside cocoon.

family, particularly during the dry season. The moth measures a little over half an inch across the expanded wings and is ash-grey in colour; there is a white wavy line along the hind margin of each front wing and, when the insect is at rest, these wavy lines, coming together along the back, form diamond-shaped marks, from which the common name of the moth comes.

The female lays her tiny yellowish-green eggs on the upper surface of the leaves of cabbage and cauliflower plants and these hatch in a few days into green caterpillars that feed on the under surface of the leaves and, if they are numerous, quickly reduce them to a network of veins only. The caterpillars spin a thin gauzy covering of silk beneath which they shelter and feed. They are about half an inch long when fully grown and spin white silken cocoons on the underside of the leaves, inside which they change into pupae. A few days later the adult moths emerge. There may be as many as ten generations a year and, as each female may lay fifty or more eggs, it is not surprising that they increase very rapidly in numbers when conditions are favourable.

The worst insect pest the potato-grower has to contend with in this country is the potato tuber moth, *Phthorimaea operculella*, another insect that has been widely spread over the world by man's commerce. The moth measures about five-eighths of an inch across the expanded wings and is greyish brown, speckled with darker markings on the

front wings.   The female lays her tiny white eggs on the potato plants
in the field or on the tubers in the ground or the store-house.   The
caterpillar feeds on the leaves, mining between the upper and lower
surface or joining two young leaves together with silk and feeding
between them.   If it is feeding on the tuber it burrows below the surface.
When fully grown it is about half an inch long, greenish white in
colour, with a black head.   It seeks out a sheltered spot when fully
grown, spins a silken cocoon and changes into a pupa.   There may
be five or six generations a year.   Besides potatoes, the caterpillars
will feed on tobacco, *stinkblaar* (*Datura*) and other members of the
potato family.

The above pests, together with many others are members of a
very large family of small moths known as the *Tineidae*.   This family
probably contains more species than any other and there must be well
over 1,000 species in South Africa alone.   The moths are small, with
narrow wings, and nearly all are dull coloured night fliers, although
there are a few brightly coloured species that fly by day.   The veins
on the hind wings are different and fewer in number than those on
the front wings and the pair on each side is linked when in flight by
a frenulum.   The moths have a tubular proboscis for sucking nectar
and, therefore, form the first family of the sub-order *Frenatae* or
Heteroneura.

The Codling Moth and its Kin

The codling moth (*Cydia pomonella*) is the most serious pest of
apples, pears, quinces and walnuts: it will also attack apricots.   The
moth itself is not often seen as it hides during the day and flies only
at night, and it is not attracted to lights.   It is small, inconspicuous
and only about three-quarters of an inch across the outspread wings.
It can most easily be recognised by the large bronze oval spot at the
tip of each front wing; the remainder of the front wing is grey, striped
with darker grey, and the hind wing is pale brown.

The female lays her eggs singly, depositing them on the leaves
and fruit, and she may lay fifty to one hundred eggs during her two
or three weeks of life as an adult.   The egg is white, round and flattened
and about the size of an ordinary pin's head.   It hatches in four to
twenty days, depending on the temperature, and the newly-hatched
caterpillar at once seeks out a fruit into which it can bore.   Usually
it enters at the calyx end of the fruit or at a spot where one fruit touches
another or is in contact with a twig—places where it is sheltered and
where it can get support while it is burrowing.

The caterpillar feeds inside the fruit for four to six weeks, by
which time it is fully grown, about three quarters of an inch long and

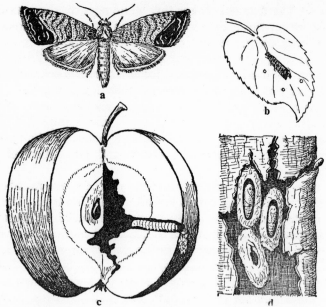

FIG. 67—The Codling Moth, *Cydia pomonella:* (*a*) moth; (*b*) moth in resting attitude and eggs on apple leaf (natural size); (*c*) caterpillar inside apple; (*d*) cocoons and pupae beneath bark.

white or pink in colour, with a brown head. It then leaves the fruit, generally at night, and creeps down the branch to find a sheltered spot in which it can spin its silken cocoon. If the tree is young and there are no cracks in the bark, it will make its way to the ground and pupate under a clod near the base of the tree. On older trees, however, there are usually plenty of cracks and crevices in the bark into which it can creep.

It spins a white silken cocoon inside which it rests for some days before changing to a pupa. After a fortnight or more the pupa wriggles its way partly out of the cocoon and then the moth emerges. The first moths of the year, the spring moths, appear in the orchards in September and October, just when the young fruit is forming. There are two generations a year, the second generation of moths making their appearance in December and January, and there may be a partial third generation in March. These generations overlap and moths, eggs, caterpillars and pupae may be found in the orchards during the greater part of the summer. The caterpillars that are fully grown towards the end of summer spend the winter resting inside their cocoons and they only change into pupae in the following spring, to give rise to the first generation of moths of that season.

The codling moth belongs to a very large and widely spread family

PLATE 31

(a) Caterpillar of the Wax Moth, *Galleria mellonella*, on honey-comb

(b) THE CONVOLVULUS HAWK MOTH, *Herse convolvuli*. Its proboscis, shown uncoiled in the photo-graph, is about 4 inches long.

PLATE 32

(a) Caterpillar of the Death's Head Moth. It is about 5 inches long, green with purple stripes.

(b) THE DEATH'S HEAD MOTH, *Acherontia atropos*

of small moths known as the *Tortricidae*. The caterpillars live concealed in rolled or joined leaves, in fruits, stems, roots or flower-heads and they are more or less slender, slightly hairy and have the usual number of abdominal feet, five pairs. The pupae wriggle partly out of the cocoons before the moths emerge and the empty pupal cases are left projecting from the cocoons. The moths have a proboscis by means of which they can suck nectar and their wings are linked by a frenulum.

Bagworms

Many insects construct portable homes for themselves, but perhaps the most remarkable and interesting of them all are the caterpillars known as bagworms or basketworms. These belong to a family of moths known as the *Psychidae* and they are very well represented in Africa. One of the commonest and best known members of the family is the wattle bagworm, *Acanthopsyche junodi*, which is found on thorn trees and which is also a serious pest in wattle plantations.

The male wattle bagworm moth measures about one and a quarter inches across the expanded wings and his wings are transparent and have few scales on them and are devoid of markings. He flies about swiftly in the daytime, but his mouthparts are imperfect and he cannot feed; his life as an adult is, therefore, short. The female is quite

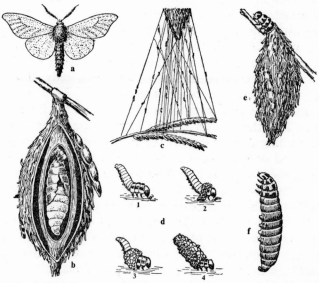

FIG. 68—The Wattle Bagworm, *Acanthopsyche junodi*: (*a*) male moth; (*b*) female moth inside her bag; (*c*) newly hatched caterpillars on silken threads; (*d*) newly hatched caterpillar constructing its case; (*e*) fully grown caterpillar in its case; (*f*) caterpillar removed from case.

S

different from her mate; most people would, in fact, fail to recognise her as a moth at all because she has no legs or wings or eyes and her body is fat and maggot-like; she is so helpless that she never leaves the bag in which she grew up. The male seeks out the bag in which she is lying motionless, head downwards, inserts his long, extensible abdomen into the bag and fertilises her. Soon after this he dies.

Shortly after the mating she begins to lay her numerous, tiny eggs, about fifteen hundred of them in all. The eggs accumulate in the empty pupal skin behind her, mixed with the fluffy scales from her body, and finally, when the egg-laying is complete, only her dead, shrivelled body remains, with the mass of eggs and scales in the bag behind her. All this occurs in the spring and the eggs hatch about a fortnight later, in the middle of September. The tiny, newly-hatched larvae leave the bag and spin silken threads amid the twigs around them and they climb up and down these threads for two or three days, without feeding. This apparently is a provision of nature to bring about the spread of the insects to other trees; strong winds may blow them away or insects and birds, flying through the silken threads, may carry some of the threads away with the little caterpillars still clinging to them.

Before it settles down and starts to feed, the young caterpillar constructs a home for itself. It does this by biting off fragments of the leaves and binding them together with silk, so that a semicircular girdle is formed, attached at each end to a leaf. Then the insect puts its head through the loop, frees the two ends and joins them together so that a collar is formed just behind its head. By adding more silk and fragments of leaves to the front edge, the collar is lengthened until the whole body is covered and then, and then only, does the little caterpillar walk away and commence to feed. As it grows it adds more silk and leaves and twigs to its home so that the familiar, ragged-looking bag is formed, with the fat brown caterpillar inside. Only when it is feeding does it expose the front portion of its body.

By the end of summer the bagworm is fully grown, with a bag nearly two inches long. It now fixes its bag firmly to a twig, binding it securely with a band of silk so that the winds and storms of winter cannot shift it. Then it retreats into the bag and spins a snug inner tube of silk inside which it can sleep, head downwards, throughout the winter. On the advant of warmer weather in the following spring it changes into a pupa and finally into a adult moth, active and winged if it is a male, sluggish and helpless if it is a female.

Although wattle bagworms would seem to be well protected by their bags, the mortality among them is very high. The large number of eggs laid by each female is also an indication that this must be so, otherwise they would increase to astronomical numbers. The bags with dead caterpillars in them remain attached to the trees and it is easy to collect them and ascertain the cause of death. Out of some 60,000 bags collected in this way in Natal it was found that 1 per cent. of the caterpillars were destroyed by birds and rats, 19 per cent. by insect parasites, 16 per cent. by fungous disease, and 17 per cent. by other diseases, making a total of 53 per cent. altogether. But this mortality is as nothing compared with the destruction of the young, newly-hatched caterpillars: less than one quarter of 1 per cent. of the young larvae survive the early perils of their life. Probably the great majority of them fail to get carried to a suitable food plant and die of starvation.

The caterpillars of the different species of bagworms found in Africa inhabit cases that exhibit great variety of form and of materials used in their construction, covering their silken abodes with fragments of leaves, or sticks, or thorns, pieces of grass, small stones and other objects. Parthenogenesis, or virgin birth, is known to occur among certain kinds of bagworms, including some African species; if a male fails to find one of the maggot-like females, she lays her eggs without mating and they hatch normally: in some cases the males are very rare or they may be absent altogether, but the eggs hatch without their aid.

Carpenter Moths

The quince borer, *Coryphodema tristis*, is a greyish brown moth that measures one to two inches across the expanded wings. It is

rarely seen as it hides during the day and only flies after dark and is not attracted to lights. As it has only rudimentary mouthparts it cannot feed and lives only for about a week as an adult. The female lays her eggs in the spring in irregular masses on the bark of quince, apple and pear trees. She deposits them in cracks in the bark,

FIG. 69—The Quince Borer, *Coryphodema tristis*. The moth is grey and measures about one and a half inches across the out-spread wings.

in old burrows and in the angles where one branch joins another, and covers them with fluff from her body. Although the eggs are very small, the masses are easily seen as pink fluffy tufts. The eggs take about two months to hatch and the young caterpillars feed at first on the bark and later burrow down into the wood.

The presence of the caterpillars is revealed by the fragments of chewed wood, like sawdust, that they push out of their burrows.

The bark surrounding the infested area becomes wet with sap that oozes out and the branch may die as a result of the injury caused by the caterpillars. In about eighteen months the caterpillars are fully grown, an inch and a quarter long, with brown heads and pale yellowish bodies mottled with irregular reddish brown spots. Then, by the end of March in their second year of life, the caterpillars spin their tough silken cocoons, mixed with sawdust, inside their burrows about an inch from the entrance. About a month later they turn into pupae in which stage they pass through the winter. Finally in October or November the adult moths emerge and, being unable to feed, they live for only a few days.

The quince borer belongs to the family known as the *Cossidae*, moths that are often popularly spoken of as goat moths or carpenter moths. They are moderately large or very large moths, some members of the family reaching a wing expansion of seven inches. Most of them lay their eggs on the bark of trees or in the tunnels from which they have emerged and the caterpillars bore into the wood. They often cause serious injury to forest, shade and fruit trees.

Some cossid caterpillars make cases for themselves out of bits of grass which they arrange very neatly crosswise. They live inside these cases and carry them about with them, and may, therefore, easily be mistaken for bagworms. The large thorn-tree goat moth, *Xyleutes capensis*, is about four inches across the outspread wings, white, mottled with small brown spots and lines. The huge caterpillar of this moth, dirty-white in colour and with four rows of round brown spots along its body, may be found burrowing inside thorn trees.

Clearwings

The pretty little moths known as clearwings might be mistaken for butterflies by the uninitiated, as they fly swiftly by day in the bright sunlight, and their antennae are often dilated or knobbed. They can be recognised, however, by the fact that scales are absent from the greater part of both pairs of wings, hence their popular name. Also the front wings are very narrow and quite unlike the broad wings of butterflies. Some of them resemble wasps and bees because of their clear wings, slender bodies and bright colours.

The caterpillars are tunnellers in the branches of trees and bushes and in the roots, and pupation takes place inside the larval galleries. The pupae are armed with spines and hard sharp cutting plates on the head so that they are able to work their way to the surface before the moths emerge.

Slug Caterpillars

In the spring and again in the late summer, green caterpillars about an inch and a quarter long, with flattened bodies covered with spines, may be found feeding on the leaves of oak and plum trees. Because of their shape and because of the apparent absence of legs they are often spoken of as slug caterpillars. There is a pale blue stripe down the middle of the back, and on each segment, except the third and the eighth, there is a pair of black dots bordered with white; the sides of the thorax are deep red. The spines are hollow and terminate in short, sharp points that pierce the skin if the caterpillar is handled. At the base of each spine is a tiny poison gland and the poisonous secretion enters the wound made by the spines and may cause inflammation and swelling.

When fully grown, the caterpillar spins an oval cocoon around itself on a twig. This brittle, egg-like cocoon is at first white but soon

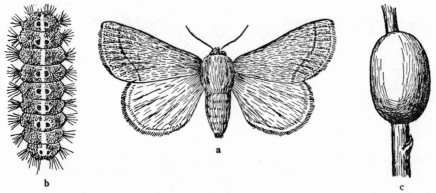

FIG. 70—The Plum Slug Caterpillar, *Parasa latistriga*. Moth in the middle, caterpillar on the left, cocoon on the right. The moth has pale green front wings and yellow hind wings and measures about one and a half inches across outspread wings.

turns brown. After resting inside the cocoon for about ten days, the caterpillar changes to a pupa and about three weeks later, during February, the moth emerges. The moth is about an inch and a half across the outspread wings, the front pair being pale green with a light brown outer border, whilst the hind wings are pale yellow, The female lays her flat oval eggs on the underside of the leaves of the food-plant, arranging them like the tiles on a roof, each egg partly overlapping the next. There are two generations a year, the first moths emerging in October and November and the second generation making its appearance in February.

The oak and plum slug caterpillars (*Parasa latistriga* and its close relatives, *Parasa johannes* and *P. vivida*) belong to the family of moths known as the *Limacodidae*. These are mostly small moths, dull brown in colour or, in some cases, green. The body is short and the wings are rounded. As the moth has no proboscis it cannot feed. The caterpillars have thick, short fleshy bodies with very small thoracic legs and small suckers on the underside of the abdomen instead of the usual claspers. Some of them are armed with poisonous spines. The pupa is enclosed in an oval cocoon of silk, with a definite lid that is pushed open by the pupa before the emergence of the moth.

Meal Moths and Their Kin

The Mediterranean flour moth, *Ephestia kuhniella*, is a well-known and widely spread pest that infests flour, bran and other cereal products. It is a small dark grey moth measuring about three quarters of an inch across the outspread wings and lays its eggs in the flour or meal in bins or on the sacks. They are small, white when first laid, but turn brown before hatching, which takes place in from five to ten

FIG. 71—The Mediterranean Flour Moth, *Ephestia kuhniella*.   (a) eggs; (b) caterpillar; (c) pupa; (d) moth. The moth is grey and about three quarter of an inch across outspread wings.

days. The white caterpillars feed on the meal, spinning crude silken tunnels wherever they go and fouling the food-stuff with their strong silk threads and their excrement. They take three to five weeks to reach full size, when they are about half an inch long. They spin silken cocoons inside which they pupate and the adult moths appear about a fortnight later. Each female moth lays about three hundred eggs and, under African conditions, they continue breeding throughout the year, and so they quickly increase in numbers and do serious damage in flour mills and pantries if they are left undisturbed.

The Indian meal moth, *Plodia interpunctella*, is a relative of the above and also very well known in pantries in this country. The moth is handsomely marked, with front wings that are half creamy white and half reddish brown and hind wings of a dusky grey colour: it measures about three quarters of an inch across the outspread wings. The female lays her eggs in meal, dried fruits, breakfast foods, in fact in almost any stored product that is edible. The caterpillars burrow through the food, fouling it with their webs and their excrement and quickly rendering it unfit for human consumption. During the colder months of the year they hibernate as caterpillars, but they continue their activities as soon as warmer weather returns.

Because the Mediterranean flour moth and the Indian meal moth are easily reared in large numbers in the laboratory, they are used for the mass production of certain parasites that are needed to combat other pests, such as the Karoo caterpillar mentioned below. The caterpillars are fed on a mixture of flour and bran and reared in cages at a temperature of about 75 degrees Fahrenheit. When the moths emerge they are collected by suction, on the vacuum cleaner principle, and placed in tins with bottoms of wire gauze. These are placed on flour and the moths lay their eggs through the gauze in the flour. When the egg-laying is complete the flour is sifted and so thousands of eggs are obtained for the mass rearings. The moths will also lay their eggs in powdered chalk and, as this is more easily sifted than the flour, it is often used for egg-collection.

The Karoo caterpillar, *Loxostege frustalis*, is a well-known pest in the sheep-farming areas as it destroys the foliage of the valuable fodder bush, *Pentzia incana*. In some years it appears in vast numbers and does great damage to the veld whilst in other years it is not nearly so common. The caterpillar is about an inch long when fully grown, green or almost black, and it spins a silken web over the plant while it is young but ceases to do so as it grows older. It reaches full size in two to four weeks, depending on the weather condi-

FIG. 72—The Karoo Moth, *Loxostege frustalis*. The moth is brown with cream-coloured spots and measures about an inch across the outspread wings.

tions, and then it makes its way to the ground and buries itself in the soil, where it spins a cocoon. It may rest for some months as a caterpillar inside the cocoon or it may change into a pupa after a rest of a few days and the adult moth emerges about a fortnight later— the speed of the change depending again on the weather conditions. The moth measures nearly an inch across the outspread wings and is brown with cream coloured spots on the fore wings. It is active both by day and by night and is attracted to lights in enormous numbers on warm moist evenings. The eggs are deposited singly or in small clusters on the underside of the leaves of the food-plants, and they hatch in five to ten days.

This insect, like other moths, has a number of parasites that prey upon it including tachinid flies (see page 299) and certain hymenopterous parasites (see page 316); under normal conditions these parasites keep the pest more or less under control but when climatic conditions favour the moth it increases enormously in numbers and does great harm to the veld. It is not economic to spray the Karoo bushes in order to kill the caterpillars, and so an attempt is being made at what is known as biological control. Parasites that will attack the Karoo caterpillar are bred in large numbers from the Mediterranean flour moth and the Indian meal moth in the laboratory in Pretoria and these are released on the veld where the Karoo caterpillar is abundant. As these moths are members of the same family, the same parasites will attack them, and it is hoped that the introduced parasites will aid the natural ones to keep the pest in check.

The wax moth, *Galleria mellonella*, is well known to beekeepers in Africa as it is very common and widely spread. This is a dull grey moth varying in size from an inch and a quarter to nearly two inches across the expanded wings. The female creeps into a hive at night, particularly into a hive where the bees have been weakened and reduced in numbers by disease and where the combs are not as well guarded as they are in a strong hive. Combs that have been removed from the hive and stored also attract her, particularly if the cells contain pollen. She lays her eggs in crevices and cracks or inside the cells. The eggs hatch in about ten days and the caterpillars, dirty white in colour, feed on the comb, boring their way through it in all directions and lining their tunnels with silk. A few of these caterpillars will quickly ruin a comb, reducing it to an unsightly mass of riddled cells with silken tubes and excrement hanging from them. A strong colony of bees can usually keep this pest out of their home, but a weak colony may be overrun and the bees will desert the hive, leaving the caterpillars to complete the destruction of the combs.

The caterpillar is fully grown in about a month and it then seeks out some corner in the hive where it can spin its cocoon of tough white silk. Frequently it gnaws an oval hollow in the wood with its strong jaws to form a snug resting place for itself. If the caterpillars are numerous the cocoons will be found piled in dense masses in a corner of the hive or on top of the frames, between them and the roof of the hive. There are three generations of the moths a year in this country and the worst damage usually occurs during the late summer months.

The lesser wax moth, *Achroia grisella*, is a pale greyish brown moth about three quarters of an inch across the expanded wings. The caterpillars of this moth are sometimes found destroying honey

PLATE 33

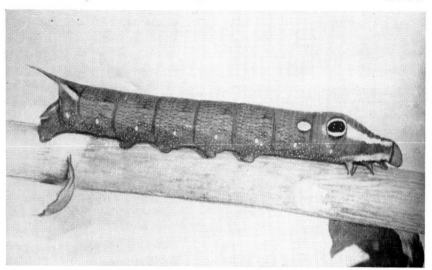

(a) Caterpillar of the White-lined Sphinx, *Chaerocampa celerio*

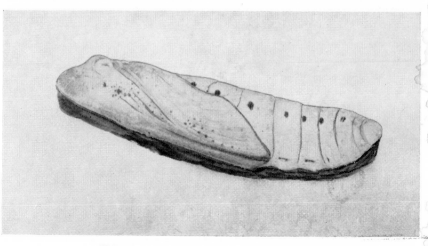

(b) Pupa of the White-lined Sphinx, *Chaerocampa celerio*

PLATE 34

(*a*) THE THORN-TREE EMPEROR MOTH, *Gynanisa maia*, male.   It is about 5 inches across the outspread wings.

(*b*) Eggs of the Thorn-tree Emperor Moth, *Gynanisa maia*

combs in association with its larger relative, but it is not so common nor is it so harmful. Its galleries are smaller and the webs are finer and more on the surface. Besides the debris in the bee hive, the caterpillar will attack dried fruit and other stored products.

The above moths belong to an enormous family of small to medium sized moths which are regarded by some authorities as consisting of a number of separate families, but usually they are all grouped together as the *Pyralidae*, divided into about a dozen sub-families. The caterpillars have varied habits and many of them live in concealment: they are mostly slender and nearly bare and with little or no colour pattern; many of them wriggle backwards or forwards in their burrows when disturbed.

Although many moths of this great family are serious pests there is at least one species that is decidedly beneficial. This is the grey prickly pear moth, *Cactoblastis cactorum*. An inch to an inch and a half across the outspread wings, it is greyish brown in colour, with

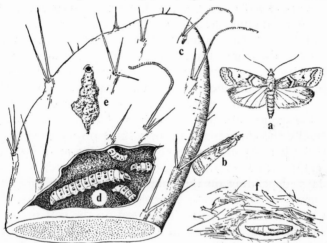

Fig. 73—Prickly Pear Moth, *Cactoblastis cactorum:* (a) moth; (b) moth resting; (c) eggs on tips of thorns; (d) caterpillars; (e) excreta and mucilage from hole in leaf; (f) pupa in cocoon amid debris.

indistinct markings on the front wings and paler hind wings. Like its food-plants, prickly pears, it is a native of America, but it was brought to this country some twenty years ago to help in the eradication of prickly pears that infested some million or more fertile acres in South Africa and rendered them useless for any agricultural purposes. It had previously been introduced into Australia and proved very successful there in destroying prickly pears, and accordingly the South African government decided to try it out under our conditions. An entomologist was sent to Australia and he brought back several

T

thousand eggs of the moth in 1932. This was the third time the eggs had been brought to this country but, on the previous occasions, in 1925 and 1927, it was considered too dangerous to release the moths, for fear they might turn their attention to cultivated plants, and they were destroyed. Work in Australia had shown, however, that the moths could live only on prickly pears and further investigations in the Union proved the same thing, and so it was decided to breed them in large numbers and let them loose on the veld. Eventually over 500,000,000 eggs were distributed among prickly pears on the veld, mainly in the eastern part of the Cape Province and the moth became established and did good work in destroying the pernicious weeds. Unfortunately, they were not as successful here as in Australia and this was due to several causes, including extremes of temperature, hail, fungus and bacterial diseases that killed the caterpillars, predacious insects, baboons, monkeys, rodents and birds. As a result, other insects, such as the cochineal, *Dactylopius opuntiae* (see page 124) and the beetle, *Lagochirus funestus* had to be introduced to assist the moths in combating the pest prickly pears.

The adult moth has rudimentary mouthparts and does not feed: consequently it lives only for about a week in the adult state. The female deposits her eggs in the form of a chain, called an egg-stick, one egg adhering to another, end to end, by a brownish mucilaginous substance emitted by the moth. Each egg is shaped like a tiny flat cheese and there are about one hundred of them in a stick an inch long. Usually she chooses the tip of a spine on the prickly pear pad as the site for her egg stick, and the slender columns of eggs look like curved prolongations of the spines. The eggs hatch in twenty to seventy days, depending on the temperature.

The newly-hatched larvae congregate at the base of the spine and then burrow into the pad. They feed on the soft tissues as they tunnel through them, returning to a silk-lined retreat where they rest together after feeding. Their excreta are thrust out of the entrance hole where they form an untidy mass held by sap that has oozed from the hole. The caterpillars are gregarious throughout their lives and, at times, they may leave the interior of the pad and cluster on the outside, near the entrance hole, where they rest for some time before re-entering the pad to feed again.

The caterpillars moult five times and are fully grown in six or seven weeks in summer, but take much longer in winter. They are then about an inch long, of a rich salmon colour marked with black and they leave the pad, drop to the ground and each seeks out a sheltered spot where it can make its cocoon. The cocoon is white, stained red at one end by the secretions of the larva, and the pupal stage lasts three to ten weeks. Meanwhile, the prickly pear pads that have been attacked rot, and a badly infested plant may die. In this way the caterpillars destroy the plants and, under favourable conditions, may eradicate them altogether over large areas.

Plume Moths

The beautiful little plume moths are readily distinguished from all others by their deeply fissured wings. The front wings are split into two, or, more rarely, three or four sections and the hind wings into three, making them appear to have five or six narrow wings on each side. There are a number of species found in this country but little is known about them. The small, slender caterpillars usually

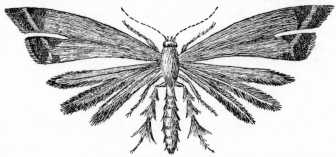

FIG. 74—An African Plume Moth, *Crocydoscelus ferrugineum*. It measures three fifths of an inch across the outspread wings.

feed exposed on flowers and leaves but some of them bore into stems and seed-pods. Plants of the daisy family (*Compositae*) are their favoured food-plants. Pupation takes place in light cocoons generally constructed above ground in a sheltered spot on the food-plant. The family is known to scientists as the *Pterophoridae*.

Lappet Moths

In November and December, and again in February, March and April, hairy caterpillars about one and a half inches long when fully grown may be very abundant on pepper trees. They may also be found, in lesser numbers, feeding on the leaves of *taaibos* (*Rhus* species), for this is their natural food-plant, but the introduced pepper trees seem to be more to their taste. The body of the caterpillar is black with two narrow yellow lines on each side, but the coating of orange-coloured hairs gives the insect a yellowish appearance.

The caterpillars are gregarious, feeding together in small groups, and if the tree is defoliated and they are hungry, they are apt to resort to cannibalism, the larger caterpillars killing and devouring the smaller ones. They cast their skin four times in the course of growth and reach full size in about fifty to sixty days. When fully grown they

crawl to the ground and swallow particles of soil which they grind
to a fine powder with their mandibles.   Then they creep about restlessly,
hunting for a suitable place to spin their cocoons.   They may crawl
back up the tree, or on to fences or walls, or into cracks in the bark
and there they spin their oval cocoons of dense silk, plastered on
the inside with a paste made from saliva and the fine soil particles
previously swallowed.   The cocoons are brown and about three
quarters of an inch long, flattened on the side attached to the support.

After resting for two or three weeks inside the cocoon, the caterpillar changes into a pupa and the adult moth makes its appearance
about a fortnight later, if it belongs to the first generation of the year.
But caterpillars of the second generation, reaching full size in April
or May, hibernate as larvae inside their cocoons and the moths only
emerge in the following October.   The female lays her straw-coloured
oval eggs in clusters which form a band about an inch long round a
twig or petiole of a leaf; there are usually about two hundred eggs
in a cluster. The eggs turn blue-black in about two weeks, just before
hatching.   Because it is at times a serious pest of pepper trees this
insect has been given the popular name of pepper-tree caterpillar;
its scientific name is *Bombycomorpha pallida*.   The moth is pure white
with a small round yellow spot on each front wing; it is about one
and a half inches across the expanded wings.

The brown pine-tree moth, *Taragama concolor*, is a member of
this family that sometimes does serious damage in pine plantations.
The female moth is about an inch and a half across the expanded

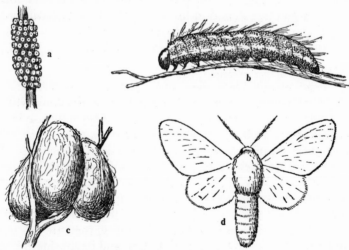

FIG. 75—The Pepper Tree Moth, *Bombycomorpha pallida*: (a) eggs; (b) caterpillar; (c)
cocoons; (d) adult female. The moth is white, and measures about one and a half inches
across the expanded wings.

wings, whilst the male is smaller and only about an inch across the wings: both are nut-brown, with paler hind wings in the case of the female, and darker hind wings in the male. The moths make their appearance in winter and the female lays her spherical white eggs in small batches on the tips of pine needles. The full-grown caterpillar is about two inches long, of a colour that closely matches that of the pine bark and it has long silky hairs along the sides of its body. Before

FIG. 76—The Lasiocampid Moth, *Mesocelis montana*: (a) male moth—he is chocolate brown with white spots and measures about one and a quarter inches across the outspread wings; (b) female moth, quite wingless and with feeble legs; (c) caterpillar.

pupating it encloses itself in a spindle-shaped cocoon of brown silk, generally on the bark of the tree, in an angle where a branch forks. The second generation of moths emerges in November and December.

Towards the end of spring, in October and November, hairy caterpillars about two inches long may be found feeding on the common *fyn taaibos* or Kannabas, *Passerina vulgaris*, on the mountain slopes in the south-west Cape. They are dark brown with yellow head and thorax and yellow patches along the sides. The full-grown caterpillars may be seen scurrying restlessly over the ground, searching for suitable spots in which to spin their cocoons. They are looking for some hollow beneath a stone or a crevice between two stones, or a hole amid exposed roots, or a heap of debris in which they may hide. The cocoons are large, oval, compact structures of silk mixed with the hairs from the caterpillar's body. If one of these cocoons is handled the sharp tips of the hairs may pierce the skin and break off, causing a mild irritation.

The pupa inside the cocoon is light brown in colour and from three quarters to an inch and a half in length, the smaller ones being males and the larger females. The male moth is a handsome creature, about an inch and a quarter across the expanded wings, deep chocolate brown with a conspicuous white oval spot on each wing. His mouthparts are reduced so that he cannot feed. The female is very different from her mate and she is quite wingless, with very small head, eyes and antennae and with tiny, short legs that are practically useless. She never leaves her cocoon. He seeks her there, mates with her and then dies. She lays her oval yellow eggs, about one hundred in number, inside her cocoon, wriggling as she does so, so that the fine yellow scales on her body are rubbed off and form a soft bed for the eggs. Finally only her dead, shrivelled body remains, with the eggs wrapped in their dense, soft coat of scales. The eggs lie dormant in the cocoon all through the summer, autumn and winter and only hatch in the following spring. There is, therefore, only one generation of these moths a year. This insect has no common name but is known to science as *Mesocelis montana*. A similar or closely allied species is found in the Transvaal and Natal.

The above moths belong to the family *Lasiocampidae*, moderate to large-sized moths with stout bodies and densely scaled wings. They do not feed in the adult state as their mouthparts are imperfect. The caterpillars are hairy and spin firm, oval cocoons of hair and silk. Many of them are gregarious and spin silken webs on their food-plants—hence the name of tent-caterpillars applied to these species.

The empty cocoons of certain Lasiocampid moths (*Pachypasa*, *Gonometra* and *Trabata* species) are used as ornaments by certain tribes in Africa. They are strung together to form bracelets or anklets and small pebbles are introduced into the cocoons through slits cut in them. Then, when these ornaments are worn for a dance, they rattle in a fashion that is pleasing to their wearers.

Hawk Moths

The death's head moth, or *by-mot* as it is called in Afrikaans, *Acherontia atropos*, is widely feared in this country as it is reputed to have a sting that can inflict a deadly wound. It is, as a matter of fact, quite harmless. The so-called sting is the rather short proboscis that is coiled up beneath the head when not in use and that is extended when the moth wishes to sip honey. There are some slender, sharp spines on the hind legs that might prick the fingers slightly if the moth is handled, but that is the worst it can do. The needless alarm evoked by the appearance of the moth is enhanced by the rather sinister-looking yellow mark on the thorax that resembles a skull and that gives the moth its popular name. It can also utter a squeak of protest if it is handled and this is liable to startle a person not prepared for it.

There is still some doubt as to the exact means by which the moth utters its peculiar call. Like all other insects, it has no voice in the real sense of the word. Formerly it was said the moth made the sound by rubbing its two palps rapidly together, but nowadays it is believed that the insect trumpets like a miniature elephant by blowing air through its proboscis. But as insects have no lungs, it is difficult to understand where the air comes from. The death's head moth can squeak even before it has emerged from the pupa.

This moth is fairly common in most parts of Africa although it is not often seen as it is not attracted to lights. Beekeepers and potato-growers are the ones who come across it most often. It is about four and a half inches across the outspread wings; the front wings are a deep brown, mottled with lighter brown, while the hind wings are yellow with two dark brown lines across them. The stout body is brown with yellow markings down each side.

The male moth has a scent gland on each side of his abdomen, where it joins the thorax. These organs consist of tufts of long, reddish scales lodged in a cavity and he can thrust the tufts out at will; at the same time the glands produce a liquid which gives off a musklike odour. When the tufts are withdrawn and the openings to the cavities closed, there is no smell. Apparently he only makes use of these organs when courting the female.

The death's head moth has a very wide geographical range, from England right down through Europe and Africa to the Cape. It is a powerful flier and can migrate considerable distances in search of food and of plants on which to lay its eggs. There are several records of these moths having been caught on ships far out at sea, both in the Mediterranean and off the coasts of France and Portugal. These moths are also found throughout Asia: those in India and China are slightly different in colouring from ours and they are regarded as a separate species by some naturalists, while others assert they are only varieties. They are not found in America or Australia.

The female lays her eggs on a number of different kinds of plants, but she usually chooses plants belonging to the potato family. The eggs are small when compared with the size of the moth, and light green in colour. They are laid singly on the leaves and scattered over a wide area and they take about a fortnight to hatch.

The full-grown caterpillar is a very striking insect, being five or six inches long, green or yellow in colour, with seven slanting purple stripes along each side. Like the rest of the family, it has a curved tail on the hind end of its body, the function of which is unknown. Although the caterpillars are so large and so brightly coloured, they are not easy to find in a field of potatoes. They rest on the underside of the leaves and their colours and stripes harmonize very well with the colours and shadows of their surroundings. Their presence is revealed by the destruction wrought to the foliage and by the large, black droppings that litter the ground beneath the infested plants.

If a caterpillar is disturbed it will draw in its head and sometimes it will make a clicking sound that is clearly audible. The sound may be imitated by clicking the finger-nail under the thumb-nail: it has been compared with the sound made by an electric spark. Sometimes the clicks are repeated so rapidly that they make a noise like a watch being wound. Apparently the insect produces the sound by clashing its mandibles together—by gnashing its teeth, as it were.

When it is fully grown the caterpillar leaves the plant and seeks out soft soil. Here it buries itself five or six inches beneath the surface and makes a large, earthen cell by pressing back the soil with its head. It does not spin a cocoon. It rests for a fortnight or so inside its cell and then it changes into a pupa. During the summer the pupal stage lasts only two or three weeks, but if the caterpillar reaches full size late in autumn it spends the whole of the winter beneath the soil as a pupa, the adult emerging only when warmer weather arrives in spring.

The convolvulus hawk moth, *Herse convolvuli*, is another large hawk moth that is widely spread and that is found throughout Africa. The caterpillars are found feeding on morning glory and its allies, *Ipomoea* species, and they are at times a serious pest on sweet potatoes. When fully grown they are five or six inches long, mostly brown in colour with yellow or white slanting stripes along the sides, and the typical tail on the end of the abdomen. They pupate in the soil like those of the death's head moth. The moth is greyish brown and about five inches across the outspread wings. It is marked with pink and brown stripes on the abdomen and has a very long tongue that is carried coiled up like a watch-spring beneath its head when at rest.

The silver-lined hawk moth, *Chaerocampa celerio*, is another common and widely spread species. It is buff brown in colour, with white lines on the thorax and a prominent white band across each front wing; each hind wing is red at the base and has two black bands nearer the outer margin. It measures about three inches across the outspread wings. The caterpillars of this common hawk moth often do damage to vines; they may also be found feeding on thorn trees and occasionally on tobacco and sweet potato plants, as well as on *Ampelopsis* creepers. They are green at first, but usually turn brown as they grow older; they have eyelike spots near the head, one on each side, black with a yellow ring round them. Pupation takes place in the soil. There are three generations of this moth a year, the first generation appears in the spring and this gives rise to the moths of the second generation in December and January, followed by the third in March; the caterpillars of the third generation spend

PLATE 35

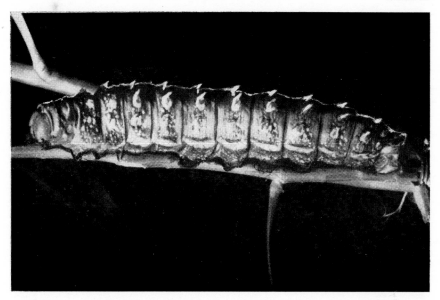

(*a*) Caterpillar of the Thorn-tree Emperor Moth, *Gynanisa maia*

(*b*) Pupa of the Thorn-tree Emperor Moth, *Gynanisa maia*

PLATE 36

(a) THE WILLOW-TREE EMPEROR MOTH, *Gonimbrasia tyrrhea*, male

(b) A COMMON CUTWORM MOTH, *Euxoa segetis*. It is about 1¼ inches across the outspread wings.

the winter as pupae in the soil. The moths deposit their spherical white eggs singly on the upper or lower surface of the leaves of the food-plants.

The hawk moths are a family, *Sphingidae*, of moderate sized to large moths that are mostly very striking in appearance with long, coiled tongues, narrow wings and swift flight, hovering in front of flowers as they feed. The caterpillars are smooth and easily recognised by the curious horn on the last but one segment of the abdomen; the function of this tail is unknown. They mostly pupate in the soil.

Emperor Moths

The large, handsome pine-tree emperor moth, *Nudaurelia cytherea*, is well known in the south-western Cape because it is extremely abundant in some years and the caterpillars do considerable harm to pine plantations by defoliating the trees. The same species, or a variety of it, is found in Natal and the Transvaal and further north. The

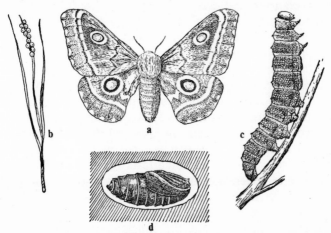

FIG. 77—The Pine Tree Emperor Moth, *Nudaurelia cytherea:* (a) female moth; (b) eggs on pine needle; (c) caterpillar; (d) pupa. The moth measures about five inches across the outspread wings.

moth measures about five inches across the outspread wings, the female being larger and more stoutly built than the male; she also has simple, threadlike feelers while his are feathery. None of the moths of this family can feed as their mouthparts are imperfect and, although they seem to be very robust and strong, they live only a few days in the adult state. Although it is a pest of pine trees, the natural food-plant of this species is the *taaibos*, *Rhus angustiofolia*, and the caterpillars may also be found feeding on the sugar bush, Cape beech, watsonias, and other native plants, as well as on wattles, eucalyptus,

U

apples, guavas and quinces. The female shows a remarkable catholicity
of choice when laying her eggs.

The moths appear in April, May and June and the females lay
their white, spherical eggs in small clusters on the twigs and foliage
of the food-plants. The substance with which the eggs are glued in
position soon turns brown, giving the eggs a blotched appearance.
A female lays from one hundred and fifty to two hundred eggs before
her ovaries are exhausted and she dies. The eggs hatch in from three
to four weeks.

The newly-hatched caterpillars make their first meal off the empty
egg-shells, remaining clustered round them for two or three days.
It seems that this preliminary meal of egg-shell is essential for the
young caterpillars, because if they are removed immediately after
hatching, they wander about restlessly and refuse to feed until they
die. Having eaten all or part of the egg-shell, the young larva begins
to feed on the foliage. It moults six times in the course of its growth
and is between four and five inches long when fully grown and of
striking appearance. Each segment of the body is closely covered
with tiny spots, coloured blue, green and yellow, arranged in bands
running round the segments.

The caterpillars may be found on the trees from June to December.
As soon as they are fully grown they leave the trees and wander about
on the ground, looking for loose soil into which they may burrow.
Having found a suitable spot, the caterpillar tunnels down to a depth
of about two inches and there hollows out a cell for itself. After
a week or so it changes into a pupa, red at first but turning black
after a day or so. The pupal stage lasts for five or six months and
there is only one generation of these moths a year. In some parts
of the country the moths may be found on the wing from January
to April and it is thought these belong to a distinct race that have a
different seasonal history from the much commoner race described
above.

A very similar and closely allied moth that is also very common
at times is the willow-tree moth, *Gonimbrasia tyrrhea*. The adults
are on the wing in October and the females lay their eggs on thorn-
trees (which seem to be their natural food-plants), wattles, pines,
willows, poplars and oaks. The full-grown caterpillar, about three
and a half inches long, is a conspicuous insect with light blue and red
markings on a velvety black background. Its life history is similar
to that described above.

The thorn-tree emperor moth, *Gynanisa maia*, is another large
and handsome member of this family that is common and widely
distributed. The moth measures about five and a half inches across

the outspread wings and is on the wing in November. The female lays her eggs on thorn-trees and the caterpillars are light green with rows of white and yellow points along the body. The cabbage-tree emperor moth, *Bunaea alcinoe*, may be caught during October. The caterpillars may be found on the cabbage tree or *kwepersol*, during December and they are black with four rows of prominent white spines; the spiracles are orange, surrounded by scarlet.

If a virgin female of any of these moths can be obtained—and this is easily done by rearing some of the caterpillars in captivity— an interesting phenomenon can be witnessed. After the stout-bodied female has emerged from the pupa and spread and dried her wings, she should be placed in a box with a gauze cover. That evening the windows of the room in which the moth is lodged should be left open. Soon after dark, if the climatic conditions are favourable (a warm evening with moisture in the air), numbers of great moths of the same species as the imprisoned female will come fluttering into the room. The box containing the imprisoned female will be the centre of attraction for them. If the visitors are examined, they will be found to be all males, with feathery antennae. Should one of the males succeed in gaining access to the female and mate with her, the others quickly lose interest and make their departure.

This attraction of a number of males by a virgin female is spoken of by entomologists as assembling and it is sometimes made use of by the collector to obtain specimens. If an enthusiast were to go out and hunt for the moths he might scour the neighbourhood for a long time in vain, but if he could obtain a single unmated female he could make use of her to attract males to his room from far and wide. This assembling of the males is found to occur with other moths besides emperor moths, but in all the species where this happens the males are the possessors of striking plumose antennae. Furthermore, if the antennae of one of these males are cut off, he at once seems to lose all interest in the female. It is therefore assumed that the sense that enables him to find her is lodged in these feelers and that he is attracted by a subtle far-spreading scent given off by the virgin.

The emperor moths, *Saturniidae*, include the largest moths in the world, certain species having a wing expanse of nearly ten inches. They are characterised by their large, heavily scaled wings with the conspicuous eye-spot in the centre of each, by the strongly plumose antennae of the males and by the atrophied mouthparts of the adults. Certain species of emperor moths yield silk of commercial value. Some authorities regard these moths as forming only a sub-family, *Saturniinae*, of the family *Bombycidae* which includes the well-known silkworm, *Bombyx mori.*

The common silkworm is too well known to need description here, but it is not generally known that the eggs of this moth can be made to hatch much quicker than normally, if they are treated in certain ways. The race of silkworms available in South Africa has only one generation a year and the eggs take about ten months to hatch. There are other races that have several generations a year and these are said to be multivoltine, to distinguish them from the race with the single annual generation, called the univoltine race. Silkworms were used in Pretoria a few years ago for rearing tachinid parasites of the brown-tail moth (see page 181) and it was necessary to have a series of well-grown caterpillars throughout the year. But the only silkworms available were of the univoltine race which spent the greater part of the year in the egg state. Experiments were therefore carried out to determine whether it was possible to cause the eggs to hatch more quickly and it was found that eggs dipped in concentrated hydrochloric acid for five minutes when they were one day old would hatch in from two to three weeks. Eggs kept in the acid for ten minutes or longer are killed, as are also newly-laid eggs because, apparently, the egg-shell is too soft until twelve hours or so after deposition.

Another interesting point about silkworm eggs is the fact that some of them can be made to hatch even though they have not been fertilised, by stroking them gently with a soft camel-hair brush. It is not known why parthenogenesis should be induced by this treatment. Silkworms that are fully grown and ready to spin their cocoons can be robbed of their silk by the following method. A caterpillar is placed in a tube just wide enough to receive it, with its head projecting. Then a silken thread can be drawn from its spinneret and put on a drum: if the drum is turned at the right speed the whole of the silk can be wound directly from the caterpillar and it is said that the colour is brighter and has a more beautiful lustrous sheen than if the caterpillar is allowed to spin its cocoon normally and the silk then wound from this.

Gregarious Caterpillars

At mid-summer and again in late autumn brown hairy caterpillars may be seen clustered together on the trunks of thorn-trees, in the forks of the branches, or under cover near the bases of the trees. They remain motionless in a dense crowd all day long and only become active at night, when they spread out over the trees to feed. Before dawn they all return to their former resting place and settle down again like a lot of sardines in a tin. When fully grown they spin dense parchment-like cocoons on the branches, or in a crevice in a rock near the tree, or in some similar place. Two or three months later the moths emerge and it is probable that, like other members of their family, they make use of a caustic fluid in order to escape from their prisons. This has not, so far, been observed in this country, but it is known from investigations of allied species overseas that moths of this family have two methods of breaking out of their dense, hard cocoons. The pupae of some of them have sharp, hard processes on their heads and by turning round and round they make a circular cut in the head end of the cocoon. In other cases, the moths, as soon as they break out of the pupal skin, emit a caustic fluid from their mouths which softens the cocoon and enables them to push their way out. Certain species seem to combine both methods of making their exit. The moth is about two and a half inches across the out-

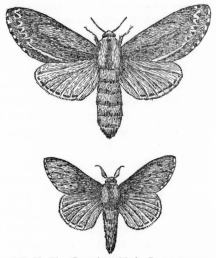

FIG. 78—The Gregarious Moth, *Braura truncata*, female above, male below. The caterpillars are gregarious.

spread wings, the females being larger than the males, and they are brown in colour. They have no popular name but are known to science as *Braura truncata*.

Two other species of this family (*Anaphe reticulata* and *Anaphe panda*) are known to have caterpillars that live in colonies. They are white moths with brown lines on the front wings and measure about two and a half inches across the outspread wings. They are found in Natal, Transvaal and further north. The caterpillars live together in large family parties of two hundred or more and they con-struct a communal home of dense brown silk on their food plant, where it is a conspicuous oval object and may be a foot

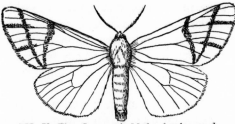

FIG. 79—The Communal Moth, *Anaphe panda*. The caterpillars of this moth live in a communal home of brown silk and go out to feed in a procession. The moth is white and about two and a half inches across the outspread wings.

or more in length. During the day the caterpillars remain inside their home but in the evening they leave it in a long procession, marching head to tail, to go out and feed. As it walks, each caterpillar spins a silken thread so that they form a trail they can easily follow when they return to their home after feeding. When full grown each caterpillar spins a thin white cocoon for itself inside the communal home and there may be two hundred or more such cocoons lying side by side in the dense outer covering. When the moths emerge they separate, each going its own way.

These moths belong to the family known as the *Nododontidae*, a family of moderate-sized to large moths, generally dull brown or grey in colour, although some are yellow and white. The caterpillars of most of them are of normal appearance and habits, but some have curious processes on the body that give them an extraordinary appearance. The moths have well developed probosces and feed on nectar and are often attracted to lights.

Cutworms and Their Kin

Some of the worst and most persistent insect pests in farm lands and gardens are the cutworms, of which there are several species. In many parts of the country the attack on young maize plants, beans, cabbages, and so on, is so severe that the lands have to be replanted two or three times. Most of the damage occurs in spring. During the winter the cutworms are present in the soil as full-grown caterpillars and these pupate as soon as warmer weather arrives in spring. Two or three weeks later the moths emerge and lay their eggs in great numbers on the leaves of their food-plants and it is from them that the cutworms develop that give so much trouble in September, October and November.

The moths belong to the very large and important family known as the *Noctuidae*, sometimes popularly called owlet moths. They measure about one and a quarter inches across the outspread wings and are dull buff in colour, with the fore wings darker than the hind wings, and all look very much alike. A single female may lay as many as a thousand eggs before she dies and these hatch in about a week into tiny black caterpillars which feed on the weeds for a few days but which soon take on their characteristic habit of lying hidden beneath the soil all day and coming out to feed at night.

When fully grown the cutworm is about an inch and a quarter long, with a smooth body and of a dull grey or brown colour. It lies coiled up in its lair beneath the soil during the day and crawls about on the surface at night to do the damage from which it derives its name. It bites off young plants at the base, leaving the top portion lying on the soil as though it had been cut off by a knife. The caterpillar eats only a little from each plant it cuts down and it may destroy a number of seedlings in one night.

When a piece of ground is ploughed or dug over, the plants on it are destroyed and the cutworms in that area are temporarily deprived of much of their food supply, but they can survive for some time on any weeds or plant remains in the soil and then, when the seedlings come up, they are there ready for their destructive work. After it is fully grown the caterpillar buries itself an inch or so below the surface and there changes into a smooth, reddish brown pupa. Two or three weeks later the moth emerges. There are several generations a year.

A close relative of the cutworms is the army worm, or mystery worm, the caterpillar of the moth, *Laphygma exempta*. From time to time this insect attracts attention because of the extensive damage it does to pastures, grain and forage crops. Vast numbers of the caterpillars suddenly appear on the veld and then, a few weeks later, disappear just as quickly and mysteriously. Outbreaks in recent years have been reported from the summer rainfall areas of the Union, Northern and Southern Rhodesia, South-West Africa, Kenya and Portuguese East Africa. These outbreaks generally occur towards the end of summer, during the months of February and March.

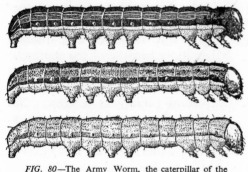

FIG. 80—The Army Worm, the caterpillar of the Noctuid moth, *Laphygma exempta*. It is about one inch long.

Above: a caterpillar of the gregarious phase, velvety black with green on the underside. *Middle:* a caterpillar of the transient phase, brown. *Below:* a caterpillar in the solitary phase, green.

The full-grown army worm is a caterpillar about an inch and a quarter long, variable in colour but usually velvety black above, yellowish-green below, with narrow pale green lines along the sides. It feeds only on plants of the grass family, including maize, wheat, barley, sugar-cane, teff and so on. Feeding takes place during the day as well as during the night, with brief resting periods, but the larva is most active during the early morning and late evening. When it is fully grown the caterpillar buries itself about an inch deep in loose soil and there forms an oval cell by binding soil particles with silk, and changes into a brown pupa. The moth emerges in one to four weeks, depending upon the temperature.

The female lays her eggs in masses, usually on the underside of the leaves of the food-plant, two or three hundred eggs in a mass and covered with downy scales from her body. She may lay two or three such masses before she dies. The eggs hatch in two to eleven days. Breeding goes on throughout the year as these insects do not hibernate at all. They are very susceptible to cold, and their natural habitat is, therefore, the low-veld and the warmer parts of the country.

In order to increase rapidly the army worm needs a fairly high temperature, a humid atmosphere and an abundance of young grass. Consequently, if there are late rains, after a farmer has burned off his veld, and if the weather is warm, the moths find the conditions eminently favourable for them and each lays a large number of eggs: perhaps seven hundred or more. These hatch out in two or three days and the little caterpillars find abundant food in the succulent young grass that has sprouted over the burned areas. They are full grown in a fortnight and the moths emerge a week or so later.

Thus the caterpillars increase very rapidly and the farmer finds his veld suddenly invaded by great armies of them and he wonders where they came from. Soon, however, colder, drier weather arrives, the food supply begins to give out, parasites and diseases multiply because of the enormous number of victims available, and the horde of caterpillars dwindles just as rapidly as it grew. But they are not all wiped out. In favourable areas some of them survive and carry on unnoticed in the normal way. Instead of a ravenous army devouring the veld there is only an occasional caterpillar here and there and nobody pays them any heed. Sooner or later—it may be years later—the combination of favourable conditions arises again, late rains, warm weather and young grass springing up over the burned veld, there is a lack of natural enemies, and the mystery worm swarms once more, for a brief period, in its millions, until nature can catch up and restore the balance again. It is believed that the moths migrate in swarms at night from infested areas to lay their eggs in some distant area before they die, but this has not so far been proved.

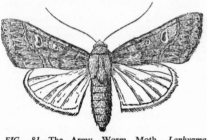

FIG. 81—The Army Worm Moth, *Laphygma exempta*. It is about one and a half inches across the outspread wings, with dark brown head, thorax and forewings and white hind wings. Some specimens have paler fawn-coloured front wings.

All this is very similar to what happens in the case of locusts and it is interesting to note that experiments in Pretoria have proved that the army worm has solitary and gregarious phases, like the locusts. Caterpillars reared in cages under crowded conditions are nearly all velvety black; this is known as the gregarious or *gregaria* phase. A small proportion of them are brown above and are spoken of as the transient or *transiens* phase. If the caterpillars are reared in isolation, only one in each tube or jar, the great majority of them are

PLATE 37

(a) Caterpillar of the Citrus Swallow-tail, *Papilio demodocus*, with its osmeterium extruded

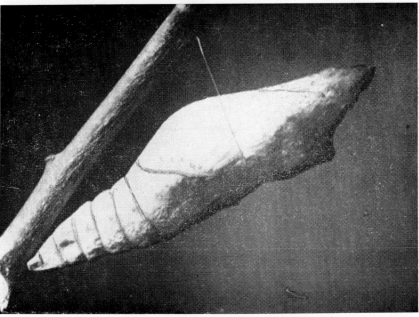

b) Pupa of the Citrus Swallow-tail, *Papilio demodocus*

PLATE 38

(*a*) THE **MOUNTAIN BEAUTY**, *Meneris tulbaghia*

(*b*) **THE PAINTED LADY**, *Vanessa cardui*

green or pink and green above and they are called the solitary or *solitaria* phase. It seems highly probable that similar phases are to be found in a state of nature; the army worms swarming on the veld are nearly all velvety black, but when they are few in numbers and scattered they are mostly green. It is not known why the change in living conditions should cause this change in colour, but it is suggested that the crowded caterpillars are much more active and that this activity brings about physiological changes that affect the colour.

The lesser army worm, *Laphygma exigua*, is very similar to *Laphygma exempta*, but it is not so common. The caterpillar will feed on most cultivated crops, such as beans, potatoes, ground nuts, cowpeas, and so on, as well as members of the grass family, whereas the true army worm feeds only on grasses.

The maize stalk borer, *Calamistis fusca*, is an African moth, apparently from the tropical and sub-tropical parts of the continent originally, but now widely spread wherever maize is cultivated. The moth measures one and a half inches across the expanded wings; its front wings are dull, coppery brown with inconspicuous markings; the hind wings are smoky brown and without markings. The first moths of the season usually make their appearance early in December when the maize plants are well established. The female deposits her

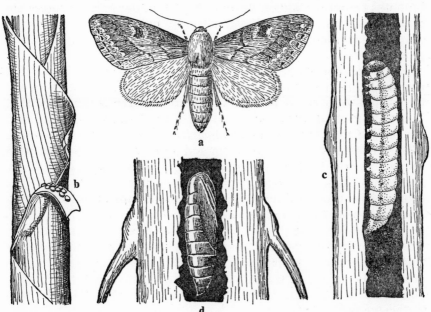

FIG. 82—The Maize-Stalk Borer, *Calamistis fusca:* (a) moth; (b) eggs (part of the leaf-sheath represented torn away from stem to show eggs beneath; (c) caterpillar; (d) pupa in base of stalk.

v

eggs in batches up to one hundred and fifty or more in a batch between the leaf sheath and the stem of the plant. The eggs stick to the underside of the leaf-sheath, and if a strip is torn away the eggs come with it, as shown in the illustration.

The eggs hatch in about a week and the young caterpillars feed at first under the leaf sheath and then they leave this shelter and migrate to the open top of the plant. By feeding on the rolled-up young leaves, they bite holes right through them and the leaves, when they unfold, show rows of holes made by the caterpillars. After a few days the larvae burrow down into the stem; if there are too many of them on the plant some of them migrate to neighbouring plants and infest them.

In about thirty days the caterpillar is fully grown, lodged in its burrow in the stem. It then prepares for its exit as a moth by burrowing towards the outer surface of the stems, leaving only a thin cap separating it from the outer air, a cap that can easily be pushed off by the moth. The larva then rests for a few days and turns into a pupa. Three weeks later the moth emerges, generally about the end of January.

The second generation of caterpillars complete their growth during March. Some of them may pupate and produce another generation of moths before the winter, but the majority usually remain quiescent through the winter in the larval stage, as full-grown borers. These nearly always descend to the lowest part of the stem, at or below ground level.

The red bollworm, *Diparopsis castanea*, is a native insect that has turned its attention to the introduced cotton plant. It is found throughout Africa and is a serious pest wherever cotton is grown. The moth measures nearly one and a half inches across the outspread wings; the fore wings are pinkish-cinnamon with a dark chocolate triangular patch at the base of each and a transverse olive-green band running parallel to the outer margin; the hind wings are dirty white. The female lays her spherical grey eggs on almost any part of the cotton plant, usually singly, but sometimes in groups of two or three. The newly-hatched caterpillar makes its way to a young boll and bores its way into it. It feeds inside the boll for three or four weeks, by which time it is fully grown and it leaves its burrow and makes its way to the ground. Here it pupates. There may be three generations of the moths a year, if the climatic conditions are favourable. Caterpillars that mature late in the season spend the winter in their cells in the ground.

The American bollworm, *Chloridea obsoleta*, is a common pest of cotton, lucerne, maize, tomatoes, peas, vines and fruit trees. It is known by several common names, such as tassel-worm or ear-worm of maize, tomato fruit-worm, tobacco bud-worm, and is found throughout the greater part of the world. The moth is about one and a half inches across the outspread wings with brown forewings and the hind wings marked with a broad dark border. The female lays her small yellow eggs on the leaves, buds and flowers of the food-plant and she may deposit as many as fifteen hundred in her life of three or four weeks.

The eggs hatch in from two to eight days. The caterpillars feed chiefly on the buds, flowers and fruits of their numerous food-plants and, when fully grown, they are about an inch and a half long and vary widely in colour, from pale green to almost black. In most of them there is a yellowish white band along each side. The larval stage lasts for two to four weeks and then the caterpillars bury themselves in the soil to pupate. During the summer the pupal stage lasts only two to four weeks, but caterpillars that reach full size late in the autumn spend the winter months under the ground as pupae.

Most moths that are pests do their damage as caterpillars and are harmless as adults, but it is just the opposite with the fruit-piercing moths. There are at least three species in this country that do a considerable amount of damage to ripening fruits, particularly in orchards near wild trees and bush. They are large insects with greyish-brown wings measuring about two and a half inches across when extended. They are strong fliers and fly out of the trees when disturbed during the day, but they are more active at night and most of the feeding on the fruit is done during the hours of darkness.

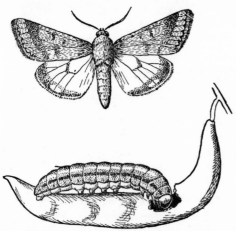

FIG. 83—The American Bollworm, *Chloridea obsoleta*, one of the worst and most widely spread of all garden and farm pests. Moth above, caterpillar below.

Most kinds of moths feed only on nectar; many have mouthparts that are degenerate and useless and they do not feed at all in the adult state. The fruit-piercing moths, on the other hand, have strong proboscles that, when extended, are about an inch long and have sharp tips with sawlike cutting edges along the sides which enable the moths to pierce holes in fruit that may be quite hard. They will attack apples, pears, grapes, peaohes, plums, guavas and citrus fruits.

Ripe fruit is preferred but they will also feed on fruit that is ripening. A moth sucks the juice from the fruit by inserting its proboscis to full length after piercing a neat round hole in the skin; the proboscis is withdrawn at intervals and re-inserted sideways so as to get at the juice from a fairly wide area.   In this way a dry spongy mass of tissue is left under the skin and this later on collapses and rots.

The three common species of fruit-piercing moths are *Achaea lienardi*, *Serrodes partita* and *Sphingomorpha chlorea*. The life histories of these moths have not been fully worked out but it is known that their eggs are deposited chiefly on native plants. The caterpillars are nocturnal, feeding at night and hiding by day. Caterpillars of the commonest and most widely spread of the three, *Achaea lienardi*,

have been found on wattles and tamboetie trees in Zululand and on sneezewood, milkwood, wild currant, *without*, *boerboom* and mountain plums in the eastern parts of the Cape Province.

The *Noctuidae* form one of the largest and, from an economic point of view, the most important family of all the Lepidoptera. They are mostly dull-coloured moths

FIG. 84—The Common Fruit-piercing Moth, *Achaea lienardi*. The markings on different specimens are varied but the white spots on the hind wings are constant.

of moderate size and are attracted to lights. The caterpillars are smooth and they pupate, as a rule, in an earthen cell below ground.

Tiger Moths

All caterpillars have short bristles, or setae, on their bodies. Even the smooth, greasy-looking larvae of the Noctuids have some seven short bristles on each side of each segment. But many caterpillars have long secondary bristles or hairs on their bodies, in addition to the inconspicuous primary setae. The hairy covering is believed to protect them from such enemies as birds and it is generally stated that only cuckoos will eat them. These caterpillars with dense hairy coats are sometimes spoken of as "woolly bears" and many of them, but by no means all, belong to family of moths known as tiger moths, *Arctiidae*.

In mid-winter at the Cape large brown hairy caterpillars may be seen scurrying over the ground. The body is black with red spiracles and bears tufts of stiff brown hairs, mingled with longer black bristles. These caterpillars have no particular food plant but seem to travel

FIG. 85—Some African Noctuid Moths : 1. *Heraclia africana*, black with yellow spots, hind wings red with black border; 2. *Perigea grandirena*, front wings pale olive green with brown spots, hind wings brown with coppery sheen; 3. *Paida pulchra*, yellow with dark brown markings; 4. *Hespagarista echione*, dark brown with yellow markings; 5. *Aegocera fervida*, front wings brown with yellow markings, hind wings bright yellow with brown border; 6. *Laphygma exempta*, front wings greyish-brown blotched with darker brown, hind wings whitish; 7. *Copifrontia xantherythra*, front wings bright yellow with brown markings, hind wings buff coloured; 8. *Ovios capensis*, front wings olive-green with dark border, hind wings yellow with dark border; 9. *Mimleucania leucosoma*, front wings brown marked with white and darker brown, hind wings white; 10. *Proxenus leuconephra*, front wings brown, hind wings buff. All natural size.

from one plant to the next and to feed indiscriminately. When fully grown and ready to pupate, they are exceptionally active, seeking for a suitable place to spin their cocoons. On finding a spot that suits it, the woolly bear spins a loose cocoon of soft silk, surrounded by a rough covering of soft earth and dead leaves. It then rests for about a week before changing into a short, blunt brown pupa, with the cast-off skin of the caterpillar adhering to the hind end. After about six weeks a large moth emerges, with a heavy red abdomen banded

with black, yellow fore-wings spotted and lined with black and dull yellow hind wings also marked with black. This is the Cape tiger moth, *Dionychopus amasis*. A close-ly allied species, *Diony-chopus similis*, is found in other parts of the country and its hairy larvae feed on apricots, geraniums and other cultivated plants.

Another very common and widely spread tiger moth is *Diacrisia eugraphica* and it may often be seen at lights:

FIG. 86—The Cape Tiger Moth, *Dionychopus amasis*. Moth above, caterpillar below.

a pretty moth about two inches across the outspread wings, white with two black wavy lines on each front wing. The hairy caterpillars may be found on various kinds of plants on the veld and in the garden in December and again in April. They pupate in loose silken cocoons on the surface of the soil, amid debris. The moths are on the wing in November and again in March.

The tiger moths are usually placed in a family by themselves but some authors regard them as forming only a sub-family, *Arctiinae*, of the large Noctuid group. They are all small to moderate-sized moths and are varied in their coloration and markings, but many are white or yellow with red and black markings on bodies and wings. The caterpillars are densely covered with hair which is uniformly placed over the body and generally brown in colour. The pupa is always enclosed in a rough cocoon of silk, hair and dead leaves.

Brown-Tail Moths and Their Kin

About thirty years ago a native moth began to attract attention as a pest of pine plantations. It was unknown before this as it apparent-ly limited its attentions to its indigenous food-plants, but to-day it is well known as the pine brown-tail moth, *Euproctis terminalis*, and is found in the Transvaal, Orange Free State and Natal. The female moth is about an inch and a half across the wings, deep yellow in colour with a satiny lustre on the fore wings and a dark brown tuft on the end of the abdomen that gives it its name. The male is smaller than the female and has plumose antennae; he is an active flier, with a rapid, zig-zag flight; he cannot feed as these moths have only vestigial mouthparts.

The female usually lays her eggs in a single, elongate cluster near the end of a pine twig, or she may lay them on the bark of the main trunk, or on the needles. She covers her eggs with down from her abdomen, dark buff in colour, but the eggs themselves are yellow and spherical. Each cluster may contain up to three hundred eggs and they are laid during February and March. The eggs hatch in from three to four weeks.

The caterpillar, when fully grown, measures from one to one and a quarter inches in length and is black, with a narrow white line down the middle of the back and a buff-coloured band along each side. It has tufts of long white hairs on each side of each segment and down the middle of the back there is a row of tubercles that bear tiny poisonous hairs. These minute hairs are barbed and they pierce the skin if a caterpillar is handled and set up severe irritation. To a lesser extent, the egg clusters, cocoons and adults are also armed with the poisonous, barbed hairs. All stages of the brown-tail moth should therefore be handled with care.

The caterpillars do great harm in the pine plantations by defoliating the trees during the winter and spring. They nibble through the

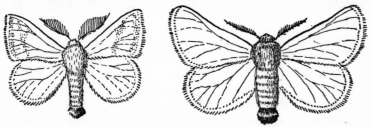

FIG. 87—The Pine Brown-tail Moth, *Euproctis termnalis*. Female right, male left. The moths are deep yellow in colour with a dark brown tuft at the end of the abdomen and measure about one and a half inches across the outspread wings.

needles so that the greater part falls to the ground. When fully grown they make their way to the ground where they spin loose cocoons amid the fallen pine needles and pupate. Since the silk of the cocoons is interwoven with the hairs of the caterpillars, severe poisoning may result from careless handling of them. The pupa is dark reddish brown with groups of yellow hairs on the abdomen. The adults emerge in from four to six weeks.

The thorn-tree brown-tail moth, *Euproctis fasciata*, is very similar to the above, but the moth has dark bands on the front wings. The caterpillar, about one and a quarter inches long when fully grown, is found on thorn trees at mid-summer and again in the autumn, as there are two generations a year. It is black with short white hairs between the segments and red tubercles along the back. There are thick tufts of black hairs on the back and tufts of grey hairs along the sides. The adults make their appearance in January and October, the winter being spent in the pupal state. The eggs are deposited in clusters on twigs of the food-plant and are covered with hairy, cream-coloured scales by the female, the whole forming a cushion-like mass. Pupation takes place in a thin cocoon constructed amid the leaves and twigs of the food-plant.

These moths belong to a group sometimes known as tussock moths, usually placed in a family by themselves known as the *Lymantriidae*, but some authors regard them as a sub-family of the *Noctuidae*, the *Liparidinae*. They are mostly small to medium-sized moths, stoutly built, and the males always have pectinate antennae. They cannot feed as adults as their mouthparts are imperfect. The female usually has the prominent tuft of hairs on the end of her abdomen. In some cases the female is quite wingless, but she has functional legs and can walk about. The little brown moth, *Bracharoa dregei*, with feathery feelers, is the male of such a species: his mate is fat, brown and hairy, but she has no wings and he has to seek her out in her cocoon where she remains and lays her eggs. The caterpillars of this moth may be found feeding on *Dimorphotheca* plants in May.

Looper Caterpillars

Although they differ so much in form and appearance, all cater-pillars are built on the same pattern. Each has a head and thirteen segments to its body, three thoracic and ten abdominal. The head bears a pair of very short antennae, with the simple eyes, usually six in number, on each side, near their base. The jaws are large and strong, with a pair of maxillae behind them and the pointed spinneret projecting between them; these mouthparts are profoundly different from those of the adult and they are completely changed when the larva turns into a pupa.

There are nine spiracles along each side of the body, one on the first thoracic segment and one on each of the first eight abdominal segments; spiracles are absent from the second and third thoracic segments seemingly because the wing buds develop beneath the skin

PLATE 39

(a) THE GARDEN ACRAEA, *Acraea horta*

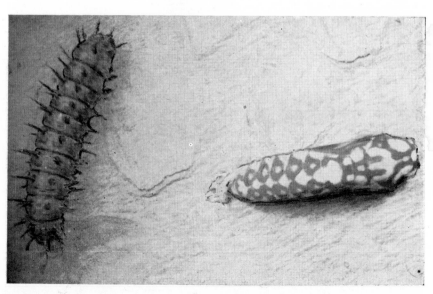

(b) Caterpillar and pupa of the Garden Acraea, *Acraea horta*

PLATE 40

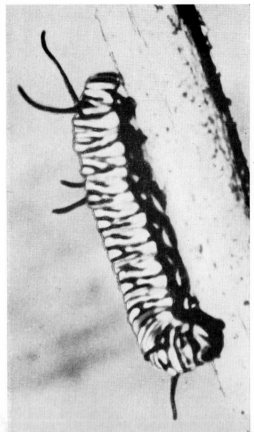

(a) Caterpillar of the African Monarch, *Danaus chrysippus*

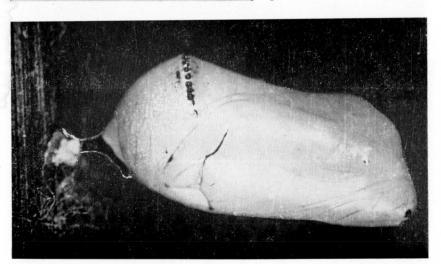

(b) Pupa of the African Monarch, *Danaus chrysippus*

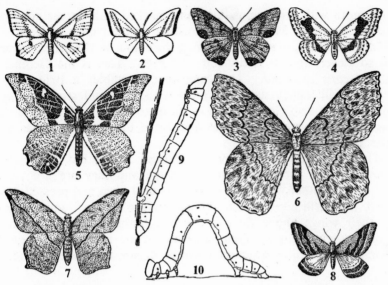

FIG. 88—Some African Geometrid Moths. *1. Traminda ocellata*, pale green. *2. Chlorerythra rubriplaga*, front wings pale green, hind wings cream. *3. Anisodes lyciscarda*, buff with dark grey markings. *4. Somatina vestalis*, white with brown markings. *5. Victoria fuscithorax*, white, heavily marked with bright green. *6. Pingasa abyssinaria*, white with black and grey markings. *7. Semiothisa simplicilinea*, pale brown mottled with darker brown. *8. Ortholitha cryptospilata*, front wings grey with brown markings, hind wings pale brownish-grey. *9.* Caterpillar of a geometrid moth in resting attitude. *10.* Caterpillar of a geometrid moth walking. All natural size.

in these segments and spiracles and tracheae would get in their way. There is a pair of legs on each thoracic segment and these six are the true legs. In addition, there are temporary legs, found only in the caterpillar stage, on some of the abdominal segments; these are sometimes called prolegs, or false legs, or claspers, but a better name by which to distinguish them is abdominal feet. As a general rule there are four pairs of these abdominal feet, on the third to sixth abdominal segments, and a fifth pair of claspers on the last segment, but some of these are absent in certain caterpillars.

Everybody must be familiar with those caterpillars that walk in a peculiar fashion, bringing their hind legs close up to the front legs and arching their body as they do so. These are called loopers, or geometers—"earth-measurers"—because of their mode of walking. If one of these slender caterpillars is examined it will be found that it has only one pair of abdominal feet, on the ninth segment of the body, in addition to the pair of claspers at the hind end. As they have no feet by which to hold the middle part of their body they loop it up out of the way as they walk. These caterpillars are characteristic of the large family of moths known as the *Geometridae*.

w

A moth with grey wings lined and marked with darker grey may often be seen from March to July resting on the trunks of trees with its wings flat and spread out, matching the colour of the lichen-covered bark so closely that it is difficult to detect. This is the Geometrid moth, *Ascotis selenaria*. The caterpillar resembles a twig and, if disturbed, will stretch itself out motionless, stiff and straight, like a twig, so that it also closely matches its surroundings. It feeds on the foliage of pepper trees and citrus and, when fully grown, buries tiself in the soil to pupate.

The geometrid moths vary considerably in size but the majority are small. The wings are relatively large and they are not folded one above the other when at rest, but are held open and pressed down against the surface on which the moths are settled; some species hold their wings above their backs like butterflies. The antennae are of moderate length, often pectinate in the males. The females of some species have degenerate wings or are completely wingless.

CLASSIFICATION

ORDER 18: *LEPIDOPTERA*—BUTTERFLIES AND MOTHS

The classification of the *Lepidoptera* is based largely on the venation of the wings. The wings of all insects are built on the same general plan of venation as the veins have all originated from the same number of tracheae, some of which have been lost by reduction or coalescence, while other new ones have been formed by branching. In the *Lepidoptera* eight branches are responsible for all the veins in each wing. Originally the fore wing and the hind wing were exactly the same, as is still the case with the *Jugatae*, but in all the others the hind wings have fewer veins than the front ones.

It is impossible to go into details concerning the venation of the wings in the many different families of moths in a book of this nature. The student who wishes to specialise in this group must consult a work such as Dr. A. J. T. Janse's *The Moths of South Africa*, published by the author and obtainable from the Transvaal Museum, Pretoria. Furthermore in order to identify the species, it is in many cases necessary to examine the genitalia, which are rather complex and not easy to describe; this matter is also dealt with in Dr. Janse's great work and fully illustrated.

SUB-ORDER 1: *Jugatae* (or *Homoneura*)

Moths in which the venation of the fore and hind wings is the same. They never have a spiral proboscis. Front wings linked with hind wings by a small lobe called a jugum.

FAMILY 1: *Micropterygidae*

Small moths with metallic colouring, diurnal. Some have jaws and are the only members of the whole order with such mouthparts. So far only one species has been recorded from Natal.

FAMILY 2: *Hepialidae*—GHOST MOTHS, SWIFTS

Mostly grey or brown, narrow-winged moths with vestigial mouthparts. The caterpillars are usually subterranean, feeding on roots, or are borers in wood.

SUB-ORDER 2: *Frenatae* (or *Heteroneura*)

Moths with venation of fore and hind wings markedly different. A spiral proboscis present in the moths, except in groups where it has degenerated. Front and hind wings linked by a frenulum as a general rule.

FAMILY 3: *Tineidae*

A huge family of small moths, usually with narrow wings bordered with long hairy fringes. Majority are night-flying with dull colours, the fore-wings usually with vague markings and the hind wings without a pattern. Most have a well developed proboscis and can feed as adults.

FAMILY 4: *Tortricidae*
This is another large family of small moths, with densely scaled wings of dull colours. The majority fly at dusk with a rapid, darting flight. The caterpillars are small, slender, smooth and live in concealment, burrowing into the fruits, buds or other parts of their food-plants or rolling the leaves to form a shelter.

FAMILY 5: *Psychidae*—BAGWORMS
This family includes the well-known bagworms, caterpillars that construct cases which they carry about with them. The male moths are small to moderate-sized, with dingy colours, with scales few or almost absent and no definite pattern on the wings. The females are wingless and remain inside their cases.

FAMILY 6: *Cossidae*—GOAT MOTHS, CARPENTER MOTHS
These are moderate-sized to large moths, of dull grey or brown, with vague patterns on the wings. The wings are long and narrow, frequently with few scales. There is no proboscis. The caterpillars are long-lived and mostly bore in wood.

FAMILY 7: *Sesiidae*—CLEAR-WINGS
Small to medium-sized moths with long narrow and usually transparent wings. The body is long and slender, often with red or yellow markings. The moths are active by day and may be seen flying in the hottest sunshine. The caterpillars bore into the stems and roots of their food-plants.

FAMILY 8: *Limacodidae*
The moths are small to medium sized, usually brown or apple green in colour. The body is short and the wings rounded. There is no proboscis. The larvae are called slug caterpillars because they have thick, fleshy bodies, small retractile heads and degenerate legs; some of them are armed with poisonous spines.

FAMILY 9: *Pyralidae*
Another very large family of small moths. The colours are varied but dull browns or greys are the most frequent. They are slender-bodied with long narrow wings without fringes, and with long, thin legs. The proboscis is small or may be absent. Mostly night fliers that come to lights. The caterpillars are small, slender and smooth and live in concealment.

FAMILY 10: *Pterophoridae*—PLUME MOTHS
Small, slender moths with narrow wings that are divided into plumes, the front wing being usually split into two and the hind wing into three divisions, making five plumes on each side. The legs are long and slender and the proboscis is well developed. The colours are usually pale, greyish white or light brown being the commonest. The caterpillars are short and oval, often clothed in hairs or spines. They feed openly on their food-plants.

FAMILY 11: *Zygaenidae*
The members of this family are often brightly coloured and fly by day, with a slow, heavy flight. They are apparently protected by an unpleasant taste and smell and their striking reds, blacks and greens are warning colours. Some members have the hind wings reduced to slender tails. The caterpillars are short and stout, being thickest in the middle, and they are sluggish and feed openly on their food-plants.

FAMILY 12: *Lasiocampidae*
Usually moderate to large-sized densely-scaled moths, brown in colour. The antennae are pectinate in both sexes but more strongly so in the males than in the females. The proboscis is absent. Most members of this family are nocturnal and will come to lights. The caterpillars are armed with lateral tufts of hair which are easily detachable and which, in some cases cause severe irritation if they enter the skin. The larvae are often gregarious, constructing a common shelter of silk in which they rest during the day.

FAMILY 13: *Sphingidae*—HAWK MOTHS
Moderate-sized to large, handsome moths with narrow, pointed wings and strong, swift flight. The antennae are, as a rule, slightly thickened in the middle and hooked at the tip. The proboscis is well developed and may be very long. The caterpillars are smooth and may be recognised by the prominent dorsal horn or tail near the hind end of the body.

FAMILY 14: *Bombycidae*

Most authors include in this family only the common silkworm and its allies, but Dr. Janse regards it as a much bigger assemblage of five sub-families, including the emperor moths, the *Saturniidae*. The moths are medium to large, with stout bodies, large wings and no proboscis. The antennae of the male are strongly pectinate. Several species yield silk of commercial value.

FAMILY 15: *Notodontidae*

Moderate-sized to large moths, generally dull in appearance, brown or grey being commonest colours. There is a proboscis and the moths will come to lights. The caterpillars are varied: some are quite normal, whereas others have curious processes on different parts of the body.

FAMILY 16: *Noctuidae*

A very large and important family, mostly of moderate size but including also some small and some very large moths. The colours are usually sombre, the fore wings being brown with an inconspicuous pattern and the hind wings paler. There is usually a proboscis. The moths are night flying and are attracted to lights. The caterpillars are smooth or with very fine hairs and they are brown or green as a rule. This family includes many serious pests.

FAMILY 17: *Geometridae*

Another very large family. Moths of slender build with relatively large wings that are held flat when at rest. Vary considerably in size but the majority are small. Proboscis is well developed. In a few species the females are wingless. The caterpillars are the well-known loopers, with only two pairs of abdominal feet.

CHAPTER XVI

BUTTERFLIES

The Rhopalocera

Formerly butterflies were regarded as forming a sub-order, the *Rhopalocera*, or "club-horned," to distinguish them from moths placed in another sub-order, the *Heterocera*, or "varied-horned" Lepidoptera. To-day experts consider that the differences between butterflies and moths are so slight that this division into two sub-orders is not justified and that butterflies form only a super-family, divided into six sub-families. As is well known, most butterflies are brightly coloured, they fly by day and the tips of their antennae are swollen. Their caterpillars are never hairy, although some of them are armed with spines, and the pupae are not enclosed in cocoons, except in the case of some of the more primitive species. A more fundamental difference between butterflies and moths is found in the fact that the wings on each side of a butterfly are not linked together by a jugum or a frenulum, except again in a few of the most primitive species. There are certain skipper butterflies found in Australia of which the males have a frenulum on each hind wing, like moths, but in all others the frenulum is absent; instead, the hind wing has a rounded lobe in front, known as the humeral lobe, which presses against the underside of the fore wing when the insect is in flight.

Skippers

The most primitive of butterflies, the most mothlike, are the dull-coloured skippers, so called because of their rapid darting flight. These common little butterflies may be recognised by their large heads, with the antennae comparatively wide apart at the base, by their front legs, which are fully formed and functional, by the two pairs of spines on each hind leg, by the veins on the wings, none of which is branched, and by the way in which they hold their wings when at rest. Some of them hold their wings flat, when settled, like a moth, others lift them above their backs, but they do not bring them close together, like other butterflies, and often the wings on each side are separated.

One of the commonest of our skippers, to be found throughout the country and on the wing at almost any time of the year, is the little brown, yellow-spotted butterfly known to science as *Cyclopides metis*. About an inch across the outspread wings, it can be recognised by the golden-yellow spots on the dark purple-brown ground colour, the underside being similar to the upper. The female lays her hemi-spherical white eggs, flattened on the underside, singly on blades of grass and they hatch in about a week.

The young caterpillar creeps to the tip of a blade of grass and forms a tubular shelter for itself by binding the edges together with silk, where it remains hidden and only ventures out to feed. In four or five weeks it is fully grown, about an inch and a quarter long, green in colour, striped with darker green along the back, and tapering at each end. It casts its skin four times in the course of its growth and then it leaves its food-plant to seek for a sheltered spot to pupate. It may choose the underside of a leaf, or a twig, or a post, or the side of a stone, where it spins a silken mat in which it fastens the hooks on the hind claspers and then it spins a girdle round its middle. Supported in this manner, in an upright position, it changes into a long, narrow green pupa, pointed at each end. About a fortnight later the adult emerges.

There are well over one hundred different species of skippers found in Africa and, as far as is known, they all have life histories similar to that described above. The majority of them fly in the sunshine but some are on the wing late in the evening, even after dusk. The caterpillars are smooth, with the first segments of the body small so that they seem to have a neck and they are mostly green and feed on grass. Most of them make shelters for themselves by joining the edges of a grass blade together with silk and some, if not all, have a small comblike structure just below the anus by means of which they flick their excrement away to a distance, thus

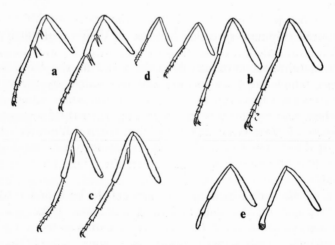

FIG. 89—The front legs of Butterflies. Male on left, female on right in each case: (a) *Hesperiidae;* (b) *Pieridae;* (c) *Papilionidae;* (d) *Lycaenidae;* (e) *Nymphalidae.*

b

a

c

FIG. 90—The Common Yellow-spotted Skipper, *Cyclopides metis*: (a) adult; (b) caterpillar; (c) pupa. All twice natural size.

keeping their homes clean. The pupae are elongated and generally
found between leaves, held in position by hooks on the hind end
and by a girdle round the middle.

The skippers are placed in a family by themselves, known as the
Hesperiidae, and they form a connecting link between the higher
butterflies and the moths.

Whites

The modern tendency is to include all other butterflies in one
family, the *Papilionidae*, which is divided into five sub-families. On
the other hand, most textbooks treat them as belonging to a number
of separate families and, as this arrangement will probably be found
most convenient by beginners, it is the classification adopted here.
The butterflies commonly known as whites, yellows, orange-tips, and
so on, form a family called the *Pieridae*. These are mostly white or
yellow, variously marked with black or brown, and they include
some of our commonest and best-known butterflies. They are mostly
of moderate size and may be recognised by their general form and
colouring, by the veins forming a closed cell on each wing, by their
fully formed and functional front legs, and by their bifid claws.

The banded gold tip, *Teracolus eris*, is common in sandy places
and is found from Abyssinia to the Cape. This butterfly is variable
in its markings and measures about two inches across the expanded

wings. The male usually has golden brown tips to his fore-wings
with a dark brown hind border, whereas the female usually has dark
brown tips to her front wings with a narrower brown hind border.
The general ground colour is white or pale yellow above with a deeper
pinkish yellow colour on the under-surface of the hind wings.

The female lays her conical white eggs singly on the underside
of leaves of native shrubs that have no common name but that are

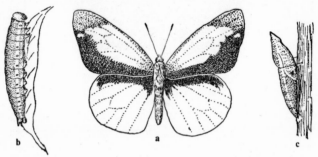

FIG. 91—The Banded Gold-tip, *Teracolus eris:* (a) adult; (b) caterpillar; (c) pupa.
All natural size.

known to botanists as *Capparis* species. The egg hatches in about
a week and the newly-emerged caterpillar makes its first meal off the
empty egg-shell. It is fully grown in four or five weeks, after moulting
four times, and is leaf-green in colour with a narrow white stripe down
the middle of the back and another along each side; it is about an
inch in length and has a forked tail end. It now seeks out a sheltered
spot on a leaf or twig and spins a small mat of silk in which it fastens
the hooks on its anal claspers. Then it spins a girdle round the middle
of its body, rests for a time and changes into a green pupa. The
adult emerges from the pupa in from two to three weeks. There are
several generations a year.

The members of this family include some of the commonest and
best known of butterflies. There are about seventy species found in
South Africa alone and more than one hundred and fifty species in
Africa. Some of them are widely distributed and are found from the
extreme south to the borders of the Sahara. Often there is a difference
between the sexes in colouring and marking. For example, in the
banded gold tip mentioned above, the female lacks the golden brown
tip to the forewing found in the male and has a black tip marked with
white spots. There may also be differences in the wet-season and
dry-season generations of butterflies; the banded gold tips of the
wet season have the black band on the fore-wing more strongly
developed than is the case with the dry-season butterflies. The cater-

PLATE 41

(a) THE COMMON TIGER BEETLE, *Cicindela lurida*

(b) Larva of the Common Tiger Beetle, *Cicindela lurida*

PLATE 42

(a) THE VEDALIA LADYBIRD, *Novius cardinalis*, on Australian bugs

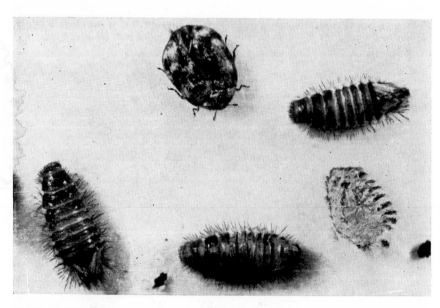

(b) THE MUSEUM BEETLE, *Anthrenus verbasci*. Three larvae and a cast skin and one adult. The beetle is about one tenth of an inch long.

pillars of this family are smooth and usually green and the pupae are always held in an upright position by hooks on the tail end, the cremaster, and by the silken girdle about the middle. In this latter characteristic they resemble the swallow-tails, but a pupa of the *Pieridae* can be distinguished from the *Papilionidae* by the shape of the head end; the pupa of a "white" has only a single pointed projection at the head end, whereas a swallow-tail pupa has always two points at this end.

Swallow-tails

The swallow-tails, *Papilionidae*, include some of the largest butter-flies in the world, some of them measuring eight or nine inches across the outspread wings. The largest butterfly in Africa is the West African swallow-tail, *Papilio antimachus*, with a wing expanse of about nine inches. The largest butterfly in the eastern parts, from Kenya to Natal, is the emperor swallow-tail or snake's head swallow-tail, *Papilio ophidicephalus*, which is between five and six inches across the wings. This species is found in forested regions and has the tail-like projections on the hind wings that give this family their common name very well developed.

One of the commonest and most widely spread of all our swallow-tails is the citrus swallow-tail, or Christmas butterfly, *Papilio demodocus*. Both sexes are alike but the yellow spots may be deeper in colour in the male than in the female. There are no "tails" on the hind wings. Although they may be seen on the wing at almost any time of the year, these butterflies are most numerous at mid-summer, hence their popular name of Christmas butterflies. The caterpillars are sometimes abundant on citrus trees and may do considerable damage to the foliage, hence their other common name, citrus butterfly.

The female deposits her spherical, yellow eggs singly on the tips of tender young leaves of the food-plants. Besides citrus trees she may choose wild celery or blister bush or Cape chestnut; like other members of the family, she shows a preference for plants with oil glands in the leaves and a strong scent and flavour. The egg hatches in about a fortnight and the caterpillar takes about a month to reach full size. It is then two inches long, smooth, green with black and orange markings, and it feeds openly without any attempt at concealment as it seems to be protected from enemies by an unpleasant taste and smell.

If one of these caterpillars is irritated, it will bend back its head and shoot out a curious forked organ from the segment just behind the head. This osmeterium, as it is called, is yellow and is forced out by muscular action and by the pressure of the blood; at the same

x

time a sickly over-powering odour of lemons is given off—the smell
has also been likened to that of rotten pineapples. The menacing
horn and the disgusting smell deter enemies from further interference
with the insect. This means of defence is common to the caterpillars
of all species of swallow-tails.

When the caterpillar is fully grown it seeks out a sheltered spot
and prepares for pupation. The whole amazing process can easily
be watched if some of these caterpillars are kept in captivity. First
of all it spins a small silken mat on the twig or branch or other chosen
spot and then it carefully fixes the tiny hooks on its hind claspers into
this mat so that it is securely held at the rear end. Resting head
upwards, it now begins to move the front part of its body from side
to side and, if it is closely watched, it can be seen to be weaving a
silken loop, fixed at each end to the surface just below its front legs.
It has its head held bent well back so that the loop passes between
its first and second pair of legs and is held securely by them. After
laying down several strands of silk in this way, which adhere
together and form a strong silken loop, it stops and rests. Then by
vigorous contortions it bends its head down and passes it through
the loop and wriggles and writhes until the silken support passes
back to the hind edge of the thorax. It is now securely held in position
by the mat at the hind end and the girdle round the middle.

Its body now shortens and thickens and finally the skin splits
at the back of the thorax and by more wriggling it is pushed back
towards the tail end and the pupa is revealed. Now comes what is
probably the most astonishing part of the whole performance. The
shrivelled cast skin round the hind end is an encumbrance that has
to be got rid of and the pupa does this in a remarkable manner. It
bends the tip of its abdomen upwards so that the skin is gripped
between two of the segments. Then it pulls the tip of its abdomen
out of the skin and, holding on only by that piece of skin nipped
between the segments, it feels with the tip of its abdomen until it
can get the tiny hooks, called the cremaster, fixed into the silken mat
below. By a series of violent jerks it makes sure that its new hold is
secure and then, with an upward jerk of the abdomen, it flings the
cast skin of the caterpillar away. The observer watching all this
cannot fail to get the impression that the caterpillar is acting with
foresight and reason, going through a complicated series of actions
in order to ensure a secure support for its pupal stage, yet it would
be quite wrong to ascribe to such a lowly creature the high degree
of intelligence required for such conscious, deliberate preparation,
and we must assume that it is guided only by blind instinct and is
quite unaware of the reasons for its actions.

The pupa matches its surroundings more or less in colour and is difficult to see. Anybody who rears some of the caterpillars can experiment by placing fully grown larvae, just when they are about to pupate, in small boxes lined with paper of different colours. Although the pupae cannot change colour, like a chameleon, the colour of their surroundings has a marked effect, for the pupa in a box lined with dark paper is much darker in colour than a pupa in a light box. This response to the colour of the surroundings is found in the pupae of many butterflies and must be of value in helping them to escape the attentions of enemies. There are two or three generations a year of the citrus butterfly and the cold months of the year are spent in the pupal state.

Mimicry

The mocker swallow-tail, *Papilio dardanus*, offers what is probably the most striking example in the world of the much-debated phenomenon of mimicry among butterflies. This butterfly is found throughout Africa south of the Sahara and occurs most commonly on the edges of forests and in clearings in wooded areas. The male is of the typical swallow-tail form with a long tail on each hind wing, pale yellow with broad black bands round the margins of his wings. There, are however, several different forms of female and they are quite unlike the male; only by breeding them in the laboratory and by capturing them when mating has it been proved that these insects, differing so markedly from one another in colouring and markings all belong to the same species.

The females do not have tails on their hind wings and they resemble other butterflies so closely that they may easily be mistaken for them. One form of female mocker is dark purplish brown and has a large yellow patch at the base of each hind wing. It is very similar in appearance to a butterfly that belongs to quite a different family, the layman, *Amauris albimaculata*. Not only is it similar in colour and markings, but also in its manner of flying, being slow and deliberate on the wing, and it is found in the same places as the layman, along the edges of forests and in clearings.

A second form of female mocker is black with large white patches on each wing and it closely resembles the friar butterfly, *Amauris dominicanus*, whilst a third form has brown instead of white patches and mimics the common African Monarch, *Danaus chrysippus*. Still other forms are found in different parts of Africa and in each case they look very much like distinct species of butterflies that are found flying in the same neighbourhood: but everywhere the males are alike, sulphur yellow with black borders to their wings and with the characteristic tails on the hind wings.

The mocker butterfly has several different races or sub-species in various regions of Africa and each of these has one to five different forms of female which usually are close mimics of certain species of Danaine butterflies (see page 207). In Madagascar the females are like the males and have tails on their hind wings. The resemblance between the different types of female mockers and their models is so close that even the most experienced butterfly collector has to look very closely at the venation on the wings to determine which is which.

This is perhaps the most remarkable example of the phenomenon known as mimicry to be found anywhere in the world. It is assumed that the butterfly called the mimic or imitator benefits because of its close resemblance to the butterfly known as the model. The model, it is believed, is protected against the attack of enemies owing to its unpleasant taste and smell. Presumably the mimic is mistaken for the model by insect-eating enemies and is consequently left alone, although it is edible. Obviously the mimic, if it is to benefit, must inhabit the same locality as the model and must have similar ways. Also the mimic must be less numerous than the model for, if it were not, the particular colouring and markings of the pair would in time lose their association with unpalability and would not serve as a warning to enemies.

The theory of mimicry has been hotly contested and some entomologists assert that the resemblance between mimic and model is purely accidental and due to causes other than natural selection. Anybody who has seen the mocker butterflies, however, in their natural haunts, flying in company with their distasteful models, cannot fail to be convined of the truth of the theory. The butterflies do not consciously imitate their models, of course: there is nothing voluntary about it at all. Those females that look like the protected models have more chance of surviving and laying eggs and so, in course of time, the mimics that look exactly like the models have been evolved. The male is not so important as the female; he is a swift flier and does not have to linger over egg-laying, therefore he is not protected by mimicry. One of the chief difficulties about the theory is the fact that mimicry is only found among a few species. If it is valuable to the mocker butterfly, why has not the citrus butterfly evolved protected females in the same way? We must assume that, for some reason or other, the female citrus butterflies do not vary in colouring and markings and there is, therefore, no material for natural selection to work upon, whereas the mocker females have been extraordinarily variable in the past.

Blues and Coppers

The *Lycaenidae* is a large family of small to moderate-sized butterflies, mostly blue in colour, although some are coppery red or dark brown or orange. On the underside of the wings the coloration is more sombre, with dark-centred eye-spots or slender lines and streaks; the hind wings are frequently provided with delicate tail-like prolongations. The legs of the adults are all functional and used for walking, but in the males the front feet or tarsi are shortened and armed with only one claw or none at all. This family is very well represented in Africa with over a thousand species.

The common copper, *Phasis chrysaor*, may be taken as our example of this group. It is a small butterfly, only about an inch across the

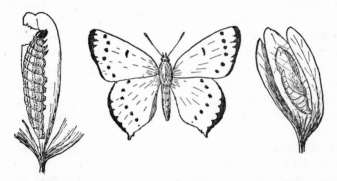

FIG. 92—The Common Cape Copper, *Phasis chrysaor*, adult in middle, caterpillar on left and pupa on right. All one and a half times natural size.

outspread wings, glittering golden orange in colour with a few small brown spots on each wing, and the male and female are alike. The adults may be seen on the wing at almost any time of the year but are commonest in summer. They are active fliers but settle frequently on low-growing plants.

The female lays her small, white, bun-shaped eggs singly on the leaves of taaibos (*Rhus* species) and *Cotyledon* plants, and they hatch in about fourteen days. The caterpillar is flattened, sluggish, greenish-grey in colour with narrow brown lines down the back. It feeds on the leaves and generally returns to the same sheltered spot each time it rests. It grows slowly, moulting seven times before it reaches full size and takes four or five months to do so. On the back of the tenth segment of its body there is a gland with a small slit opening behind a shiny, wrinkled area. This is the honey gland and these caterpillars are eagerly attended by black cocktail ants, *Cremastogaster* species, for the sake of the sweet liquid given off by the gland. An ant, on finding the caterpillar, strokes the gland with its antennae and the caterpillar responds by protruding the gland slightly and a drop of liquid oozes from the slit and this is lapped up by the ant. It is thought that the caterpillar benefits from this association because the ants protect it from parasites and other enemies. On the segment behind the honey gland there is a pair of tubercles that can be protruded at will and they are armed at the tip with bristles. The function of these tubercles is not known for certain but it seems reasonable to assume that they serve to protect the honey gland from unwanted visitors. If the honey gland is touched by a hair a small white piston-like protuberance is shot out of the opening in each tubercle and the stiff bristles at the tip are swept across the honey gland with a rapid, jerky motion which, apparently, would drive away insects trying to get at the sweet secretion; the visits of the ants only are tolerated by the caterpillar. It has also been suggested that the tubercles give off a scent that attracts the ants and enables them to locate the gland.

When it is fully grown the caterpillar seeks out a sheltered spot, between two leaves, or amid dead leaves, or in the angle of a stem, and spins a light web. It then changes to a pupa, generally lying on its back and held in position by the hooks on the hind end of its body, the cremaster, which are fixed in the web. The pupal stage lasts for fifteen days or so.

The life histories of many Lycaenids, as far as they are known, are similar to that described above, but there are some interesting variations. The beautiful star blue butterfly, *Lycaena asteris*, for example, that is found at the Cape, is one of the bigger species, measuring nearly two inches across the outspread wings. The male is bright blue above, with a short tail on each hind wing; the female is of a duller, more brownish hue. Both sexes are marked on the underside with a number of conspicuous dark brown spots on a pale background. These butterflies may be seen on the wing on the mountain slopes early in the summer.

The female lays her eggs on a shrub that is common on the mountainside and that bears sweet-smelling mauve flowers; it has no popular name but is known as *Selago serrata* to botanists. The eggs are laid singly on the flowers and they hatch into tiny sluglike caterpillars that feed on the flowers. Entomologists at the Cape who have tried to rear these insects find that the caterpillars feed and flourish for a short time in the cages, but after a while they refuse to take any more food and become restless, wandering about the cage until they die of starvation.

It is obvious, then, that these caterpillars start life in the ordinary way and feed on the flowers of *Selago*, but later they require some special conditions they cannot find when kept in captivity. That is as much as is known at present for certain. The next stage is probably connected with a curious caterpillar that may be found in the nests of certain kinds of ants. During the winter months a strange white sluglike caterpillar is sometimes found inside the nests of the common brown ants, *Plagiolepis custodiens*. The caterpillars are by no means common and usually only one is found in a nest.

Close examination of the caterpillar shows that it has a small head hidden beneath the overhanging front portion of the body, with small thoracic legs and short abdominal claspers also hidden by the overlapping margins of the body. On the tenth segment the narrow slit can be seen on the back that is the opening of the honey gland. The caterpillar is very sluggish and scarcely moves at all if left to itself. Attempts to rear this caterpillar have so far failed as they die soon after they are moved from the ants' nest.

Judging from observations made on the large blue, *Nomiades arion*, in England, it would seem highly probable that the ants carry

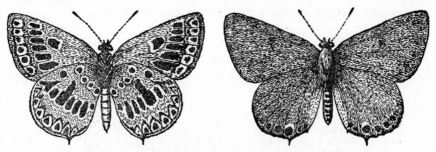

FIG. 93—The Star Blue, *Lycaera asteris*

the young caterpillars of the star blue into their nest and keep them there for the sake of the secretion given off by the honey gland. The caterpillars have become adapted to life in the nest and they have adopted a carnivorous diet, feeding on the larvae of their hosts. When fully grown they pupate inside the nest and the butterflies, when they emerge, creep out before their wings expand. All this needs confirmation by observations and it is suspected that several others of the larger species of blues found in Africa have this close, strange association with ants.

Among the Lycaenids the males of many species are far more numerous than the females, in some cases the former outnumbering the latter by as many as fifty to one. So far no satisfactory explanation has been put forward for this. The females are usually not so active or so conspicuous as the males, but this does not account for the disproportion of the sexes caught. Furthermore, among these and other butterflies (see page 208) it is the males that are scented and not the females, as is the case with moths. The phenomenon of assembling, described on page 169, is considered to be the result of a subtle scent given off by the females and it has not been observed among butterflies. But on the wings of many male Lycaenids, as well as other butterflies, there are patches of peculiar, modified scales called androconia, or "male particles". These are associated with tiny glands on the wing that give off a fluid thought to have an odour agreeable to the females. The scent patch is usually situated on the upper surface of the hind wing and there is a brush of hairlike scales associated with it. The function of this sunken pocket of specialised scales is not known for certain, but it is generally believed to be of use to the male when he is courting the female—apparently he scatters a scented dust as he flutters about her. On the other hand, it has been suggested that the scent patch is really an organ that enables him to find his mate by picking up the subtle odour it is assumed she gives out when ready for the male. Further observations on the living insects are necessary before this matter can be settled.

Beaked Butterflies

The *Libytheidae* are peculiar butterflies placed in a small family by themselves, widely spread over the world and with only one species

FIG. 94.—The Beaked Butterfly, *Libythea labdaca*. About twice natural size.

found in South Africa. This is the beaked butterfly, *Libythea labdaca*, so called because the palps on its head are much longer than in other butterflies and they project in front of the head like a beak. The front legs of the male are small and useless and without claws, similar to the front legs of the higher butterflies described below, but the front legs of the females are fully formed and can be used for walking.

PLATE 43

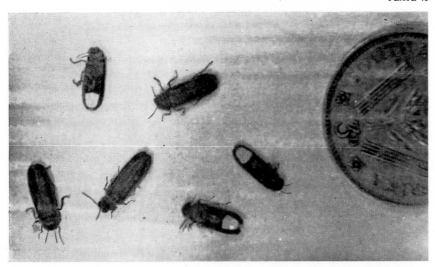

(a) THE CAPE FIRE-FLY, *Luciola capensis*, photographed beside a threepenny-piece to show comparative size. Three of the beetles are on their backs, to show light-producing organ on underside of abdomen.

(b) Female GLOW WORM, on a dead slug

PLATE 44

(a) Male GLOW WORM, underside, showing the enormous eyes

(b) POWDER-POST BEETLES, *Lyctus brunneus*, photographed together with a match-stick to show comparative size

The beaked butterfly is about two inches across the outspread wings, brown with yellow markings. It is very local and frequents wooded areas where it may be seen flying over the tops of bushes and small trees. It takes short flights from flower to flower and when it settles it rests head downwards on the trunk of a tree. This butterfly is to be found from Natal to Tanganyika and also in West Africa and is on the wing in spring and summer.

Browns

We now come to the higher butterflies that are characterised by the first pair of legs in both sexes being much smaller and more

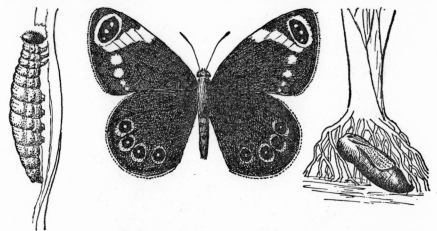

FIG 95.—The Autumn Brown, *Dira* (*Leptoneura*) *clytus.*   Adult in middle, caterpillar on left, pupa on right.   All natural size.

slender than the others, too short to be used in walking or clinging. These front legs are usually much more reduced in the male than the female, without any joints or claws on the tarsi or feet; the tarsus in the female is jointed but short and not armed with claws. All these butterflies are sometimes classified as belonging to one large family, the *Nymphalidae*, divided into several sub-families, or they may be regarded as belonging to distinct but closely related families. The first of these includes small or medium-sized species, with a few large ones among them, usually of a sombre brown colour with eye-spots on the wings, the *Satyridae*, (or *Satyrinae* if they are regarded as a sub-family).

The autumn brown, *Dira* (*Leptoneura*) *clytus*, is a common species in the Cape Province and there are very similar closely related species found in other parts. This butterfly is about two inches across the outspread wings, of a rich chocolate brown colour with yellow

Y

markings on the front wings and five eye-spots (one very small) in each hind wing; the underside is of a dull brown. It may be seen flying slowly and resting frequently over open ground, where grass is growing, from the middle of February to the end of May, but is most abundant in March. In places it may be very numerous, but if a number of specimens are caught, it will be found that the males are much commoner than the females, outnumbering their mates by as much as fifty to one.

The female scatters her eggs whilst she is settled on a blade of grass; they are smooth, yellow, round and slightly flattened on the underside. The eggs hatch in about a fortnight and the caterpillars

FIG. 96—The Evening Brown, *Melanitis leda*, so called because it flies only in the evening and at dawn

feed on grasses, hiding by day and coming out only at night to feed. They moult four times before they are fully grown and then they are about one and a quarter inches long, thickened in the middle and narrower at each end, with a largish head, dull yellow in colour with brownish markings. Although they may be numerous amid the grass they are not seen because they hide themselves so well during the hours of daylight. The full-grown caterpillar seeks out a sheltered spot amid grass roots and dead leaves and stems and there it changes into a pupa, not attached in any way but lying loose on the ground. The pupa is brown mottled with black. There is only one generation a year.

The evening brown, *Melanitis leda*, is peculiar as it does not fly by day but only in the evening and at dawn. During the day it frequents the darkest and shadiest spots in woods, resting on the ground or on dead leaves, where the colouring of the underside of its wings harmonises so well with its surroundings that it is difficult to see. If disturbed it takes a short, flapping flight before dropping again into some shady nook. It becomes active after sunset and then seeks the open where it flies about until after dark. This is a common butterfly in wooded areas from Natal right up through Africa and it is also found right through Asia. About three inches across the outspread wings, it is dull brown with a conspicuous black spot on a yellow patch in each front wing, but it is a very variable species in colour and pattern and also in the outline of its wings.

The mountain beauty, *Meneris tulbaghia*, is a large and handsome member of this family, about four inches across the wings, chocolate brown with yellow markings and with five eye-spots on each hind wing. It is found during the summer months on mountains and rocky hillsides and has a swift, strong flight. The caterpillars are pale bluish green with a black stripe down the back and feed on grasses. The pupa is short and stout, suspended by its tail, white with small black dots on it.

There are about thirty species of *Satyridae* found in South Africa and they are mostly weak fliers, flying near the ground and settling frequently, and the caterpillars, as far as known, are grass-feeders.

The Painted Lady Family

The painted lady, *Vanessa cardui*, is the commonest and most widely distributed butterfly in the world. It is found throughout Africa at all times of the year and is also an inhabitant of Europe, Asia and North America. In some years it is common in Britain, in other years it is scarce, yet it cannot survive the winter there; every year it is annihilated by the cold and the question at once arises, how is the stock replenished each spring?

This butterfly, like a number of others, is a migrant. Numbers of them fly across the English Channel from the continent of Europe every spring and they breed in England, giving rise to the autumnal generation of butterflies which are all killed off during the winter. Nobody knows why butterflies migrate in this way, but it is generally assumed that they do so when they have increased so much in their usual haunts that the food supply for the caterpillars runs short. But this is only part of the answer. In the case of the painted lady the caterpillars feed on common wayside weeds, such as nettles, thistles and mallows, and there is rarely such a lack of foodplants as to cause a wholesale migration of the adults.

From various parts of Africa reports have been received of swarms of these butterflies, flying low and all in the same general direction. Nobody knows where they go, or why. Their stout thoraces and large wing-muscles mark them as strong fliers, but it is unknown how far they can fly or what are the limits of their endurance. A flight of twenty miles across the English Channel is obviously a commonplace performance for them and specimens have been taken on ships far out in the Mediterranean.

The painted lady measures about two and a half inches across the outspread wings and is a rich tawny red with black markings and some white spots. The underside of the wings is beautifully mottled with yellow, white and brown. The red colour of the wings is peculiar in that it is soluble in hot water. Also it becomes duller with age so that an old pinned specimen in a cabinet is not nearly so handsome as a newly-emerged butterfly—but the colour can be restored to a bright rosy red by exposing the specimen to chlorine gas. The colouring and pattern, as in all butterflies and moths, are lodged entirely in the tiny scales that coat the wings like the tiles on a roof. If the wing is examined under a microscope it can be seen that the red portion is coated with red scales, marvellously formed and arranged, whilst the white spots are covered with white scales, and so on. When the scales are rubbed off the wing itself is seen to be a colourless membrane.

It is a mystery how the different colours are laid down in their restricted patches of scales to form the pattern. The most reasonable suggestion is that the scales do not all grow and form at the same time on the wings inside the pupa. When the blood contains black pigment, only certain patches of scales on the wings are ready to receive it and these scales become black and form the black spots. Later, when the blood of the pupa contains red pigment, other scales are ready to receive it and these form the red parts of the wings, and so on.

The female lays her green eggs on the leaves of thistles and other weeds, usually only one to a leaf. These hatch in about a fortnight into little black caterpillars coated with branched spines. Each caterpillar constructs for itself a shelter by binding a leaf to the stem with a few silken threads and it feeds inside this shelter. When it is fully grown, after moulting four times, it is nearly two inches long, dark brown, with a wavy light line down each side and prominent branched spines along its back. It leaves the plant to pupate and seeks out a sheltered spot, where it can hang freely head downwards and where it is not exposed too much to the weather. First of all it spins a small silken mat on the underside of a branch or an over-hanging stone, or wherever it may be, and then it fixes the hooks on its hind pair of claspers into this mat so that it can hang securely.

Its body now thickens and shortens and it curls the head and front part of its body upwards. The skin splits across the back of the thorax and, by vigorous writhing and wriggling, is worked upwards and backwards off the body, revealing the pupa, greenish yellow, gilded on the back and wing-covers and with three rows of golden spots down the back. It is this golden colour that is evident in the pupae of many different kinds of butterflies that has given rise to the name, chrysalis.

The shrivelled, discarded skin of the caterpillar hangs round the top end of the pupa, where it is fixed to the support. In order to get rid of this unwanted encumbrance the pupa has to let go its hold on the silken mat and it would seem that, as this is its only means of support, it must inevitably fall in doing so. But it does not fall. At first the pupa is held in place only by the tip of its tail which is still embedded in the cast skin, and this cast skin is held in its turn by the hooks of the hind claspers fixed in the silken mat. The pupa has knoblike projections on its tail and it grips the cast skin between two of these. Then it quickly disengages its tail and fixes the hooks at the tip, the cremaster, into the silk beside the cast skin. Finally, with a jerk, it flings away the skin and hangs there securely and freely by its new hold. This is a difficult performance that has to be carried out by every caterpillar of the large family to which the painted lady belongs, because they all hang head downwards when they pupate. About a fortnight later the adult emerges. There are several generations a year and the painted lady may be seen on the wing at all seasons.

The handsome butterflies known as *Charaxes* belong to the same family, the *Nymphalidae*, as the painted lady. They are medium to large-sized, with thick bodies and usually with two pointed tails on each hind wing. They occur chiefly in forested areas and are strong fliers, haunting the tree-tops but descending to the ground to settle on muddy patches, on animal droppings or on carrion or decaying fruit. Collectors make use of this habit when out butterfly-hunting. They put down a bait consisting of fermented fruit, bananas, paw-paws, etc., sometimes mixed with stout and brown sugar, and the female Charaxes are attracted to this; the males seldom come to such a bait, but it has been found that the droppings of a dog (it is said the dog must be fed on meat) are very attractive to them and the enthusiast carries a tinful of the dung with him as a bait for the males. Most of the species are African and many of them are widely spread.

One of the commonest is the foxy charaxes, *Charaxes pelias* that is found from the Cape to Kenya in localities where there are indigenous trees. Measuring about four inches across the outspread wings, it is brown with yellow and black markings and borders. The female lays her spherical yellow eggs singly on the leaves of the food-plant, which is usually a tree or bush belonging to the *Leguminosae*. The egg hatches in seven days and the newly-hatched caterpillar devours the egg-shell before starting to feed on the leaves. It moults four times before it is fully grown about six weeks after hatching, when it is two inches in length, green in colour and distinguished by four peculiar "horns" on top of its head. It pupates in the same way as described

FIG. 97—The Foxy Charaxes, *Charaxes pelias:* (a) adult; (b) caterpillar; (c) pupa. All slightly smaller than natural size.

above for the painted lady and the pupa is about an inch long, thick and bluish-green in colour. The adult emerges after a fortnight spent as a pupa.

The diadem butterfly, *Hypolimna misippus*, is another well-known and widely spread member of this family. It is of interest because of the striking difference between the two sexes and because the female has several forms that mimic the distasteful African monarch, *Danaus chrysippus*. The male, about three inches across the outspread wings, is violet-black with a large circular white patch on each wing. The female is quite different, being brown with black borders to the wings, closely resembling the African monarch. The brown caterpillars of this butterfly, armed with red and blackish spines and with two black horns on the head, may be found during the late summer months on apricot and other plants.

The gaudy commodore, *Precis octavia*, is a member of this family and offers what is perhaps the most striking example known of what is called seasonal dimorphism. It is a beautiful insect well known right through Africa, but few people would recognise its two forms, the wet-season and dry-season forms, as belonging to the same species.

The dry-season form is blue, with darker blue wavy lines and a row of red spots parallel with the border of the wings; it is about three inches across the outspread wings and is popularly known as the blue commodore, and as *Precis octavia sesamus* to entomologists. The wet-season form is quite different in appearance and slightly smaller; it is red with blue-black margins and is called the red commodore, *Precis octavia natalensis*. When they were first found these two butterflies were naturally supposed to be two quite distinct species, particularly as their habits are different, the red form preferring open grassy spots while the blue form favours shady spots, and as they are found on the wing at different times of the year. They were named accordingly, *Precis octavia* the red form, and *Precis sesamus* the blue form. Specimens intermediate between the two in colouring and pattern were caught, as well as pairs of the two forms mating together, and it was assumed that the two species hybridised and the intermediate forms were hybrids. But more than fifty years ago the blue form was reared from eggs laid by red females, and vice versa, thereby proving conclusively that the two are the same species and that the striking differences between them are due in some way or other to climatic conditions. It has long been known that the colouring and markings of certain kinds of butterflies can be modified by submitting the pupae to abnormal conditions of temperature and humidity, and it seems reasonable to assume that the red commodore and the blue commodore are the result of climatic conditions during the wet and the dry seasons of the year, although precisely how these conditions produce the striking differences is not known. Several other species of African butterflies show seasonal dimorphism, but none is quite so remarkable as *Precis octavia*.

The butterflies belonging to this large family, the *Nymphalidae*, are mostly robust with wings densely coated in scales, with stout, spiny middle and hind legs and with a deep groove or channel along the inner margins of the hind wings in which the abdomen fits. They are swift, active insects and many of them are large and brilliantly coloured. The caterpillars are smooth or armed with branched spines and the pupae always hang by the tail only.

Distasteful Butterflies

In summer a red and black butterfly with a lazy, fluttering flight is very common in many parts of the country. This is the garden acraea, *Acraea horta*, and it belongs to a family of butterflies, *Acraeidae*, that are protected from their enemies by an unpleasant taste and smell. The deep brick red colour and black markings warn any bird, lizard or frog that might be tempted to make a meal of it that it is not good to eat and any young and inexperienced insect-eater that snaps at these butterflies soon learns to associate the conspicuous markings and lazy flight with a disgusting taste and it leaves them severely alone, unless it is very hungry.

The garden acraea is a hardy butterfly and tenacious of life. Whereas it is easy to kill most butterflies by pinching the thorax and thereby crushing the main nerve centres, with this species anything short of actual crushing of the tissues fails to kill it. When it is pinched a yellow fluid issues from the joints and this fluid seems to be the source of the evil taste and smell. The front legs of the male are small and useless—it is a four-legged butterfly like the other members of the higher families of butterflies. The front legs of the female are somewhat better developed but they are without joints or claws on the tarsi. The female can also usually be distinguished from the male by the presence of a small, black horny pouch at the end of her tail. This curious pouch is found only in the females of this family and in a few females of the swallow-tail family, and its use is not known, but it is suggested that the shieldlike covering is formed after the female has mated in order to prevent other males from mating with her.

The female lays her eggs on the leaves of the wild peach, *Kiggelaria africana*, and of related plants, including the grenadilla. The wild peach and the grenadilla are quite dissimilar in appearance, one a tree and the other a climber, one an exotic and the other indigenous, yet the butterfly has detected the close relationship between the two. How does she select the food-plant for her young? It must be remembered that, if she makes a mistake and lays her eggs on the wrong sort of plant, her offspring will have little chance of surviving, for most caterpillars are extraordinarily conservative feeders—anybody who has tried to rear them knows that they die quickly if not given the right sort of food. It is not likely that she recognises the plants by sight because her eyes are not adapted for clear vision at any distance and, in any case, appearance is no guide to the relationship of plants—witness the wild peach and the grenadilla. Possibly she is able to detect the subtle aroma of some essential oil that is common to the plants; all we do know for certain is that butterflies and moths are excellent botanists with an unfailing instinct for picking out the right plants for their young.

The caterpillars of the garden acraea are dark brown and covered with branched spines. They are conspicuous on the plants and make no attempt at concealment because they are protected by their spines and unpleasant taste. A parasitic wasp attacks and destroys numbers of them, however; often a dead caterpillar may be found with a little

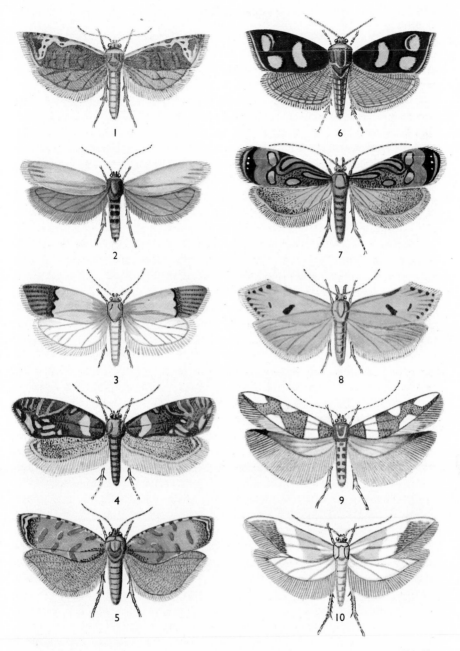

III. SOME AFRICAN MICROLEPIDOPTERA. Many of our smallest moths are extremely beautiful. The species shown on this plate are all only half an inch or less across the outspread wings. 1. *Dichelia albardana;* 2. *Gymnogramma hutchinsoni;* 3. *Odites natalensis;* 4. *Glyphipteryx grapholithoides;* 5. *Argyrotoxa viridis;* 6. *Simaethis flavimaculata;* 7. *Strobisia metallica;* 8. *Anorthosia fracticostellus;* 9. *Stagmatophora distincta;* 10. *Oxymachaeris niveocervina.*

grey, barrel-shaped object, barred with black, hanging on a silken thread below it. This is the cocoon of the parasite.

The pupa of the garden acraea is a conspicuous object, white and black with small yellow dots. It is found hanging head downwards in fully exposed positions on tree trunks, rocks, palings and walls. The adult emerges from the pupa in about a fortnight. The butterflies may be seen on the wing at almost any time of the year.

The members of the family to which the garden acraea belongs, *Acraeidae*, are mostly of moderate size, red and black, with wings that are not thickly coated with scales and that, in some species, are almost transparent. The heads and bodies of the adults are conspicuously marked with white and yellow spots. They are butterflies of slow flight and often found in quantity in their favourite haunts. Their deliberate movements and complete disregard of concealment, together with their striking appearance, indicate clearly that these insects are not persecuted by enemies. Many of them are mimicked by butterflies belonging to other groups, the *Nymphalidae*, *Papilionidae* and a few *Lycaenidae*, that are not protected by distasteful qualities.

The African Monarch and its Kin

The African monarch, *Danaus chrysippus*, is common throughout Africa—in fact, it is one of the most widespread butterflies in the world, being found from southern Europe to the Cape and from West Africa to the Far East. It is a conspicuous insect with reddish brown wings, bordered with black and white and measuring from three to four inches across the outspread wings. It is a slow, lazy flier because, like the *Acraeidae*, it is protected by an unpleasant taste and smell, and few insect-eaters will touch it. The male and female are alike, except that he has a velvety black spot in the middle of each hind wing that is lacking in his mate. This black spot is of considerable interest and well worth a little attention.

The black patch on the hind wing of the male consists of a shallow pocket or pouch opening by a small slit on the upper surface. A thick ridge covered with black scales overhangs this opening. If the patch is dissected with the aid of a pair of needles and examined under the microscope it is found to contain innumerable tiny black scales, oval in shape and different from the scales that cover the rest of the wings. This black dust inside the pockets is a scented powder that the male uses in courtship.

If you capture a male monarch and hold him by his wings folded over his back and gently squeeze his abdomen, two things like miniature shaving brushes will protrude from the tip. Each is about an eighth of an inch long, as thick as a stout pin and quite easily visible to the

z

naked eye. If you now increase the pressure of your fingers very slightly the two tufts of hairs will suddenly explode, as it were, and instead of two tiny brushes you will see two powder puffs protruding from his tail.

The male, when courting the female, flies about her, thrusts out

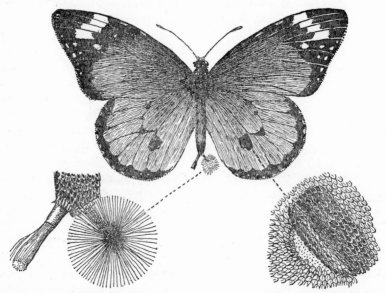

FIG. 98—The African Monarch, *Danaus chrysippus*. Male, natural size showing the scent pockets on his hind wings and the scent brushes at the tip of his abdomen. Below, the scent brushes (one open and one closed) and the scent pocket are shown enlarged.

those two powder puffs from his tail, sweeps the scented dust from the pockets on his hind wings and scatters it in the air around her. It is difficult to prove that this charming form of courtship actually takes place, but there seems to be no other reasonable explanation of the elaborate scent pocket and scent brushes of the male. Special scent scales known as androconia, or male dust, are found in many other butterflies and it is well known that the males of many species have distinct and pleasant odours, easily perceptible even to the blunted sense of smell of human beings.

The caterpillars of the African monarch may be found at almost any time of the year on the plants known as milkweeds, *Asclepias* species, and on stapelias. They are black and yellow and easy to recognise because each caterpillar has three pairs of black, threadlike tentacles on its back, the use of which is quite unknown. They are hardy insects and feed freely exposed as though they have no enemies to fear. When fully grown, the caterpillar hangs itself up by its tail and changes into a pupa marked with golden spots; the colour of the pupa varies and may be green, blue, pink or yellow. In about a fortnight the pupa turns black and soon afterwards the adult emerges.

The African monarch belongs to a small family generally regarded as the highest of the Lepidoptera, the *Danaidae*. They are conspicuous butterflies because of their size and slow flight. All are hardy and apparently long-lived for insects, as some of them are capable of migrating for long distances.

CLASSIFICATION

ORDER 18: *LEPIDOPTERA*—BUTTERFLIES

Butterflies were formerly placed in a sub-order, *Rhopalocera* "club-horned", to distinguish them from the *Heterocera*, "varied-horned" moths, but to-day the two groups are regarded as being so closely linked that the butterflies form only a super-family, the *Papilioninae* divided into a number of families or sub-families. The beginner will probably find it most convenient to classify the butterflies into separate families.

FAMILY 1: *Hesperiidae*—SKIPPERS

The most primitive butterflies, nearly all small, dull in colour and with a distinctive darting and rapid flight. They are unique among butterflies in that all the veins arise direct from cells, none branching subsequently. The head is wider than the thorax, with large eyes, and the bases of the antennae are wide apart. The first pair of legs are functional in both sexes, while the tibiae of the hind pair are usually armed with two pairs of spines, as in many moths. The caterpillars taper at both ends and spin leaves together to form a shelter. The pupae are long and tapering, often without tail-hooks or girdle and they are often enclosed in a crude cocoon of silk and grass.

FAMILY 2: *Pieridae*—WHITES

Butterflies that are predominantly white or yellow in colour. The first pair of legs are functional in both sexes. The claws of the feet are bifid or toothed. The eggs are elongated, bottle-shaped and ribbed. The caterpillars are smooth, without tubercles or spines. The pupae are angular, supported in an upright position by tail-hooks and girdle, characterised by only one point on the head.

FAMILY 3: *Papilionidae*—SWALLOW-TAILS

In many species the hind wings have conspicuous tail-like prolongations. The prevailing colours are black and yellow. This family includes the largest butterflies in the world. Front legs fully developed in both sexes with a flattened spur on the tibia. Claws large and simple, not bifid. Eggs rounded without distinct sculpturing on the surface. Caterpillars smooth and hairless, with a protrusible forked appendage, the osmeterium, just behind the head. Pupae differ from those of the *Pieridae* in having two points at the head end; they are supported by tail-hooks (cremaster) and girdle in an upright position.

FAMILY 4: *Lycaenidae*—BLUES AND COPPERS

Small or medium-sized butterflies, many with slender tails on the hind wings. Mostly blue in colour, but many are red. The front legs of the males reduced in size, usually with only one joint in the tarsus and a single claw. The front legs of the females are not so reduced and are armed with two claws. Eggs hemispherical with sculptured surface. Caterpillars short and thick, with small head and feet generally hidden beneath overhanging sides. Some caterpillars remarkable for their association with ants. Pupae are short and rounded, sometimes lying free, sometimes attached only by tail-hooks or by tail-hooks and girdle.

FAMILY 5: *Libytheidae*—BEAKED BUTTERFLIES

This is the smallest family of butterflies and there are only one or two species found in Africa. Brown with yellow spots. The palps on the head are very long and project in front like a beak. Front legs of males slender and reduced and without claws, front legs of females well developed. Eggs bottle-shaped and ridged. Caterpillars slender and smooth. Pupae suspended by the tail only, without a girdle.

FAMILY 6: *Satyridae*—BROWNS

Inconspicuous butterflies, brown being the prevailing colour, with eye-like spots on the wings. One or more of the veins on the front wings are dilated at the base. The front legs of both sexes are degenerate, the tarsi of the male having one joint only, those of the female several joints, and they are not armed with claws. The eggs are rounded, marked with grooves. The caterpillars taper at both ends, smooth or coated with very fine hairs; usually feed on grasses. Pupae short, thick, rounded, lie free on the ground or held only by tail-hooks.

FAMILY 7: *Nymphalidae*—PAINTED LADY, CHARAXES, MOTHER-OF-PEARL, ETC.

Medium-sized or large butterflies, stoutly built, often with brilliant colours. Front legs reduced in both sexes. The cell formed by the veins on the front wing is usually closed but that on the hind wing is open. The front legs in both sexes are degenerate and useless for walking; in the male they have two tarsal joints and are brushlike, while in the female they have four joints and are not brushlike. The eggs are generally ribbed, with a flat area at the top. Caterpillars bear spines or tubercles. Pupae are always suspended head downwards by the tail-hooks only.

FAMILY 8: *Acraeidae*

Small to medium-sized butterflies with narrow wings. Front legs degenerate and useless for walking. Red and black are common colours. Protected by evil taste and smell and are slow, deliberate fliers. Mimicked by species of other families. Wings thinly scaled. Females develop an abdominal pouch after mating. Caterpillars armed with branched spines. Pupae suspended head downwards by tail-hooks only

FAMILY 9: *Danaidae*—AFRICAN MONARCH, ETC.

A small family of conspicuous butterflies with slow flight, protected by evil taste and smell. Mimicked by many species of other families. Front legs greatly reduced in both sexes. Male butterfly with scent patch on each hind wing and scent brushes in end of abdomen. Cells of the wings closed. Eggs conical and ridged. Caterpillars smooth but most have one or more pairs of slender tentacles on their backs. Pupae are suspended head downwards by tail-hooks only.

CHAPTER XVII

BEETLES

The Coleoptera

Beetles make up the largest order in the whole animal kingdom, with nearly two hundred thousand known species. They include some of the largest and some of the smallest of all insects: certain long-horn beetles found in tropical regions measure up to six inches in length, whereas there are minute fungus beetles that are less than one fiftieth of an inch long. They abound everywhere but they do not, as a rule, attract much attention because of their dull colouring and their concealed ways. Many are of great economic importance.

The most striking characterisic of beetles as a group is the nature of their front wings. They aie horny or leathery, not used in flight, but serving as a protective cover for the second pair of wings and the soft back of the abdomen. These horny first pairs of wings are called elytra and the scientific name of beetles, *Coleoptera*, means horny-winged. The hind wings are membranous and, when not in use, are carried folded beneath the elytra. Many beetles have lost the power of flight and their second pairs of wings are much reduced or have disappeared completely, and the elytra are firmly joined together to form a strong covering for the abdomen. The mouthparts are adapted for biting. The life histories of different types of beetles are extremely varied but they all go through the four stages, egg, larva, pupa and adult: in other words, their metamorphosis is complete. The order is divided into a large number of families and only some of the most important can be dealt with here.

Tiger Beetles

Tiger beetles have been well named because they are among the fiercest and most voracious of all insects, both as larvae and as adults. The beetles have large prominent eyes, strong, sharp jaws and long legs and they can run rapidly over the ground. Most of them have wings and fly readily, but some have lost their second pair of membranous wings and are unable to fly. Many are brightly coloured and are active in the hot sunshine, but others are pale yellow or white and are found on the seashore and on sand-dunes, while still others are black or dark brown and nocturnal in their habits.

One of the commonest of our tiger beetles, *Cicindela lurida*, is a handsome insect, brown with a sheen like bronze and with curved yellow markings on its wing-cases; it is about five-eighths of an inch long. The underside of the body is metallic blue and green and its long legs bristle with stiff white hairs. The male and female are alike, except that she has six segments to her abdomen, whereas he has seven. She has a brown, tubular ovipositor hidden in her tail by means of which she places her eggs in the soil.

These beetles revel in the hottest sunshine and retire to rest, creeping beneath a stone or burying themselves in the sand, before the

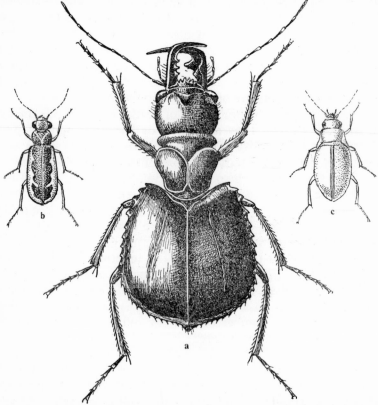

FIG. 99—Tiger Beetles: (a) *Mantichora ferox;* (b) *Cicindela marginella;* (c) *Platychile pallida.* All drawn to the same scale, twice natural size.

sun sets in the evening, and reappearing again next morning only after the sun is up and the sand is warm once more. They may be seen running about on open patches, along paths and on the banks of streams and vleis, at any time of the year. Their eyesight is keen and they take short flights if they are disturbed.

Small, neat round holes about the diameter of a lead pencil may be seen dotted about on the hard patches of sand that are the haunt

of the tiger beetles. If a slender grass stalk is pushed down one of these
holes in the ground it will be found that the tunnel goes straight down
into the soil to a depth of twelve inches or more. In order to see
something of the owner and maker of this dwelling, the observer must
sit down close to it and remain quite still for several minutes. After a
time a flat stopper appears at the mouth of the burrow, dark blue in
colour and fitting the hole perfectly. The slightest movement on the
part of the observer will cause the stopper to disappear immediately,
but if he catches and kills a fly and sticks it head downwards in the
hole, the fly will, after a short while, disappear down the hole.

The burrow belongs to the larva of the tiger beetle; it is a strange
white grub with a big, flat head, a creature as unlike its parents as it
well could be. The head and the hard first joint of the thorax form the
plug that closes the mouth of the burrow when the insect comes to the
surface. It has a pair of strong, curved jaws and four tiny eyes that
gleam like beads on each side of its head. The six legs are well developed
and it can crawl about on the ground quite nimbly if need be. On the
back of its wormlike body, on the fifth segment of the abdomen, there
is a curious hump with two curved hooks on it. This hump, with its
upward-pointing hooks, enables the larva to keep a grip on the side
of its tunnel and to move up and down it with astonishing speed.

Although the insect deepens and enlarges its tunnel from time to
time, you never see a heap of soil at the entrance, such as betrays the
work of so many burrowing insects. You will see, however, little
pellets of soil scattered about an inch or so from the hole. When the
insect is digging, it forms the pellets of soil with its jaws, puts them on
top of its head and carries them to the surface much in the same way
as a labourer carries up bricks on a hod. Arrived at the top, it gives
a jerk with its head and flings the pellets away, to return at once to
the bottom of the burrow to repeat the performance.

It lies for hours on end with its head plugging the entrance to its
home, staring at the sun and waiting with endless patience for some
insect to come blundering along within reach of those murderous jaws.
Then the head is thrown back with a jerk and the victim is seized and
dragged below to be devoured at the bottom of the burrow. The larva
may take a year or more to reach full size, its rate of growth depending
mainly on the number of victims that happen to fall into the trap. When
it is fully grown the larva makes a cell beside its tunnel, not too far
below the surface, and there it changes into a pupa. About a month
later the adult beetle emerges.

There are many different species of tiger beetles found in Africa
and all, as far as is known, have life histories similar to that described
above. The large black tiger beetles with wide abdomen and fearsome

looking jaws, *Mantichora* species, are well known in the Karoo and drier parts of the country. Although swift runners, they are wingless and cannot fly. They can inflict a severe bite if handled carelessly. The jaws of the males are exceptionally large and it is believed they use them for holding the females when mating.

Very different from the giant *Mantichora* is the little seashore tiger beetle, *Platychile pallida*, only half an inch long, very pale yellow, smooth and shining. This little beetle hides during the day in a burrow in the sand on the seashore and comes out at night to hunt for food. It is a pugnacious little creature and will attempt to bite fiercely if picked up. The tiger beetles which are so common everywhere and which are mostly bronze with yellow markings belong to the large genus *Cicindela*, and the whole family is known as the *Cicindelidae*.

Ground Beetles

The ground beetles, *Carabidae*, form a very large and important family of nearly twenty thousand species distributed all over the world. They are very well represented in Africa, with over nine hundred species recorded from South Africa alone. The most striking members of the group are the large black ground beetles, from one to two inches in length, many of them with white spots and bands on their wing-cases. They may be seen running about swiftly during the day and are found from the Cape to the Mediterranean. Although they are common and

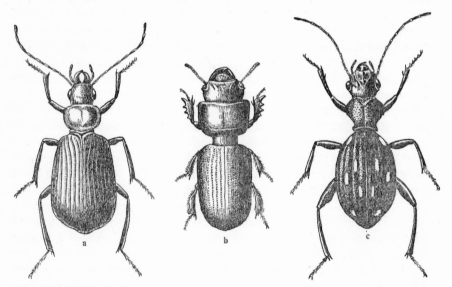

FIG. 100—Ground Beetles, *Carabidae:* (a) *Calosoma planicolle;* (b) *Passalidiusfortipes;* (c) *Anthia decemguttata.* All drawn to the same scale, twice natural size.

well known, they seem to have no popular name; most of them belong to the genus *Anthia*, and it will therefore, be convenient to speak of them as Anthia beetles.

Like all the other members of this large family, they are carnivorous and have strong, sharp jaws with which they can inflict a severe bite. Besides this, they can defend themselves by emitting a volatile, pungent fluid that discolours the human skin and, if it gets on a soft, tender spot, such as the eyes or the lips, may cause considerable pain. The Anthia beetles are fierce hunters, capturing their prey on foot: they cannot fly as their wing-cases are firmly joined together and the second pair of membranous wings beneath them have disappeared.

Bombardier beetles, *Brachinus* species, are smaller members of this family, mostly about half an inch long and red and black in colour. These interesting little beetles receive their popular name from their habit of emitting an evil-smelling, pungent, volatile fluid as a means of defence, like their larger relatives, the Anthia beetles. But in the case of the bombardier beetles the fluid, when ejected, rapidly volatilises into a gas which appears like a tiny jet of smoke from the tail end of the insect and the discharge is accompanied by an audible sound. Well known in Europe, there are also a number of species of these beetles widely distributed in Africa.

The calosoma beetles, *Calosoma* species, are striking members of this family, an inch to an inch and a half in length, greenish bronze or shiny black, and they may be seen running about on bushes and trees, hunting for the caterpillars that form their prey. The little omophron beetles, *Omophron* species, are quite different in appearance, although members of the same family. They are only about a quarter of an inch long, yellow and green, with stout, rounded bodies, and they are only found in the neighbourhood of water, where they hide themselves by burrowing in the sand. Certain species of ground beetles, such as *Rhopalomenus angusticollis*, about an inch long and black, seem to feed mainly on termites because they are generally found in or near the nests of these creatures. These, like other members of the family, can emit an offensive smell if they are irritated. Other ground beetles, such as *Passalidius fortipes*, live under stones and burrow in the ground and their front legs are obviously adapted for digging.

Little is known about the life histories of ground beetles found in this country, but they undoubtedly resemble their overseas relatives, and have active, predacious larvae. They should be found under stones, in vegetable debris, in decayed logs, and similar places and may be recognised by their sharp, sickle-shaped jaws, six legs and six simple eyes on each side of the head. At the end of the abdomen there is a pair of cerci and the tip is tubular.

Water Beetles

Shining black water beetles, *Cybister* species, are often attracted to lights at night for they are strong fliers and migrate from pond to pond under cover of darkness. If one of them strikes against the lamp and flops on to the table or floor, it can only writhe awkwardly because its legs are so modified for swimming that it walks clumsily and with difficulty. The hind legs are the principal swimming organs; they are flattened and the tibiae and tarsi are fringed with long, stiff, brown bristles. It uses these legs like oars and can 'feather' its oars on the return stroke much more neatly than any human oarsman. The tarsi are so jointed to the legs that they can turn on their long axis, so that,

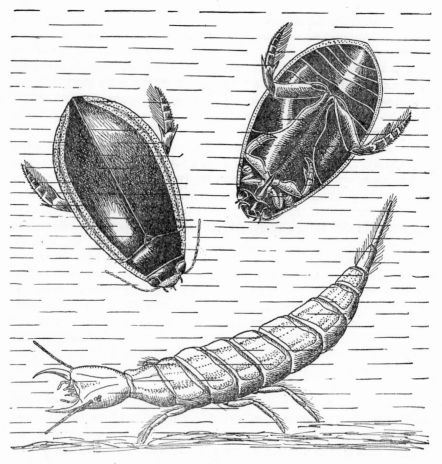

FIG. 101—The Common Water Beetle, *Cybister tripunctatus*. Adults, upper and under-side, above; larva below. The beetles are about an inch long.

when it kicks out backwards, the bristles stand out in a stiff array and offer the maximum resistance to the water. But when it draws its legs in for the next stroke, the tarsi turn so that the bristles lie flat and there is little to impede the forward momentum.

The body is flat and extraordinarily smooth. If one of these beetles is picked up it is liable to shoot from between the fingers like a wet orange pip. The head, thorax, abdomen and elytra are all streamlined, so that there are no angles or projections to obstruct the swift progress through the water. On the underside, just behind the bases of the second pair of legs, there is a strong, sharp spine that projects backwards. If the beetle is held tightly in the fingers it may try to wriggle its way out and the spine may pierce the skin and draw blood. While it is struggling to escape, the beetle also gives off a white fluid from the joint between the head and thorax and, if it is held close to the nose, it will be found to have a disgusting odour, worse than rotten eggs. Furthermore, the water beetle has two anal glands which secrete a fluid that smells like ammonia; this fluid can be discharged from the anus with a small explosion when the insect is irritated.

Although the water beetle spends most of its time in the water it is an air-breather. The two elytra fit tightly and closely over the back, enclosing a space between them and the back of the abdomen. The spiracles are situated in this space, along each side of the abdomen, and the last pair, at the hind end, are the largest. When the beetle wishes to renew its air supply it simply stops swimming and floats slowly to the surface, for its body is just a little lighter than water, and the hind end is lighter than the front, so it floats to the surface tail upwards. When the tip of the abdomen projects above the surface the air-supply between the elytra and abdomen is renewed and the beetle dives again.

The beetle is carnivorous, capturing and devouring other water insects, small worms, tadpoles, etc. It is long lived for an insect, as specimens have been kept alive in captivity for over a year. The male can be distinguished from the female by the swollen, circular pads on his front legs. These pads are armed with a number of tiny suckers connected with glands which give off a glutinous fluid that enables the male to cling to the smooth and slippery body of the female when mating.

The female lays her eggs singly in the stems of different kinds of water plants, making deep slits to receive them. The egg hatches in about three weeks and gives rise to a six-legged larva of a pale brown colour, armed with a pair of sharp, curved jaws. It is carnivorous, like its parents, and also an air-breather, rising to the surface at intervals and breathing through two spiracles at the tip of the tail.

The jaws each have a canal running through them that opens at the tip. Poison is injected into the victim through these canals, and, after the victim is dead, digestive juices from the stomach also pass through the canals into the dead body. Thus digestion takes place outside the body of the larva and the insect sucks in the dissolved tissues of its victim, leaving only the empty shell. The larva cannot chew and swallow in the ordinary way as its jaws are not adapted for chewing and its mouth is permanently closed. When it is fully grown the larva leaves the water and burrows into the wet soil beside the pond and there changes into a pupa.

The carnivorous water beetles form the family *Dytiscidae*, of which there are many species found in Africa. They are black, some with yellow margins to their elytra, very smooth and shining, and they range in size from about half an inch to one and a half inches in length.

Whirligig Beetles

Whirligig beetles may be seen gyrating on almost any pool at almost any time of the year. They are sometimes seen on still water, but they prefer pools in gently flowing streams because the current brings to them the dead or dying insects which have fallen into the water and which form their main food supply. If one stands beside a stream and watches the beetles as they glide ceaselessly over the surface they will be seen to swim towards and investigate every small object that comes floating past. If a fly or other insect is caught and killed and dropped into the water above them, the beetles will seize upon it as soon as it floats down to them and will tear it to pieces like a pack of miniature wolves, each swimming away with whatever portion it has managed to secure for itself. If one of their own

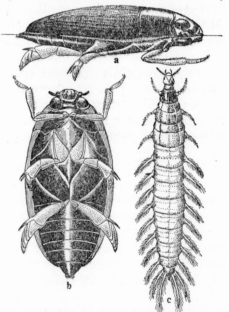

FIG. 102—The Whirligig Beetle, *Aulonogyra capensis:* (a) beetle seen from side, showing double eye; (b) underside of beetle; (c) larva.

band is caught and crushed and dropped among them they will devour it also.

When alarmed, the whirligigs speed up their gyrations until they can scarcely be followed with the eye. A repetition of the alarm will cause them to dive beneath the surface and to career wildly about below. Each one carries a bubble of air with it which looks like a silver ball on its tail, so that it can breathe for some time, even though completely submerged.

Like the *Dytiscidae*, whirligig beetles are wonderfully well adapted for their mode of life. They are streamlined and smooth, with the head sunk in the thorax so that there are no jutting angles or corners; the hind legs are fringed with bristles and make efficient oars. The middle legs are similar to the hind ones, but not so long or powerful, but the front legs are quite different and not used in swimming at all. They are long and armed with short sharp bristles and they serve as organs for grasping the prey. The beetle's antennae are also peculiar and modified for an aquatic life. The basal joint is broad and serves as a lid to close the cavity in which the antennae lie, thus keeping them dry although they are beneath the water.

But the most remarkable adaptation is found in the structure of its eyes. Each one is divided into halves and one half is on top of the head while the other is beneath. The whirligig, therefore, seems to have four eyes, two of which look upwards into the air and two which look downwards into the water. Thus it can keep a good look-out for enemies in both elements. Whirligigs taken from the water and placed on land can only flop about clumsily, but they are good fliers, although they cannot take off from the surface of the water or from flat ground. If it wishes to fly off in search of fresh hunting grounds, it must climb up on to the stem of a water-plant or the side of a stone and then, when it is well clear of the water it can stretch its wings and fly away.

The beetle usually utters a faint squeaking sound before taking to flight and it produces this noise by rubbing the hind edges of its elytra against the tip of its abdomen. If it is caught and handled roughly it gives off a white fluid from the joints of its thorax and this has an unpleasant odour, like cockroaches.

The female whirligig lays her elongate, oval eggs in a row upon the leaves of water-plants. The larva is a slender creature that looks something like a small centipede at first sight. It has a small head, six long legs and a pair of feathery gills on each segment of the abdomen, with two pairs on the last segment, making ten pairs in all. The larva creeps on the bottom of the pool and feeds on any small creatures it can capture. According to observations made in Europe, the full-grown larva spins a silken cocoon, grey in colour and pointed at each end. It is so well hidden among water-weeds or stones that it is seldom found.

A number of different species of whirligig beetles are found in

Africa and they all, as far as is known, have similar habits and life histories. They form the family known as the *Gyrinidae*, all very uniform in appearance, being ovoid or elliptical, more or less flattened, smooth shining black or bronzy-brown.

Ants' Guests

The small beetles belonging to the family *Paussidae* are among the most remarkable of them all. The largest are not quite half an inch in length and most of them are only a quarter of an inch or less. They are never found running about in the open but only in ants' nests, or when flying at night. In the great majority of species the antennae are of extraordinary shape, with the terminal joints fused together to form a curiously shaped club. When irritated, the beetles can eject a volatile, caustic fluid explosively from the anus, like the bombardier beetles described above.

These beetles are tolerated guests inside ants' nests and it is believed that the ants get from them an aromatic secretion of which they are very fond. The glandular tissue that produces the secretion is lodged in the enlarged antennae, the head, thorax and apex of the abdomen. There are tufts of yellow hairs and groups of pores that mark the glands and these are licked by the ants. When some of

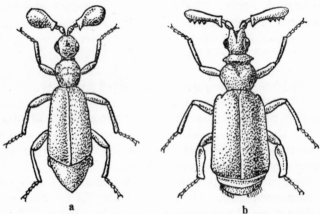

a   b

FIG. 103—Two Paussid Beetles found in Ants' Nests: (a) *Paussus arduus;* (b) *Paussus barberi*. The beetles are about a quarter of an inch long and brown in colour.

these beetles are kept in an artificial ants' nest they remain motionless most of the time and seem to be asleep and the ants ignore them. Occasionally, however, the ants will drag them about, usually seizing them by the antennae. It is said that the beetles feed on the eggs and larvae of the ants. There are three hundred species of *Paussidae* known and a number of these are recorded from Africa.

Rove Beetles

The rove beetles, *Staphylinidae*, may be recognised by their short elytra that cover only the front portion of the abdomen. The second pair of membranous wings are large and well developed and, therefore, have to be folded in a complex manner to get them under the first pair when not in use. If a rove beetle is watched just after it alights it will be seen that it moves its abdomen in a peculiar way and the membranous wings fold up and disappear beneath the elytra in a remarkable manner—but the beetle does not use the tip of its abdomen to assist in this process, as was formerly believed.

Most rove beetles are very small and they are usually found in decaying organic matter, including dung and dead animals. Many of them are predacious and feed on any small creatures they can capture.

About three hundred species are known which are found only in the nests of ants and termites. One of the most remarkable of these is *Paracorotoca akermani*, a small rove beetle, only about an eighth of an inch long, yellow in colour, with its swollen abdomen carried curled up over its back and resting on the short elytra that are specially modified to support it. This beetle is found in the mounds of the fungus-growing termite, *Eutermes natalensis*; it is not common, as a prolonged search carried out some years ago revealed only fourteen specimens in four hundred nests. It is not known how the beetles spread from one mound to another as they cannot fly and soon die if removed from the shelter of the termites' nest. The beetle has curious thin-walled swellings on its body, one just behind its head, two at the back of the thorax and one on each side of the abdomen. It is believed that an exudation is given off from these swellings which the termites lick up greedily and for the sake of which they tolerate the presence of the beetles in their nests. The beetles

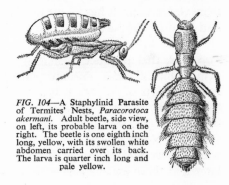

FIG. 104—A Staphylinid Parasite of Termites' Nests, *Paracorotoca akermani*. Adult beetle, side view, on left, its probable larva on the right. The beetle is one eighth inch long, yellow, with its swollen white abdomen carried over its back. The larva is quarter inch long and pale yellow.

have sharp, well developed jaws and it is thought that they feed on young termites; the beetle larvae that have been found in the nests and that are almost certainly those of the rove beetles are also considered to be predacious and to feed on young termites.

Although the beetles, like the termites, live in perpetual darkness, they have well developed eyes. They are quite active and run about among their hosts and, when disturbed, jerk their bodies to and fro, just as the termites do. The swollen abdomen is filled with stored fat and with the large reproductive organs. The female produces only a few large eggs and it is thought these hatch inside her body. Owing

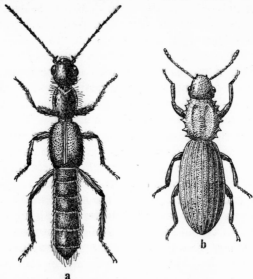

a

FIG.105—(a) The Blistering Rove Beetle, *Poederus sabaeus*. It is about three-eighths inch long and black (*Staphylinidae*). (b) The Saw-toothed Grain Beetle, *Orzaephilus surinamensis*. It is one sixth inch long and brown in colour (*Cucujidae*).

to the difficulty of keeping the beetles and the termites alive when taken from the mound, it has so far not been possible to study the life history and habits of these strange insects in any detail.

There are certain species of rove beetles, belonging to the genus *Paederus*, that produce blisters if they are crushed against the human skin. One of these, *Paederus sabaeus*, is widely spread and common in many parts of Africa. It is a small black beetle that is often attracted to lights at night and it might be mistaken for a flying ant. Should one of these alight on a person and then get crushed and rubbed into the skin, the blood and juices, entering tiny scratches made by the hard wing covers and chitin of the insect, cause blisters to form two days later and these leave a scar after they heal.

The Cadelle

The cadelle, *Tenebrioides mauritanicus*, is a small black beetle, about a third of an inch long, which is found in mills, storehouses, shops and dwellings, and in other places where human food-stuffs are stored. It has been spread all over the world by man's commerce and is well known in Africa. Such things as wheat, maize, oats, biscuits, nuts, dried fruits and nutmegs may be infested and severely damaged by this pest.

IV. MIMICRY AMONG BUTTERFLIES. 1. The Mocker Swallowtail, *Papilio dardanus*, male. 5. The Citrus Swallowtail, *Papilio demodocus;* the male and female are alike, except that the yellow spots in the male are often deeper in colour than in the female. Nos. 2 to 4, The Mocker Swallowtail, female; 2. form *hippocoonoides*, mimicking the Friar *Amauris naivius*, race *dominicanus*, No. 6; 3. form *cenea*, mimicking the Layman, *Amauris albimaculata*, No. 7; 4. form *trophonius*, mimicking the African Monarch, *Danaus chrysippus*, No. 8.

The female lays her eggs in batches of about twenty on the stored product and she may lay 1,000 or more eggs before she dies. These hatch in one to three weeks, according to the temperature. The larvae take two or three months to reach full size and they moult three or four times in the process. They are then nearly three-quarters of an inch long, white, with a black head and with two strong blunt processes on the hind end of the body. They burrow into wood or cork or any other suitable material they can find that will give them shelter whilst they pupate. The adult beetles emerge from the pupae in about a fortnight. Generally eggs, larvae, pupae and adults may be found in infested stores at the same time, as the generations overlap.

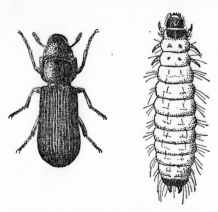

FIG. 106—The Cadelle, *Tenebrioides mauritanicus.* Adult on left, larva on right. The beetle is black and about one third inch long.

The cadelle belongs to the family *Trogostidae*, the members of which are mostly small and dark in colour. Several species are found in decaying logs and others in fungi.

Dried Fruit Beetles

The dried fruit beetle, *Carpophilus hemipterus*, is only about an eighth of an inch long, and is black, with light brown patches on its elytra. The elytra are short and leave the last two segments of the abdomen exposed. The female lays her eggs on ripe fruit whilst still on the trees, or inside the fruit if it is damaged and she can get inside. She will also deposit her eggs on fruit drying in the sun, or on dried fruit in packing sheds and storerooms. The larvae feed on the dried fruit and are about a quarter of an inch long when fully grown, creamy white, with the head and hind end

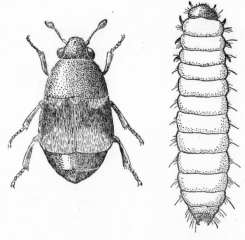

FIG. 107—The Dried Fruit Beetle, *Carpophilus hemipterus*. Adult on left, larva on right. The beetle is only about one eighth inch long, black with brown markings on elytra.

AA

of the abdomen dark brown. They take about a month to reach full size and the pupal stage lasts a fortnight. There are several generations a year. A few of these grubs inside a box of dried fruit will quickly ruin it because of the unsightly appearance caused by the presence of excreta, larval and pupal skins and tunnels in the fruit.

There are several species of small beetles that attack dried fruit, all very similar to the one described above, and they belong to the family *Nitidulidae*. These are small squat beetles with clubbed antennae and many of them have short elytra that leave the last segments of the abdomen exposed. Many members of this family may be found in flowers; some are found in fungi and others in decaying animal matter.

The Saw-toothed Grain Beetle

The saw-toothed grain beetle, *Orzaephilus surinamensis*, is the commonest beetle found in grocers' stores, where it will attack almost anything that is edible, including grain, bran, flour, dried fruit, sweets and biscuits. It is a small beetle, only an eighth of an inch long, or a little more, brown in colour, with five or six toothlike projections on each side of the thorax that give it its common name (see fig. 105). The female lays her eggs in small batches, hiding them in cracks and crevices in the food-stuffs, or she may lay them singly in finely ground foods such as flour. The eggs hatch in three days if it is warm, or they may take a fortnight or longer in cooler conditions. The larvae are small, white and brown six-legged grubs which moult three or four times before they are fully grown, in about a month. Under African conditions these beetles breed all the year round and there are several generations a year.

The saw-toothed grain beetle belongs to a family of small beetles, *Cucujidae*, that are of diverse forms, but mostly with flattened bodies and with the terminal joints of the antennae enlarged. Some are found beneath the bark of trees and in the tunnels of wood-boring insects and a few, like the saw-toothed grain beetle, are pests of stored products.

Ladybirds

The lunate ladybird, *Chilomenes lunata*, is to be found in most gardens, on rose bushes and on other plants infested with aphids. Like the great majority of the family, *Coccinellidae*, this shiny red and black beetle is carnivorous and preys upon aphids. If one of them is caught and handled roughly a yellow fluid will be seen to ooze from between the joints of its legs. This fluid is extremely bitter and serves as a protection to the ladybird, making it unpalatable to birds, lizards, frogs and other insect-eaters. As it is distasteful it has no need to conceal itself and it is conspicuously marked and coloured as a warning.

The female lays her yellow, cigar-shaped eggs in clusters, generally on the underside of leaves, with twenty or thirty eggs in a cluster. They are usually to be found on plants that are infested with aphids, for the female herself feeds on the plant lice and she leaves her eggs

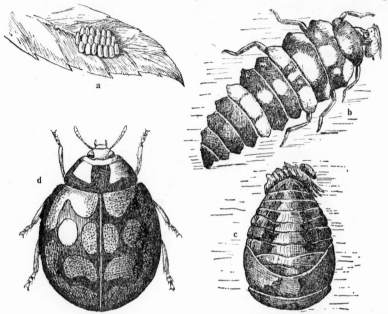

FIG. 108—The Lunate Ladybird, *Chilomenes lunata:*   (a) eggs; (b) larva; (c) pupa; (d) adult.

where the young, when they hatch, will not have far to search for their prey. The eggs hatch in about a fortnight into small black larvae with six legs and three simple eyes on each side of the head. They feed on the aphids, spearing them with their sharp, sickle-shaped jaws and sucking their juices. As the larva grows bigger it is marked with conspicuous spots of pale yellow on the black background. It casts its skin four times before it is fully grown, by which time it is about three-eighths of an inch in length.

The full-grown larva generally leaves the plant and seeks out a stone or wall where it fixes itself head downwards by means of a sticky secretion that oozes from its tail end. Then its body thickens and shortens and, after a few hours, the skin splits and reveals the yellow pupa inside. In about ten days the adult beetle emerges from the pupa. It is pale yellow at first but its colour slowly darkens to red, with crescent-shaped black markings that join end to end.

There are well over two thousand species of ladybirds known in the world and they are nearly all predacious and carnivorous, feeding as larvae and as adults on aphids, scale insects and mealie bugs and they are decidedly helpful in keeping these pests in check. The little Australian ladybird, *Novius cardinalis*, dark crimson in colour and marked with black, is well known because of the important part it has played in destroying the very harmful Australian bug, *Icerya purchasi*. Many years ago the citrus industry in California and South Africa was threatened with disaster owing to the rapid increase and spread of the Australian bug, a pest which it is very difficult to combat by means of sprays because of its protective coating of waxy threads. Then the little cardinal ladybird was discovered in Australia and sent to California. It thrived there and soon reduced the bugs to negligible proportions, as it feeds largely upon the eggs of the pest, tearing open the egg-bags of the females and devouring the contents. The cardinal ladybird was brought from California to South Africa and is now well established here, with the result

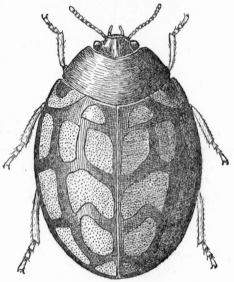

FIG. 109—The Large Vegetarian Ladybird,
Epilachna dregei

that the Australian bug is no longer a serious pest.

Other kinds of ladybirds have been introduced into Africa to help in the fight against such pests as mealie bugs. Although nearly all the members of this family are carnivorous and extremely useful insects, there are a few species, *Epilachna* species, that have taken to a vegetarian diet and that are minor pests of potatoes, maize, pumpkins and other plants. These vegetarian ladybirds may be recognised by the fact that they are not shiny, like the others, but dull, and they are red and black in colour.

The large vegetarian ladybird, *Epilachna dregei*, is one of the largest and broadest of the ladybirds and is widely spread in South Africa and the Rhodesias, where it is found feeding on the leaves of potatoes, pumpkins, turnips, beans and other plants. The adult is black with eight or ten buff spots. The eggs are laid in clusters on the underside of the leaves and the black, spiny larvae that develop from them eat holes in the foliage and are fully grown in about a month. They then pupate on the plants and the adults emerge a fortnight later.

There are two generations a year, the first adults that appear in the spring having hibernated; these give rise to the second generation, which makes its appearance in the middle of January.

Skin and Horn Beetles

The leather beetle, *Dermestes vulpinus*, is very common and widely spread as it has been carried all over the world by man's commerce. It is found in old bones, carcases, skins, hides, leather, dried

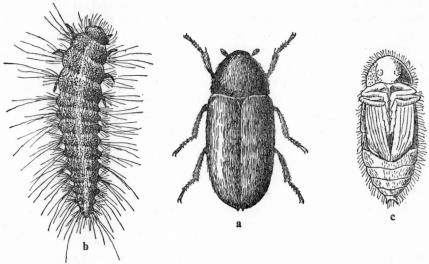

FIG. 110—The Leather Beetle, *Dermestes vulpinus:* (a) adult; (b) larva; (c) pupa. The beetle is about half an inch long.

fish, bacon and other goods. The beetle is black and about half an inch long and feeds on any dried meat or skin it can find. The female lays her oval, white eggs in small batches in cracks and crevices in the food material and these hatch in a few days into active larvae that are black and hairy. These grubs feed on the dry animal matter and moult six to ten times before they are fully grown in two or three months, when they are nearly three-quarters of an inch long.

The full-grown larva leaves its food and seeks out a place where it can pupate. It has the habit of boring into anything at hand to make a sheltered tunnel for itself: wood in badly infested store-rooms may therefore be severely damaged and the mortar between bricks may be honey-combed with the burrows, while cork is very attractive to them as a place for pupation. The pupa is enclosed in the last larval skin which forms a further protection for it and the adult emerges about ten days later.

The larder or bacon beetle, *Dermestes lardarius*, is very similar to the leather beetle but may easily be distinguished by the pale yellow band across the elytra, with six brown spots on it. This beetle is found infesting stored provisions such as bacon, ham, meats, cheese, skins and stuffed animals, dried fish and dog biscuits, and it has a life history similar to that described above.

Anybody who has formed a collection of insects is certain to have made the acquaintance of the destructive little museum beetle, *Anthrenus verbasci*. Sooner or later small heaps of brown dust begin to appear beneath the specimens in the store-boxes and, if nothing is done to check the damage, the whole collection is eventually reduced to an unsightly accumulation of dust and fragments of legs and wings. The museum beetle is a pretty little insect, about one tenth of an inch long, with a round, flattened body. It is black, but its body is covered with tiny scales that give it a marbled appearance, a mixture of grey, red and black. It can be seen in the store-boxes, among the ruined specimens, but it is also to be found out in the open, usually on yellow flowers of the *Compositae*, or daisy family.

When the female is ready to lay her eggs she seeks out any dried animal matter she can find and she is quickly attracted to any skins, insects or other museum specimens that have not been protected by some poison. She will, if she can, make her way through narrow cracks into the boxes and lay her eggs directly on the specimens. If she cannot get inside she will deposit her eggs in the crevices of the lid, or in some similar opening, and leave her young to find their own way inside when they hatch. Short of pasting paper all round to seal the lid it is almost impossible to keep the beetle or her grubs out of the store-boxes.

Apparently the adult beetle does not feed on the museum specimens itself; it flies to the window and makes its way outside and feeds on the pollen and nectar of flowers. Often, however, these beetles cannot get out of the boxes because the crevices through which they crept as newly-hatched larvae are too small to allow their escape. Under such circumstances they mate and lay their eggs without taking any food as adults.

The larva is a hairy grub, brown in colour, with six legs and a small black head. Its only food consists of the dried remains of insects and other specimens which may be years old and contain very little, if any, moisture. It is a mystery how the little creature obtains its essential water supply from the desiccated remains in the store-boxes. It has been suggested that it can manufacture its own water from the hydrogen and oxygen in its food. If this is so, the chemistry of its stomach is extraordinary and the little creature can do what few other living things can do.

The larvae are hardy little creatures and can survive long fasts; if all fails them, they can carry on for a time by devouring their own cast skins. Scarcely any form of dry animal matter comes amiss to them: horn, hair, feathers, skins, dried insects, all furnish them with food. When the larva is fully grown its skin splits down the back but the skin is not cast off; it is retained as a loose cover for the pupa lying face downward inside it. Eventually the adult emerges two or three weeks later.

The above beetles belong to the family known as the *Dermestidae*, all small or moderate sized and all feeding on such materials as furs, hides, wool, dried meats and other animal products. Their job in nature seems to be the completion of the useful work performed by such scavengers as flesh flies and carrion beetles. Dermestid beetles are not to be found in a carcase on the veld when it is swarming with maggots but, later on, when only a few dried shreds of flesh and hide are left clinging to the bones, these beetles turn up and polish off the remains.

Glow-worms and Fire-flies

The common fire-flies at the Cape, *Luciola capensis*, are small beetles, about a quarter of an inch long and dull brown in colour. Both the males and females are winged, but the males seem to be much commoner than their mates and their lights are brighter. The male fire-fly can easily be recognised by his enormous, spherical eyes, of a dark violet colour, which occupy almost the whole of his head and meet in the middle line. The eyes of the female are smaller and fairly widely separated. Apparently she does not flit about much, for, if a number of the insects are captured while they are flying in the evening, they will all be found to be males. Although the beetles each have a pair of sharp, curved jaws they do not seem to feed at all in the adult state.

The light-producing organ of the fire-fly is lodged on the underside of the abdomen, at the tip. If this part of the body is examined, it will be found that the last two segments are pale yellow in colour and of a peculiarly dense and smooth appearance. On this part of the body the outer integument is transparent and beneath it there is a layer of spherical masses of cells filled with a white substance. This layer is well supplied with tracheae and nerves. Behind this layer is a second layer of cells filled with tiny urate crystals; this layer serves as the reflector.

The light-producing substance is lodged in the spherical white cell-masses and is called luciferin. This is acted upon by a ferment contained in the insect's blood, called luciferase. Both these substances have been isolated, but nothing is known about their chemical composition. The light is due to the oxidation of the luciferin under the action of the luciferase and the process seems to be reversible—that is to say, the luciferin can be used over and over again.

The cold light of the fire-fly is very efficient. It contains no infrared or ultra-violet rays: all the rays are visible, and scarcely any of the energy is wasted in the production of useless heat. The insect seems to be able to switch the light on and off at will, the control apparently being effected by nervous regulation of the air-supply to the layer of white cells. If one of the beetles is crushed between the fingers, the white cells give off a greenish glow like phosphorus, and this slowly fades away.

Very little is known about the habits and life history of our fire-flies. It is probable that the female lays her eggs in the soil and among dead leaves where the bush is thick. These hatch out into larvae that look very much like tiny female glow-worms, flat, segmented, dark brown, with six legs and a tiny head. They are almost certain to be carnivorous, killing and devouring any small, soft-bodied creatures they can capture by means of their sharp, curved jaws. The larvae probably pupate in the soil and there is only one generation a year.

Female glow-worms, about an inch in length and dark brown or black, may be found in damp spots at almost any time during the summer. The winged males are very much like fire-flies but much bigger; their light-producing organs are poor, consisting only of two small spots on the tip of the tail. These brown beetles, with great black eyes bulging out beneath the head, are occasionally attracted to lights in the evening, but fire-flies never are.

While it is the male fire-fly which attracts attention with his flickering light as he flies about, it is the female glow-worm, with her steadily glowing lamp, that catches our eye among the weeds in a ditch or on a bank. Her light-producing organ is similar in structure and function to that of the fire-fly and it is situated on the same part of the body.

Glow-worms are carnivorous and seem to feed chiefly on snails and slugs. According to Fabre, the insect injects a poison through its mandibles and this substance serves a double purpose—it anaesthetises the prey and liquifies its tissues, forming a sort of dark-coloured broth which the beetle sucks up through its hollow mandibles. The adults take little or no food.

It is usually said that the luminescent organs of the glow-worms and fire-flies serve as signals for bringing the sexes together, but it is difficult to understand why the winged male in the one case and the wingless female in the other should be the ones with the bright lamps.

PLATE 45

(*a*) **A TORTOISE BEETLE.** Adult on left, larva on right and pupa above, all on leaf of food-plant

(*b*) Two pupae of the Tortoise Beetle, showing the two-pronged fork on hind end of abdomen

PLATE 46

(a) THE BROWN LONGHORN, *Delochilus prionides*

(b) THE BLUE LONGHORN, *Promeces longipes*, often wrongly called "Spanish Fly"

The larvae and even the eggs also give off a feeble glow and the light in their case certainly cannot serve as a sexual attraction.

There are about two thousand different species of glow-worms and fire-flies known in the world and they belong to the large family of beetles called *Cantharidae* (or *Telephoridae* or *Malacodermidae* by some authors). They are all soft-bodied, rather elongate beetles and all are predacious. Many of them do not possess light-producing organs and they are diurnal, being found on flowers and foliage. Their larvae are generally found in soil, amid dead leaves and under bark; they look like small female glow-worms and they are also predacious.

Death Watch Beetles

The common furniture beetle, *Anobium punctatum*, is a native of Europe but it has been spread all over the world and is now common

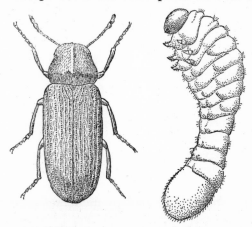

in many parts of Africa, particularly in the coastal areas. It attacks old seasoned timber and may do serious damage to furniture and fittings in houses. This beetle and a closely allied species are often called death watch beetles because of the ticking sound they make in their burrows during the mating season. The tapping noise is thought to be a sexual call and is made by the beetle jerking its body forward several times in rapid succession, each time striking the lower

FIG. 111—The Common Furniture Beetle, *Anobium punctatum*. Adult on left, larva on right. The beetle is reddish brown and about one fifth inch long.

part of the front of the head against the surface upon which it is standing.

The furniture beetle is about a fifth of an inch long, brown in colour, with the prothorax ridged along the middle and forming a hoodlike covering over the head in front. It may be seen in the neighbourhood of infested timber at almost any time in the spring and summer, is active at night, and is a strong flier. It can therefore easily make its way to other buildings to spread the infestation.

The female lays her eggs in cracks and crevices in the woodwork, thrusting them into postion with her ovipositor which can extend to more than half the length of her body. The eggs hatch in three to four

BB

weeks into tiny white grubs that tunnel into the wood. They grow slowly, feeding on the wood, and under favourable conditions may take eight or nine months to reach full size, although if the wood is very old and dry they may take two years to reach maturity. The full-grown larva is about a quarter of an inch long and is curved and has the front part of the body somewhat swollen.

It now directs its tunnel towards the surface of the wood and hollows out a chamber just below the surface in which it changes into a pupa. Three or four weeks later the adult emerges and bites a neat round hole about a twelfth of an inch in diameter to make its way to the exterior. The holes made by the adults and the small heaps of dust that fall from these holes are the first signs that the wood is infested. If they are not checked the beetles may continue breeding in a piece of furniture for years until it is completely spoiled.

The furniture beetle belongs to the family *Anobiidae*, small beetles many of which are destructive to wood and to various kinds of stored products. The bark anobiid, *Ernobius mollis*, is another member of this family which is a native of Europe that found its way to South Africa in infested packing cases a few years ago. It is now well estab-lished and attacks unbarked coniferous timber. The biscuit beetle, *Sitodrepa panicea*, is another member of the same family, a small reddish brown beetle about one sixth of an inch long, which attacks biscuits, leather and drugs and which is widely spread in Africa, as is the cigarette beetle, *Lasioderma serricorne*, which feeds on dried vegetable products, including tobacco, ginger, rice, figs, and pepper.

Shot-hole Borers

The shot-hole borers, *Bostrichidae*, are small or moderate sized beetles, ranging from one eighth to one inch in length and brown or black in colour, which attack felled timber or dried wood and also standing trees. They are cylindrical in shape and their hood-shaped thorax projects over the head. The horned shot-hole borer, *Bostry-choplites cornutus*, is a common and widely spread member of this family. It is about half an inch long, dark brown, and has the front angles of the prothorax projecting like two stout horns. It attacks bamboo and eucalyptus logs and poles, but very little is known about its life history. Like other members of the family, it is active at night and is a strong flier.

The bamboo borer, *Dinoderus minutus*, is one of the smallest of the shot-hole borers, measuring only about an eighth of an inch in length and it also is dark brown. This insect is a native of the Far East but has been distributed widely through the world in infested bamboo and cane and is prevalent in many parts of Africa where it does considerable damage to bamboo, cane chairs and wicker-work. The beetle bores into cut bamboo at any spot where the hard outer rind has been injured and makes a tunnel in which mating takes place and inside which the tiny white eggs are laid. On hatching, the larvae burrow up and down the wall of the bamboo and their tunnels become packed behind them with a fine dust consisting of inedible fragments and excrement. When fully grown the larva is yellowish white, about an eighth of an inch long, curved and with a swollen thorax. It pupates in a chamber it hollows out at the end of its tunnel and a week or so later the adult beetle emerges, biting its way out of the bamboo

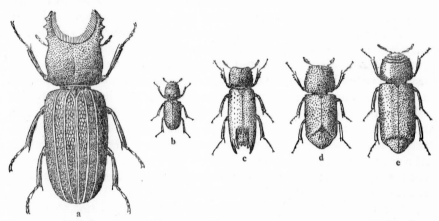

FIG. 112—Shot-hole Borers, *Bostrichidae:* (a) *Bostrichoplites cornutus;* (b) *Dinoderus minutus;* (c) *Xylion adustus;* (d) *Sinoxylon transvaalense;* (e) *Xyloperthodes nitidipennis.* All drawn to the same scale and about four times natural size.

through a neat, round hole. There are three or four generations of these beetles a year and they can, therefore, increase rapidly in numbers and do much damage.

The Acacia shot-hole borer, *Sinoxylon transvaalense,* is common throughout Africa south of the equator and infests the wood of trees and shrubs belonging to the *Leguminosae,* as well as a wide range of other timbers. It is about a quarter of an inch long, black, and has a pair of spines near the hind end of its elytra. A pair of these beetles burrows into the wood for the purpose of mating and egg-laying. The tunnel runs in for a short distance at right angles to the surface and then turns and runs parallel with the grain of the wood. This tunnel is kept scrupulously clean and the beetles remain in it for some time, apparently to guard the eggs and the newly-hatched young from parasites and other enemies. The larvae burrow and feed and pupate in the usual manner and there may be two or three generations a year.

There are many species of shot-hole borers native to Africa, ranging in size from very small to an inch or more in length, and all have the swollen prothorax that overhangs and conceals the small head when viewed from above. Their antennae end in a three-jointed club. They are all borers in wood. Some of them show the beginnings of a crude sort of social life because they are gregarious in their habits and the males help the females in boring the first tunnel for the egg-laying.

Powder Post Beetles

The powder-post beetle, *Lyctus brunneus*, is very common and widely spread and is responsible for a great deal of damage to timber in buildings. It is small, only about one eighth to one sixth of an inch in length, with a narrow body of dark reddish-brown colour. It has a well developed pair of wings beneath its elytra and can fly quite readily; it is active at night and sometimes attracted to lights. The female deposits her long, narrow eggs in pores in the wood, generally at the ends where it is sawn. She will not lay on surfaces that are polished or protected by paint. Limba, wattle, oak, marula, kiaat, eucalyptus and many other kinds of wood are liable to attack if they contain sapwood—that is to say, wood from the outer part of the tree which contains sugar and starch; the beetle cannot develop in heartwood cut from the inner part of the trunk. Stinkwood is also occasionally attacked if it includes sapwood.

The egg hatches in two or three weeks and gives rise to a tiny white larva that tunnels in the wood, feeding as it goes. It reduces the wood to a fine powder which is tightly packed in the tunnel behind it. There must be starch and a certain amount of moisture in the wood, which is why hard, dry heartwood is left severely alone by these beetles. Under normal conditions it takes about ten months for the larva to reach full size. This period may be shortened if the infested wood is kept in a warm room and if there is more than the usual amount of food material present in the timber. Similarly, it may be considerably lengthened if the temperature is low, the wood is very dry and there is little nourishment in it.

The fully grown larva is only about a fifth of an inch long, slightly curved and with the front end of the body thicker than the hind end. It now bores its way up towards the surface of the wood, stopping only when there is a thin layer between it and the outer air. Here it hollows out a small chamber in which it changes into a pupa and about a month later the adult beetle is ready to emerge. If the weather is warm the beetle will soon cut its way to the surface, making a small round hole about the size of the letter 'o' in this type and leaving a small tell-tale heap of sawdust on the floor beneath the hole. But if the weather is cold and the room unheated the beetle may lie motionless in its cell for weeks before emerging. Ordinarily, the complete life cycle takes from nine to twelve months, but under favourable conditions this period may be shortened to seven or eight months, and if conditions are unfavourable the beetle may take two or even three years to reach maturity.

A few beetles in a piece of timber will do little damage, but if they are allowed to breed unchecked they will eventually reduce the sapwood to a hollow shell of powder, with the surface riddled with holes. Only the wood of broad-leaved trees appears to be attacked; they are never found in coniferous timber.

The powder-post beetles belong to a small family of wood-boring beetles known as *Lyctidae*.

Buprestid Beetles

The *Buprestidae* form a large family of wood-boring beetles many of which are conspicuous with brilliant metallic colouring, bronze, blue, green, gold and other colours. They are mostly found in forests and are active during the day, readily taking to wing and flying strongly from one tree to another. They are elongate beetles, tapering to a blunt point at the hind end of the body and they range in size from quite small insects to large and showy species over an inch in length. These beetles do not attack dead wood, as a rule, but the females lay their eggs in cracks and crevices of the bark of standing trees and bushes.

The eggs hatch into larvae that may be recognised by their shape: the prothorax is flat and much broader than the rest of the body. They are sometimes spoken of as flat-headed borers, but this is a misnomer because the head is small and it is the prothorax that is broad and flat. These borers gnaw wide flattened galleries just beneath the bark, destroying the thin growing layer between the bark and the wood, called the cambium, and thereby doing considerable harm to the infested plant. They have no legs but the distended front portion of the body enables them to get a firm hold in their tunnels as they gnaw their way forward.

Click Beetles

Click beetles, *Elateridae*, are elongate insects, mostly of sombre black or brown, but a few are red or have metallic colours. If one of these beetles is placed on its back it will "sham dead" for a time and then, with a slight clicking sound, will leap into the air and probably right itself and run off. The prothorax of the click beetle is jointed with the rest of the body so that it can move freely but, when it is on its back, the two parts are held rigid, with the body slightly arched. There is a hard pointed projection on the underside of the prothorax that fits into a notch between the bases of the second pair of legs. This projection apparently presses down hard on the notch and suddenly slips out into the cavity below, causing the insect to jerk itself into the

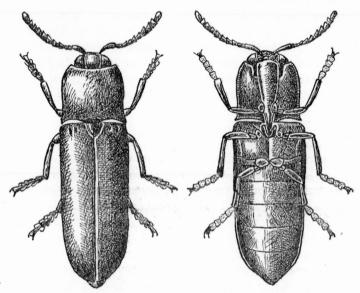

FIG. 113—The Large Click Beetle, *Tetralobus rotundiformis*.   Upper and under side.
It is nearly two inches long and black.

air. It is difficult to understand exactly how this action is brought about and it seems strange that the body of the beetle should be so considerably modified for a purpose that is apparently of little value. Some click beetles can leap quite well, others feebly and some not at all.

The larvae of click beetles are found in decaying wood or in the soil. The smooth shining yellow grubs, with tough skins, that are found in the soil feeding on the crowns and lower parts of the stems of wild and cultivated plants and that are popularly known as 'wireworms' are the larvae of click beetles. These insects do little harm in the veld but when the ground is ploughed and crops are planted they may, for a time, do much damage to wheat, potatoes, tomatoes and other crops. They do not thrive in ground that is continuously cultivated and they usually disappear after the first few seasons of abundance. The larvae are slow-growing and may take three or four years to reach full size.

Meal Worms

Meal worms are the larvae of two species of beetles, *Tenebrio molitor* and *Tenebrio obscurus*, which are reared as food for small animals kept as pets and in zoological gardens. These two beetles have been spread all over the world and they are established in Africa, where they may be found doing damage to stored grains, flour and other food stuffs. The beetles are half to three quarters of an inch in length and are dark brown or black and usually occur in dark, moist places, in neglected corners of stores and mills where sweepings and refuse have been allowed to accumulate. The white, oval eggs are laid singly or in small batches in the food and they hatch in about a fortnight into elongate, yellow larvae with six legs. These insects are omnivorous and, besides feeding on flour and bran, will eat meat, dead insects and even

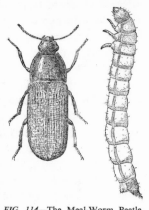

FIG. 114—The Meal-Worm Beetle, *Tenebrio molitor,* and larva. The beetle is five-eighths inches long and dark brown. (*Tenebrionidae*).

feathers. Naturalists who rear them in bran as food for their pets give them bits of vegetable leaves occasionally and they also add a few drops of water from time to time, as the larvae do not flourish in dry food; on the other hand, the food must not be too moist, as moulds develop that harm the beetle grubs.

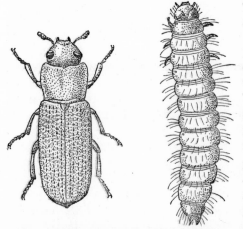

FIG. 115—The Confused Flour Beetle, *Tribolium confusum.* Adult on left, larva on right. The beetle is one-fifth inch long and reddish-brown.

These beetles belong to the very large family, *Tenebrionidae*, of which more than ten thousand species are known. The adults differ widely in size, form and appearance, but their larvae are all very much like the meal worms. Many are ground beetles, brown or black, and unable to fly because their second pair of wings are vestigial. Many species are found in Africa and they occur in all sorts of places, from the wet tropical forests to the dry, sandy deserts.

Perhaps the best known of them are the large black or brown toktokkies, *Psammodes* species, that are widely spread throughout our country.

These are heavy-bodied, wingless beetles that derive their common name from their habit of knocking on the ground at intervals, apparently in order to attract the opposite sex. The tapping noise is made by raising the abdomen and bringing it down on the ground several times in quick succession. The long, smooth, yellow larvae of these beetles live in the soil and feed on the roots of grasses and other plants. Occasionally they occur in numbers in fields of wheat, oats, barley and maize and may do considerable damage to the young plants.

The confused flour beetle, *Tribolium confusum*, is another member of this family that is a pest of stored cereals and products made from them. It is reddish brown and slightly less than a quarter of an inch in length. It has been spread all over the world and is the commonest beetle found in bran, flour, rice, ground-nuts, and other stored products. Its life history is similar to that of the meal worms and there may be five generations a year. It can, therefore, increase rapidly in numbers if it once infests a store or pantry.

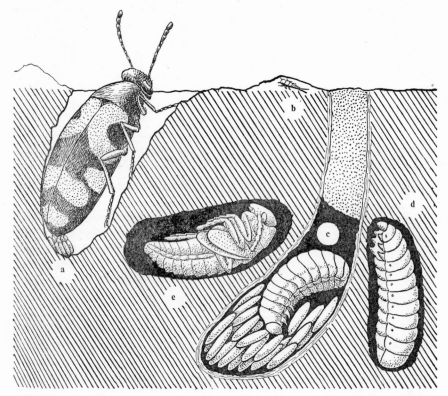

FIG. 116—Life History of a C. M. R. Beetle: (a) female laying eggs; (b) newly hatched larva, or triungulin; (c) larva feeding on grasshopper's eggs; (d) resting stage; (e) pupa.

PLATE 47

(*a*) Larva of the Brown Longhorn, *Delochilus prionides*

(*b*) THE EUCALPYTUS BORER, *Phorocantha semipunctata*. It is about three quarters of an inch long.

PLATE 48

(a) THE RED AND BLACK LONGHORN, *Ceroplesis aethiops*

(b) THE BULB WEEVIL, *Brachycerus obesus*

Blister Beetles

Blister beetles, *Mylabris* species, are very common throughout Africa and are of considerable interest because they do good at one stage of their career and harm at another, and because their bodies contain a powerful drug known as cantharidin. There are many different species of them and they range in size from about three-quarters of an inch to nearly two inches. Most of them are black and yellow in colour, some are black and red and others are all black. The colours of the former Cape Mounted Rifles were black and yellow, so these insects are sometimes called C. M. R. beetles. They belong to the interesting family *Meloidae* (or *Cantharidae*), which includes the oil beetles as well as the blister beetles.

These beetles are found on flowers throughout the summer months, especially on plants of the pea and bean family. They eat the petals and often do harm to crops of peas and beans because they destroy the flowers and thus prevent the formation of pods. They walk about and fly slowly and deliberately, as though they do not fear pursuit, because of the poisonous substance in their blood, cantharidin, which protects them from insect-eating enemies, such as birds and lizards. Their striking colours warn their enemies to leave them alone. Cantharidin is used to a limited extent in medicine in cases where it is necessary to blister the skin. It is also used in a very dilute form in certain hair tonics because it is supposed to help to prevent baldness, but it is doubtful whether it has any such effect. This drug has long had a reputation as an aphrodisiac, but it is extremely poisonous and may cause serious illness or death. It can be extracted from the beetles by soaking a number of them in alcohol or chloroform for some time and then allowing the liquid to evaporate.

The female beetle lays her eggs in the ground. Although she is ill-fitted for the task, she labours prodigiously for half an hour or more to dig a hole about an inch deep in hard soil, using her slender legs and jaws as tools. Then she turns round and backs into the hole and deposits in it some twenty or thirty fairly large eggs, oval and white. Then she comes out of the hole and fills it in by raking the loose soil back into it and stamping it down with her feet. After this she goes off to repeat the process somewhere else a day or so later, and she continues to lay batches of eggs until her ovaries are exhausted, and then she dies.

The eggs hatch in three or four weeks into tiny, active creatures about as long as the letter 'i' in this type, white, with a large head, six legs and two stiff bristles on the tail. The newly-hatched larvae look very much like small lice as they run about over the hot ground, seeking for spots where grasshoppers and locusts have laid their eggs.

CC

Many of them die because they fail to find such spots.

The newly-hatched larva of the blister beetle must find an egg-pod of a locust or grasshopper within a few hours of its birth, otherwise it dies of exhaustion and hunger. By some mysterious means or other, perhaps by a keen sense of smell, it will find the eggs if it is anywhere near them and it will bore down into the soil to reach them. When it is lodged safely inside the pod it casts its skin and becomes a fat, white maggot with very short legs, quite a different creature from what was first hatched. It no longer needs to run about, and for the rest of its career as a larva it is very sluggish. It feeds on the eggs and grows rapidly. Towards the end of summer it burrows into the ground beside the pod and changes its form again. It now becomes what is known as a false pupa, a resting stage in which it passes the winter months. Its skin is tough and white and it has very short legs; it cannot move about, but it is not yet a true pupa.

When the warm weather arrives again in September it casts its skin once more and enters the next stage of its career as a larva. It may now enter the egg-pod again and feed on any eggs that are left in it, or it may, after a short period, change into a pupa without taking any more food. At first the pupa is white but slowly it darkens in colour and finally, after three or four weeks, the skin is cast for the last time and the adult emerges. It rests for a time in its cell under-ground until its skin hardens and then it makes its way to the surface, to feed on flowers, to lay its eggs and to die.

The oil beetles are stout-bodied insects with short elytra and they cannot fly because they have lost their second pair of wings. They are black or dark blue and from half to three-quarters of an inch in length. When seized they exude through the joints of the legs a yellow fluid which contains cantharidin and it is from this habit that they receive their popular name. These beetles are not common but are widely spread and may occasionally be seen on the veld and on flowers during the summer months. They belong to the genus *Meloë* and nothing is known of their life history in this country, but closely allied species overseas are known to be parasitic on certain kinds of solitary bees. The female lays a large number of eggs and these hatch into tiny active creatures similar to those described above and called triungulins. They creep up on to the flowers and there await the arrival of the bees, to which they cling and are then carried to the bees' nests. Large numbers of them perish because they fail to find a suitable host, but a triungulin that succeeds in getting into a cell in the bee's nest leaves the bee and devours first the egg and then the store of honey and pollen provided by the bee for its young. The larva goes through similar changes of form to those already described for the C. M. R. beetles.

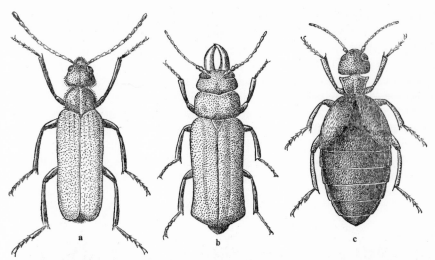

FIG. 117—The Oil Beetle Family, *Meloidae:* (a) *Cantharis pallidipennis*, black with yellowish-red elytra; (b) *Synhoria hottentota*, red in colour; (c) *Meloë angulatus*, black. All are about one inch long.

The beetles of the genus *Cantharis* (of which the "Spanish fly" of southern Europe is a well-known example) are also well represented in Africa and they are all apparently parasitic in their immature stages, although nothing is known of their life history here. The brick-red beetles, *Synhoria hottentota* and *Synhoria rhodesiana*, are also members of this family which should prove to have a very interesting life history when it is known. These beetles, about an inch long, are only found in the nests of carpenter bees and nobody knows at present what is the relationship between the beetles and their hosts.

Pea and Bean Weevils

The small weevils which infest peas and beans belong to the family *Bruchidae* and are very well represented in Africa. Besides some half a dozen species which have been introduced from overseas and which are pests of various kinds of peas, cowpeas and beans, there are many species which breed in the seeds of thorn-trees and other leguminous plants. They can be obtained in numbers simply by collecting the ripe seeds of these plants and keeping them in receptacles until the beetles emerge.

The pea weevil, *Bruchus pisorum*, is common and troublesome along the south coast but does not seem to have made its way inland to any extent. The adults appear in spring, just when the young pods are forming on the pea plants, and the females lay their elongate yellow eggs on the outside of the pods, gluing them singly in position by a gummy fluid that exudes with the egg. The young larva, on hatching,

burrows into the pod and enters one of the developing peas. Often
two or three larvae may enter one seed, but there is only enough food
in the seed to bring one of them to maturity. After a time one of the
larvae gets ahead of the others, it grows faster, and for some unknown
reason the others stop feeding and die, leaving the field clear for the
survivor. If they all went on feeding inside the pea, eventually they
would all die because of insufficient food, but invariably only one
larva carries on after the first few days and it is not known what
causes the premature death of the others.

By the time the peas are ripe the larva has reached a length of
about one-sixteenth of an inch and is a fat white grub with very short,

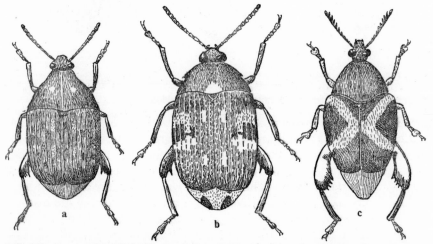

FIG. 118—Pea and Bean Weevils, *Bruchidae:* (a) the bean weevil, *Acanthoscelides obtectus;*
(b) the pea weevil, *Bruchus pisorum;* (c) the cross-bearing bruchid, *Caryopemon crucifer.*

useless legs. It continues to feed and grow inside the ripe, stored pea
and is fully grown at the end of three months. It pupates inside the
cell it has hollowed out for itself inside the pea and about three weeks
later the adult beetle emerges. But it does not leave the cell; it remains
dormant inside its snug retreat until the following spring. Thus there
is only one generation of these beetles a year and they attack only
young green peas developing on the plants in spring. They do not
breed in dry peas.

The bean weevil, *Acanthoscelides obtectus,* is commoner, more
widely spread and more destructive than the pea weevil. This small
brown beetle, less than one-eighth of an inch long, does not attack the
green bean pods, but the female waits until the pods are ripe and have
partially split open. Then she creeps inside and lays her elongate, oval
white eggs loosely inside the pod, among the ripe beans. The newly

hatched larvae burrow into the beans and are safely lodged inside when the beans are harvested and stored. They are so small that several can come to maturity in one bean. The beetles that develop from these larvae emerge in the bag of beans about three months after they are harvested and they mate and lay their eggs without leaving the bag. Unlike the pea weevils, therefore, the beetles can go on breeding in stored beans until the seeds are riddled with holes and completely ruined.

The cowpea or Chinese weevil, *Callosobruchus chinensis*, and the

FIG. 119—The Cowpea Weevil, *Callosobruchus chinensis*, showing eggs, larva, pupa, two adults and an exit-hole in the cowpea.

four-spotted cowpea weevil, *Bruchus quadrimaculatus*, are also found in this country and they are at times serious pests of stored cowpeas. As with the bean weevil, the attack begins when the cowpeas are ripening in the field and continues in the store until the seeds are destroyed. The small white eggs are glued on to the seeds by the females.

Leaf-eating Beetles

Tortoise beetles, *Aspidomorphus* species, often attract the attention of gardeners because of their striking shape and colour. There are several different species of them, some of which are quite common, and they belong to the large family of leaf-eating beetles known as the *Chrysomelidae*. The adult beetles are about a third of an inch long, flattened and shaped something like a tortoise, golden green in colour with a beautiful metallic lustre. Unfortunately, this handsome appearance is lost soon after death; the colour fades to a dull grey, so that a collection of these beetles in a cabinet gives little indication of the handsome appearance of the living insects.

Some are found on convolvulus (*Ipomoea*) creepers in spring and again in late summer, others feed on the leaves of plants of the potato family, and still others on wild veld plants. The green tortoise beetle, *Aspidomorphus* shown in the photograph, is common on tall straggling shrubs with yellow flowers of the daisy type (*Othonna* species) and an account of its life history will serve as typical for the rest because they are all very similar in their habits and ways. The female lays her eggs singly on the leaves, dotting them about indiscriminately. Each is yellow, oval and surrounded by a blob of transparent liquid that quickly hardens so that the egg seems to be enclosed in a tiny disc of glass attached to the leaf. Usually, but not always, the female disguises her egg by depositing some excreta on top of it.

The egg hatches in ten to twelve days and gives rise to a little green grub with a row of flattened, branched spines down each side of its body. On its hind end it has a two-pronged fork that sticks up jauntily in the air. It retains this tail throughout its life, until it changes into a beetle, and it serves a curious and important function. The newly-hatched larva at once proceeds to dig a pit in the fleshy leaf, eating away the tissues so as to form a shallow hole in which it is comfortably lodged. It does not eat completely through the leaf but always leaves the skin on the opposite surface intact as the base of its home.

Thin black threads of excreta given off by the grub as it feeds are not dropped but become entangled in the fork on the tail and are retained there. When it is a few days old it stops feeding for a time and casts its skin. The moulted skin also is not thrown away. It shrivels up and slips backwards along the body on to the fork and is held there, mingled with the excreta. So it goes on throughout its life until, by the time it is fully grown, it has a strange unsavoury burden on its tail consisting of four cast skins, one above the other, and a black, gluey mass of excrement. If it is disturbed it waves this accumulation in the face of its enemy, as it were. The green colour of the larva harmonises well with that of the leaf, but the black shining lump feebly wagging to and fro is very conspicuous and attracts attention. Besides serving a protective purpose, the quaint habit of carrying its excrement on its back may also have a sanitary value by preventing the food from being soiled with waste matter.

When the larva is fully grown it fixes itself firmly to the leaf by digging in the claws of its six short legs. As it takes no more food in this stage the lump at the back dries up and falls off, leaving only the bare fork with the two parallel prongs. Then the skin splits and reveals the flattened, green pupa. Finally, about a fortnight later, the adult tortoise beetle emerges. There are two generations of the beetles a year; the adults which are about in the autumn go into hiding when the colder weather arrives and hibernate, becoming active again in spring and laying the eggs that give rise to the first generation of the following year.

As far as is known all the tortoise beetles have a life history similar to that described above, but many of them have a different method of laying their eggs. Instead of scattering their eggs singly, the females make little capsules, each of which contains eight eggs. The capsule is, as a rule, pale brown, about an eighth of an inch long and looks like a tiny paper bag stuck on the leaf.

The pests known as tobacco slugs are the larvae of two closely allied leaf-eating beetles, *Lema bilineata* and *Lema trilineata*, natives

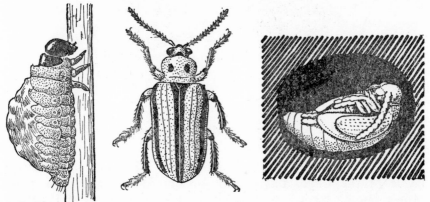

FIG. 120—The Cape Gooseberry Beetle, *Lema trilineata*.   Larva on left, adult in middle, pupa on right.   The beetle is yellow with black stripes and is a little more than quarter of an inch long.

of South America which have been introduced into South Africa and which are common on plants of the potato family, such as potatoes, Cape gooseberries, tobacco and stinkblaar (*Datura*).   The adult beetles are small black and yellow insects, about a quarter of an inch in length; the back is flattish and the elytra have three black stripes down the back; the underside of the body is usually black but the colour varies. The female lays her oval, yellow eggs in clusters on the underside of the leaves; they are covered with a sticky substance and gradually darken to a dark brown colour.   They take about six days to hatch and the larvae feed ravenously on the leaves, reaching full size when about ten or twelve days old.   They are then about a quarter of an inch long, with black heads and legs and they are covered on the back with slimy excrement which serves as a protection from enemies.   This repellent substance is brought into position by undulating movements of the body.   If the larva is disturbed it rears up its head and emits a drop of brownish fluid from its mouth.

When fully grown the larva drops to the ground and buries itself in the soil to the depth of about an inch.   Here it forms a cell by cementing the particles of soil together to form the walls and changes into a pupa. About a week later the adult beetle emerges. There are five or six generations a year.

There are many species of Chrysomelid beetles of which the larvae have this strange habit of carrying their excrement on their backs as a

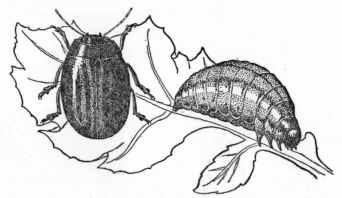

FIG. 121—The Banded Chrysomelid, *Chrysomela fasciata*, and its larva.

protection, but there are others that do not. The common leaf-eating beetle of the Cape, *Chrysomela fasciata* for example, has a fat brown smooth larva that feeds on the leaves of plants of the daisy family and does not bear any unsavoury load of excrement.

Long-horned Beetles

The long-horned beetles, *Cerambycidae*, are an important family of wood-borers and they include some of our largest insects among their numbers, certain species from Central Africa measuring four inches in length. Smaller kinds, ranging up to about two inches in length, are common; many are dull brown in colour, but there are some that are black or black and red and others that are bright metallic blue or green. The slenderly built metallic blue species, about an inch in length, are often called "Spanish flies" in this country, but this is a misnomer as the true "Spanish fly" is a beetle belonging to the oil beetle family and not to the long-horns.

A pale brown long-horn beetle, *Delochilus prionides*, is common and widely spread and often comes to lights at night. It is about an inch and a quarter in length and may be taken as a typical member of the family. If one of these beetles is picked up it will make a feeble squeaking or creaking sound. It does this by rubbing the hind margin of the prothorax against a roughened area between the bases of its elytra; the movement can easily be seen if the beetle is watched while

PLATE 49

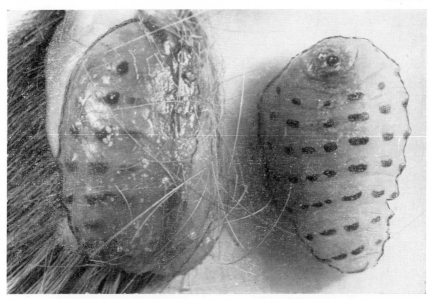

(a) "WARBLES," *Dermatoestrus antilopinus*, beneath the skin of a Grysbok. The larvae are about an inch long.

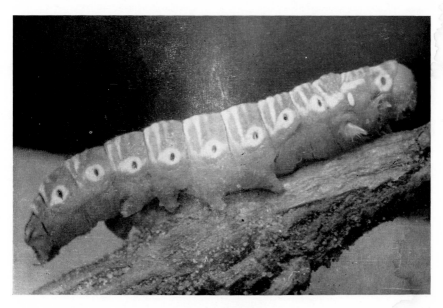

(b) A Caterpillar with a Tachinid Fly's egg on it

PLATE 50

(a) THE BLIND BEE LOUSE, *Braula coeca*, on a Worker Honey Bee

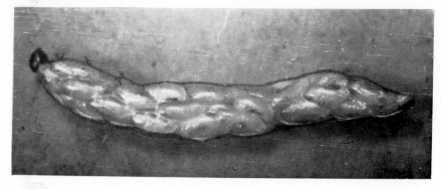

(a) Polyembryony, many larvae of a parasite inside a dead caterpillar; all the larvae have developed from one egg.

it is squeaking. It is difficult to imagine what use this squeaking call can be to the beetle. The noise is not loud enough to serve as a call-note, nor will it scare enemies away. We do not even know whether the insects can hear the sound themselves. The beetle has no ears but, like many other insects, it has a number of what are known as chordotonal organs scattered over various parts of the body. "Chordotonal" means a string or fibre for detecting tones and a chordotonal organ consists of one or more microscopic rodlike structures, situated just beneath the skin and connected with nerve fibres. Apparently the insect can detect vibrations in the air by their means and they seem to serve as primitive ears.

Chordotonal organs are also found along each side of the fat white larva of the long-horn beetle, looking like denser spots in the thin white skin and situated just below the spiracle in each segment. Hearing, as we know it, would be of little use to the sluggish worm lodged in a tunnel in a log: very few sounds can reach it in such a retreat; but the organs are probably of value to the larva in enabling it to detect vibrations set up by the jaws of another larva feeding close to it. The larvae are cannibalistic. When a number of young emerge from a cluster of eggs deposited in a crack in the bark by the female beetle, they devour one another until the survivors are too widely scattered to reach one another. In their tunnellings after this the grubs skilfully avoid the burrows of their fellows, turning aside when approaching another burrow too closely. The chordotonal organs along their sides may enable them to detect the proximity of others.

The larva grows slowly, probably because of the poor quality of its food. It has to get the whole of its nourishment from the wood and it may take three or four years to reach full size. When fully grown it hollows out a chamber in which it changes into a pupa. Usually the larva tunnels towards the surface of the log and makes its pupation chamber just below the bark. It is a mystery how the grub finds its way in its dark tunnel, yet when it is ready it makes it way unerringly towards the exterior. The larvae of many, but not all, species of long-horns plaster the walls of the pupal chamber with a sort of liquid chalk that comes from its Malpighian tubules, and this forms a hard, smooth, water-proof lining to the cell. The end of the tunnel leading into the chamber is then blocked with a wad of shavings and frass and finally the insect changes into a pupa. At first the pupa is white and translucent and looks as though it has been carved out of glass, but slowly the colour darkens and in two or three weeks the adult emerges and bites its way into the outer world.

A common long-horn where plantations of gum trees are found is the eucalyptus borer, *Phorocantha semipunctata*. This is a handsome

DD

beetle about an inch long, deep chocolate brown in colour, with a yellow band across the middle of the elytra and two neat oval yellow spots at the hind end. Like the rest of the family it has a pair of long antennae. This beetle is a native of Australia and apparently found its way to Africa about fifty years ago in railway sleepers of eucalyptus wood imported from Western Australia. Since then it has flourished here and spread widely. It does not attack healthy trees. Apparently the flow of sap is too great in such trees for the young larvae that feed on the juicy tissue just below the bark. But if a tree is weakened by disease or if it is felled, then the female beetles appear on the scene and lay their eggs in cracks and crevices in the bark. As a rule the attack takes place just after the trees are cut down, while the logs are lying on the ground. The females do not lay their eggs in logs which are dry and well seasoned.

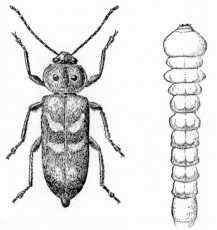

The female lays her eggs in batches of fifty or so and when the white, blind, legless larvae hatch they burrow outwards from this central point, feeding on the thin layer of soft tissue between the bark and wood. As they increase in size the burrows get wider and the part they leave behind them is tightly

FIG. 122—The European House Borer, *Hylotrupes bajulus*, Female beetle on left, larva on right. The beetle is from half to three quarters of an inch in length

packed with a mixture of sawdust and excrement. In this way the curious pattern of radiating grooves of increasing diameter is formed just beneath the bark of an infested log. When the larvae are bigger they bore down obliquely into the wood and may penetrate to a depth of three or four inches. The full-grown larva is white, about an inch and a half long.

The European house borer, or Italian beetle, *Hylotrupes bajulus*, is a native of Europe and has long been known as a serious pest there. A few years ago it was found to have established itself in Cape Town and Port Elizabeth, probably having been conveyed to these ports in the wood of boxes containing goods from Europe, and it is now widely spread. The beetle is about three-quarters of an inch long, black, but with a coating of short grey hairs on the front part of the body and forming four grey spots on the elytra. Two smooth shining black knobs on the prothorax make it fairly easy to recognise this beetle. The European house borer breeds only in wood from coniferous trees, such as the fir and pine, and it does considerable damage to roofing timbers, flooring boards, window frames, tables and other articles made from this wood. Like most wood-boring beetles it is found only in the sapwood, and not in the heartwood which contains little food for it.

The female lays her eggs in cracks and crevices in the wood and she may lay up to two hundred eggs or more before she dies. The eggs hatch in two to three weeks and the larvae take two to five years to reach full size, the length of time depending on the temperature and on the amount of food material in the wood. The pupal stage lasts for about a month. This beetle will also breed in dead pine trees and logs on the veld, as well as in fencing poles, garden seats and other external structures made of coniferous timber.

The majority of the members of the family, *Cerambycidae*, are scavengers, hastening the decay of dead, dying and fallen trees. There are a few that are injurious to felled timber and a few that cause damage to standing trees. One of these is the common and widely spread fig-tree borer, *Phryneta spinator*. The adult is a stout-bodied insect, from one to one and a half inches long, the male being smaller than the female, black, mottled with grey and yellow hairs on the elytra which are easily rubbed off. The female makes a T-shaped slit in the bark of a fig tree, generally near the ground, and lays an egg in it. This hatches in about a fortnight and the young larva feeds on the bark for a time before burrowing into the wood. It lives inside the tree for about two and three-quarter years and then pupates in a cavity just below the bark and the adult emerges about a month later. The adult beetles also cause damage by gnawing the bark of fig, willow, apple, apricot and other fruit trees.

Weevils

The weevils, *Curculionidae*, form the largest family, not only of insects, but of all living things. Over 30,000 species have already been described and named and there are undoubtedly many thousands more that still await description. They are characterised by the prolongation of the front of the head to form a snout or rostrum and by their elbowed, clubbed antennae. In some species the rostrum is short and broad while in others it is long and narrow and may even exceed the rest of the body in length. The mandibles are lodged at the tip of the rostrum and the females of many, but not all, species use it as a boring instrument for making holes in which they lay their eggs. The rostrum of the male is often shorter than that of the female and it is not known what function it serves in his case. The female cycad weevil of South Africa, *Antliarrhinus zamiae*, which lays her eggs in the cones of cycads, has a rostrum three times as long as the rest of her body, whereas that of the male is only about half as long as his body. Some weevils are midgets, smaller than the letter 'o' of this type, while others are comparative giants two inches or more in length. All of them are feeders on vegetable substances. In the larval state they are all fat, white grubs without legs and generally hidden inside some fruit or stem.

The bulb weevil, *Brachycerus obesus*, is a striking member of this family, about an inch long, with a black head and thorax and a dark red abdomen. The adult bulb weevil cannot fly, although most of its numerous relatives are excellent fliers. The round, hard back of the abdomen really consists of the elytra fused together to form a hard protective cover. So tough are the wing-cases that it is very difficult to get a pin through them when a specimen is being mounted for the cabinet. If one of these beetles is trodden on it will not be crushed unless the ground is hard and stony, because it will be pressed into soft soil and quite unharmed.

This weevil feeds on the tender young leaves of bulbs just as they appear above the ground and in this way may do much harm to gladioli and other bulbs in the garden. If the beetle is disturbed while it is feeding or while it is walking with its slow, clumsy gait across a garden path, it will at once "sham dead". It falls on its side and holds its legs out stiffly and no amount of prodding will cause it to show signs of life. This appears to be a clever trick on the part of the insect to deceive its enemies, but it must not be thought that it is a conscious, voluntary act. The insect has no reasoning powers and it is quite incapable of thinking out such a ruse for itself. Its nervous system is so constituted that, whenever it is disturbed, it must fall down in a sort of cataleptic fit—it cannot help itself. If one of these beetles is watched until the fit passes off and it begins to move again, it can be made to fall down again immediately by touching it, and this can be repeated many times, but gradually the succeeding fits become shorter until finally the insect no longer responds to the stimulus and only tries to escape. Most of the weevils have this curious instinct of shamming dead when they are disturbed.

The female bulb weevil lays her eggs in the crowns of the bulbs, just beneath the surface of the soil. A creamy white legless maggot hatches from the egg and feeds on the bulb, eating out a hole in which it is lodged, and eventually destroying the bulb. If the bulb is big enough the larva remains feeding inside it until it is fully grown. If not, the larva can burrow through the soil in search of other bulbs. Finally it pupates either in the hollowed bulb or in a cell excavated in the soil beside the bulb. The adult emerges when the first rains cause the bulbs to sprout in the following season.

The grain weevil, *Sitophilus granarius*, is very common and widely spread, attacking stored cereals of various kinds in houses, shops and mills. It is an elongate, dark brown beetle about a sixth of an inch long and it cannot fly as its second pair of wings is vestigial. It is quite long lived for such a small insect, the female living for ten months in the adult state and laying up to three hundred eggs during that period. She makes a neat hole in the kernel of the grain and deposits her tiny white egg at the bottom, sealing the hole afterwards with a gummy fluid that quickly hardens. The small legless white grub lives inside the grain and three or four of them may come to maturity in a single maize grain, but there is only enough food in a wheat grain for one grub. There may be four or five generations in a year and it has been estimated that a single pair may give rise to six thousand descendants in twelve months.

The rice weevil, *Sitophilus oryzae*, is very similar to the grain weevil but it has, usually, four reddish spots on the elytra and it can fly quite well. It was probably a native of India originally but it has been spread all over the world and is common in Africa. Its life history is similar to the grain weevils and it attacks all sorts of stored cereals.

The vine calandra, *Phlyctinus callosus*, is a dull brown weevil about a quarter of an inch long that is often harmful in vineyards.

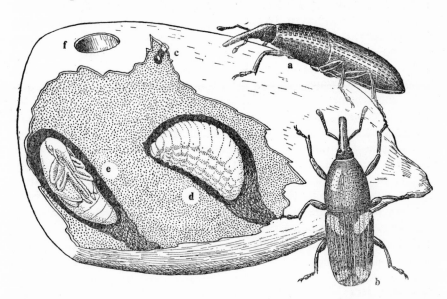

FIG. 123—The Grain Weevils: (a) the granary weevil, *Sitophilus granarius*; (b) the maize or rice weevil, *Sitophilus oryzae;* (c) egg; (d) larva; (e) pupa; (f) exit-hole of adult. The beetles are about one sixth inch long.

The adult beetles live through the winter under clods of earth, among dead leaves, beneath bark and in similar sheltered spots, but in the spring they emerge and feed on the tender new foliage of the vines. They are nocturnal, feeding at night and hiding under the bark during the day. The female lays her eggs in the soil and the larvae feed on

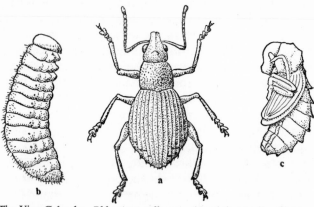

FIG. 124—The Vine Calandra, *Phlyctinus callosus:* (a) adult weevil; (b) larva; (c) pupa. The beetle is brown and about a quarter of an inch long.

the roots of the vines and other plants. The larvae are full grown by the autumn and they hibernate in the soil until the spring, when they pupate in September or October and the new generation of adults emerge early in November.

The eucalyptus weevil, *Gonipterus scutellatus,* found its way to this country from Australia about forty years ago and is now well established and widely spread wherever gum trees are grown. It is a small dark brown beetle about three-eighths of an inch long. The female lays her eggs in small batches of about ten, enclosed in a small dark brown capsule attached to a leaf. The larvae are yellowish green and sluglike and they feed on the tender young eucalyptus leaves. If they are numerous the tops of the trees may be almost completely defoliated and young trees may suffer a severe set-back. The full-grown larva drops to the ground and buries itself and pupates in a small cell it excavates for itself. This beetle threatened to become a very serious pest in eucalyptus plantations but a tiny egg parasite was introduced from Australia by the Agricultural Department and this has held it in check.

Pinhole Borers

Pinhole borers are small beetles, ranging from one-eighth to half an inch in length, which belong to the family *Scolytidae.* The adults are reddish brown, dark brown, or black and they attack dying or dead trees, logs and unseasoned or moist timber. They make small round tunnels into the wood but they do not feed on the material excavated which is thrown out of the tunnels as a fine, light-coloured powder. Although these long, narrow-bodied beetles are quite common in the warmer forested regions and although there are many different species, they are not often noticed because they spend little time in the open and live out almost their whole lives inside the timber. They breed in trees that are sickly, often because they have been burned at the base by veld fires, or in logs from trees that have recently been felled. They do not breed in dry, seasoned timber, and so are not found in buildings.

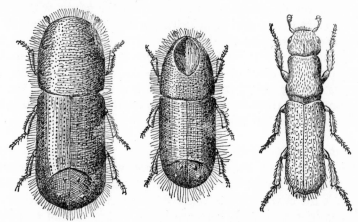

FIG. 125—Ambrosia Beetles. *Xyleborus celsus*, female on left, male in middle. *Platypus* species on right.

Although these beetles burrow into the wood, they and their young do not feed on the wood itself but on a fungus which grows in their tunnels. This fungus is much like the blue-green mould, Penicillium, and for some reason or other it has been given the name ambrosia fungus and the beetles which feed on it are called ambrosia beetles. The fungus causes the wood on which it grows to turn black and, therefore, if a piece of wood is split open and found to have narrow tunnels with blackened walls, this is an indication that ambrosia beetles have been busy in it. The burrows made by other kinds of wood-boring beetles show the natural colour of the wood.

A number of ambrosia beetles may be found living in a burrow in a log together, with their eggs and young beside them. The larva grows fairly quickly on its diet of fungus and may be fully grown when it is one or two months old; it then pupates and a month later the adult emerges. If the log still contains sap and is damp enough to grow more of the mould, the beetles continue to breed in it. If it has become too dry the beetles leave it and seek out another freshly felled log or dying tree. They carry with them, on the hairs of their bodies or in special pores and pits in their skin, the spores of the fungus. As they bore into their new home the spores are rubbed off on to the damp wood and the mould grows and provides them with a fresh supply of food for themselves and their young. In their manner of feeding these beetles remind us of the fungus-growing termites and they also show the beginnings of an organised social life.

Some species construct simple galleries in which the adults, eggs, larvae and pupae are found living together. Others make compound tunnels with side branches along which there are small cells in which the larvae develop. These larvae are fed by the adults with wads of fungus that are thrust into their cells. In other cases the larvae look after themselves, feeding on the fungus growing on the tunnel walls. In some cases at least the female, before laying her eggs, makes a carefully prepared layer of wood fragments and excreta upon which the fungus starts growing and from which it spreads along the walls of the tunnel. As these beetles cannot grow their fungus in dry wood they are never found in seasoned timber.

Stag Beetles

The stag beetles, *Lucanidae*, are not very well represented in Africa. We have no species in which the males have enormous mandibles, as is the case with the well-known stag beetle of Europe. The few species that are found here are black or brown and one to two inches in length, with nothing very striking about them. Very little is known of their life history. They probably live in rotting logs and tree-trunks and are therefore found in forested regions.

There are, however, some half a dozen different species of members of this family which are found only on the mountain tops in the south-west Cape and which are of considerable interest because of their peculiar distribution. These beetles, *Colophon* species, are about three-quarters of an inch long, black, with antennae that are clubbed and elbowed, and stout front legs that are toothed something like those of a scarab beetle. They are rare in collections; very few have been caught, partly because of the inaccessible mountain tops where they live and partly because they are nocturnal and remain well hidden by day. They cannot fly. Practically nothing is known of their habits and life history but it is thought that the larvae live in the soil and feed on roots. The interesting point about these beetles is the fact that one species, *Colophon westwoodi*, is found only on mountain tops in the Cape Peninsula, and nowhere else. Another species, *C. stokoei*,

PLATE 51

(*b*) **THE PELARGONIUM SAW-FLY,** *Athalia pelargonii.* Cocoon on left, adult female on right

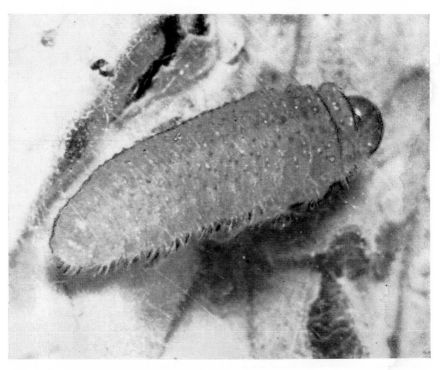

(*b*) The larva of the Pelargonium Saw-fly, *Athalia pelargonii*

PLATE 52

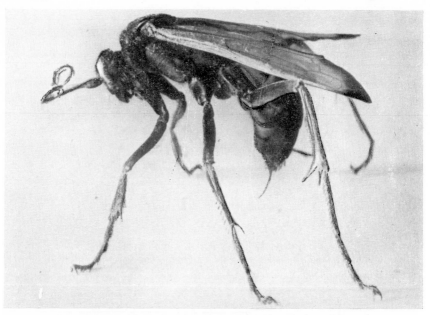

(*a*) THE SPIDER-HUNTING WASP, *Hemipepsis capensis*, female

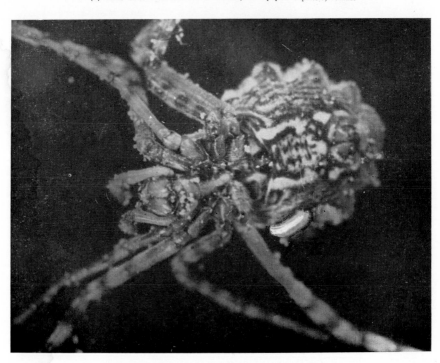

(*b*) A paralysed Spider with the egg of *Hemipepsis capensis* on it

is found only on the top of the Hottentots Holland Mountains, a third, *C. haughtoni*, only on the Hex River Mountains, a fourth, *C. cameroni*, only on the Waaihoek Mountains, a fifth, *C. izardi*, only on the Lange-

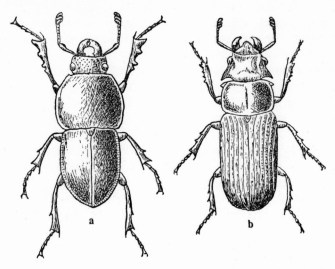

FIG. 126—South African Stag Beetles: (a) the Table Mountain Stag Beetle, *Collophon westwoodi;* (b) the Cape Stag Beetle, *Xiphodontus antilope*.

berg Range, and the sixth, *C. primosi*, on the Zwartberg Range. All these beetles except the first were named after the mountaineers who helped in their discovery. There may be other species on mountain tops in other parts of the country that still await discovery. It would seem that, long ago, the stag-beetle ancestors of these *Colophon* species were isolated when the different mountain ranges were formed; each group varied as time passed and slowly evolved into the distinct species we find to-day, each cut off from the others in its mountain home so that no interbreeding was possible.

Dung Beetles

The family that includes the dung beetles, *Scarabaeidae* is a very large one, including about 15,000 different species. The family is particularly well represented in Africa, the members of it varying greatly in size, form and habits, but they are all alike in possessing antennae that terminate in a fan of three or more flattened joints that can be folded one over the other. The most famous member of the group is the sacred scarab of Egypt, *Scarabaeus sacer*, and there are many other scarabs found throughout Africa that have similar ways. The one shown in the photograph is the wrinkled scarab, *Scarabaeus rugosus*, and it is one of the smaller members of the tribe, being only about three-quarters of an inch in length.

Both sexes are exactly alike and they are sombre black. When it scents its food from afar the scarab holds out the little three-jointed fans of its antennae, spread wide open, and it seems to be sniffing the breeze. When it is working in the dung, however, it keeps its antennae tucked away in little pockets beneath its head.

The most striking anatomical feature of the scarab is its complete lack of tarsi on its front legs. Its middle and hind legs have well-developed, five-jointed feet, but its front legs end, as it were, at the ankles. The front legs are stout and the tibiae are armed with four strong teeth. The beetle uses the legs as scoops and rakes, to break up the dropping left on the road or veld by the passing animal and to gather the best parts of it together in a ball. It makes the selected portion into a ball by patting and pressing it with its front legs and it is obvious that a pair of slender, five-jointed tarsi on these legs would be more of a hindrance than a help and they have therefore been lost.

When the scarab has made its ball of dung it proceeds to roll it away across the veld, seeking for a suitable place to bury it. It always moves backwards when doing this, holding the ball between its long, curved hind legs. Sometimes a second beetle will join it and make a great show of giving assistance in the arduous task of trundling the ball. Anybody seeing the two insects fussing about the ball might think that this is a case of male and female co-operating in providing food for the family, but this is not so. The second beetle may be of the same sex as the owner of the ball, or of the opposite sex. It is not a case of co-operation but of attempted robbery. The newcomer will make off with the ball if it gets the chance; failing this, it will remain as an uninvited guest to share the feast.

After having pushed the ball along for some distance, toiling over all sorts of obstacles, the beetle (or beetles) proceeds to bury it a few inches below the surface of the ground. An underground chamber large enough to hold the ball and to allow of movement round it is hollowed out and the tunnel leading down to the chamber is blocked with the earth that is dug out of the chamber. Finally the scarab settles down to eat and it feeds stolidly for several days, until the whole sphere of dung is consumed. It has peculiar jaws, soft and membranous, instead of hard and horny as the jaws of most beetles are, but they are quite strong enough to deal with the soft food that suffices for the scarab throughout its life.

When the ball is eaten the beetle is ready to come to the surface again and to fly off in search of fresh supplies. The insect seems to be content with the rather coarse droppings of a horse, mule or donkey for its own use, but when the time comes to prepare for the next generation the female prefers the softer and more nutritious excrement of sheep or goats, or, failing this, of cows. She scrapes together the softer part of the heap and forms a ball as before, and she may bury the ball on the spot or she may trundle it away for some distance. In either case she buries the ball, but this time she makes a much larger chamber two or three inches below the surface, a chamber in which there is ample room for her to move round and over the ball.

Now begins a long patting and smoothing process until the mass of food is perfectly round and smooth. Her curved, toothed front legs are the tools she uses in this work. Next she makes a hollow at one side of the ball and deposits an egg in it. The egg is fairly large when compared with the size of the insect that lays it, being one-eighth of an inch long, oval and white. Finally she pats and smooths the edge of the hollow, bringing it up to cover the egg so that it forms a projection on the ball, like the small end of a pear. Having completed the pear-shaped mass, with the egg lodged in the hollow at the small end, she leaves the underground chamber, closing the tunnel behind her. Then she goes off to start the same task all over again somewhere else.

The egg hatches in a week or so into a white grub with six legs and a curious hump on its back. It lies on its side inside the ball and devours the provisions provided by its mother. The outer surface of the pear hardens and forms a crust which prevents the food from drying out. Within two or three weeks the larva has devoured the whole of the contents and it lies snugly concealed in the hollow shell of dry dung. Here it changes into a chrysalis and about a month later the adult emerges.

The bronze and green dung beetle, *Onitis aygulus*, is a handsome beetle, nearly an inch long, with a dark metallic green head and thorax and underside of the body, and brown elytra with a sheenlike bronze. Although it lives and works amid wet cow-dung it is always spotlessly clean and shiny and it is difficult to understand how it maintains its immaculate appearance in such surroundings. Like the scarabs, it has no feet on its front legs and its jaws are soft and membranous; the fans on its antennae consist of nine joints. It does not trundle balls of dung over the veld but burrows right down into the cow dropping and is hidden from view.

When preparing to lay her eggs the female first of all digs a tunnel in the soil beneath the dung. This tunnel is about half an inch in diameter and may go down seven or eight inches into the ground, in a slanting direction. She throws up the excavated soil in a heap at the side of the dropping. At the bottom of the burrow she excavates a large chamber, often of irregular shape because of obstructions, such as stones and roots. The chamber is large enough to accommodate a mass of dung about the size of a man's fist. Having completed the laborious digging, she now proceeds to fill the chamber with food carefully selected from the mass above. She burrows amid the dung and chooses only the softest and most nourishing portions, carrying it below by shovelling it along with her front legs. She packs the chamber solidly from end to end, laying her eggs at intervals as the filling proceeds.

The first egg is laid after only a few loads have been brought down and packed tightly in the far end of the chamber. In this the female makes a neat spherical cell about the size of a pea and she coats the wall of this cell with a brown liquid regurgitated from her stomach. This is food she has partially digested and which is intended to serve as the first mouthfuls for the delicate larva when it hatches. Then she lays her egg, fixing it on end inside the cell. It is very large in comparison with the size of the beetle, being about the size of a grain of wheat, white and oval.

After this, more dung is packed in the chamber, a second egg-cell is made, and so it goes on until the cavity is full and about half a dozen eggs have been laid. The egg-cells are always made near the outer surface of the mass and never in the centre; this is apparently to ensure that the eggs and larvae receive enough air. The mass of dung forms a sort of communal feast, with the inhabitants situated as far from one another as possible, but the share of each one is not cut off in any way from that of the others. The eggs hatch in about a fortnight and the hump-backed larvae feed almost incessantly from the moment of their birth, eating out large hollows, until, by the time they are fully grown, they are separated from one another only by thin walls of dry fibres. Each makes a neat cell for itself amid the remains of the food and then pupates. The pupa is a beautiful object in such surroundings, looking as though carved out of white crystal. It has curious horns on its back which serve to keep its soft, delicate body away from the damp floor of its prison. After two or three weeks the adult emerges.

There are a large number of different species of dung beetles found in this country and they are as varied in their sizes and shapes as they are in their habits. In former days, when great herds of game roamed the veld, they played an important part in helping to keep the veld sweet and clean by removing the droppings and incorporating them quickly into the soil. Nowadays, owing to the destruction of the game, the advent of motor vehicles and the dwindling number of horses, they are not as abundant as they were.

Smallish beetles, from a quarter to three quarters of an inch in length, black, often coated with mud and dust, and with roughened ridges along their backs, are members of this family and belong to the genus *Trox*. Most of them can fly but some have lost their second pair of wings and can only walk slowly over the veld. When captured they emit a feeble squeaking sound. These beetles are found, sometimes in large numbers, beneath the dried remains of carcases on the veld and under dried excrement. They finish off the scavenging work commenced by the flesh flies, dung beetles and others.

The chafers and fruit beetles are also members of the *Scarabaeidae*. Numerous species are found in Africa; some are sobrely coloured, black or brown, while others are striking insects with bright colours. Some are nocturnal while others revel in the hottest sunshine. The larvae of these beetles are fat white grubs found in the soil and amid dead vegetation; usually they are coiled in the form of the letter 'C' and lie on their side. They feed on roots, humus, and decaying leaves. Some of them, such as the zebra beetle, *Stripsipher zebra*, spend the larval stage in rotten logs.

Certain members of this family may become serious pests at times. The stoutly built brown or black beetles, *Heteronychus* species, are sometimes abundant and do damage to lawns, bowling greens and cereal crops. In the spring, particularly in the south-west Cape, the little monkey beetles, with long hind legs, are extremely numerous and may be found head downwards in almost every composite flower. For a few weeks in September and October they are the bane of gardeners, and then they disappear until the following spring. They belong to the sub-family of the *Scarabaeidae* called the *Hopliinae* and there are very many different species, all much alike in size and form but varying widely in colour, and some are smooth while others are hairy. Nothing is known about their life history, although they are so very common, but it is probable that their larvae are root feeders, living in the soil.

CLASSIFICATION

ORDER 18: *COLEOPTERA* (Beetles)

Front wings horny or leathery elytra which almost always meet to form a straight line down the back and which form a protective cover to the second, membranous pair of wings. Second pair of wings often reduced or missing altogether. Biting mouthparts and complete metamorphosis.

SUB-ORDER 1: *Adephaga*

Beetles with threadlike antennae and five-jointed tarsi. Predacious and carnivorous as larvae and adults.

FAMILY 1: *Cicindelidae*—TIGER BEETLES

Antennae 11-jointed. Clypeus (lower part of front of head) wider than bases of antennae. Swift active beetles that hunt their prey on foot; many are strong fliers but some lack the second pair of wings and cannot fly. Larvae in tunnels in soil.

FAMILY 2: *Carabidae*—GROUND BEETLES

Antenne 11-jointed. Clypeus not wider than bases of antennae. Predacious, active beetles. Larvae elongate and active, feed on other insects and many are found in the soil.

FAMILY 3: *Dytiscidae*—WATER BEETLES

Antennae 10-jointed. Smooth, flattened beetles that live in water and have hind legs modified for swimming. Larvae also live in water and are predacious.

FAMILY 4: *Gyrinidae*—WHIRLIGIG BEETLES

Antennae 10-jointed, but very short and stout. Eyes divided. Swim mostly on surface of water and have legs highly modified for swimming. Larvae also aquatic and predacious.

FAMILY 5: *Paussidae*—ANTS' NEST BEETLES

Antennae abnormally developed, the terminal joints fused to form a club. Small beetles that are found in the nests of ants and termites.

SUB-ORDER 2: *Polyphaga*

Antennae and tarsi very variable. Larvae of various types and habits.

FAMILY 6: *Staphylinidae*—ROVE BEETLES

Short elytra that do not cover whole of abdomen. Tarsi 3-, 4- or 5-jointed. Abdominal segments flexible, with 8 segments visible ventrally.

FAMILY 7: *Trogostidae*

Small beetles. Tarsi 5-jointed but first joint very small. The important pest, the cadelle, *Tenebrioides mauritanicus*, belongs to this family.

FAMILY 8: *Nitidulidae*

Small beetles. Tarsi 5-jointed. Often elytra not long enough to cover abdomen, leaving one or two of the end segments exposed. Includes some important pests, such as the dried fruit beetles, *Carpophilus* species.

FAMILY 9: *Cucujidae*

Small, flattened beetles. Tarsi 4- or 5-jointed. Abdomen with five segments visible ventrally. Includes some important pests such as the saw-toothed grain beetle, *Orzaephilus surinamensis*.

FAMILY 10: *Coccinellidae*—LADYBIRDS

Rounded, convex beetles. Antennae short, 11-jointed. Tarsi apparently 3-jointed but with a very small fourth joint hidden. Adults and larvae predacious, feeding mostly on aphides, mealie bugs and their kin.

FAMILY 11: *Dermestidae*

Small or moderate-sized beetles, mostly dull coloured. Antennae short with the terminal joints swollen to form a club. Tarsi 5-jointed. Adults and larvae mostly feed on furs, hides, wool, dried meats, bacon, etc. Includes the museum beetle, *Anthrenus museorum*.

FAMILY 12: *Cantharidae*

Soft-bodied beetles, usually elongate. Antennae of various forms. Tarsi 5-jointed. A very large family including glow-worms and fire-flies.

FAMILY 13: *Anobiidae* (*Ptinidae*)

Small beetles, mostly wood-borers. Slender 11-jointed antennae with terminal joints slightly swollen. Tarsi 5-jointed. This family includes the 'death watch' beetles which are destructive to furniture, rafters and flooring. Other species are pests of stored products, including cigars, cigarettes, biscuits, flour, drugs and ginger.

FAMILY 14: *Bostrichidae*

Cylindrical beetles with head bent down and hidden by projecting prothorax. Antennae with a 3-jointed club. Tarsi 5-jointed but first joint very small. They are borers in felled timber and dried wood, occasionally attacking unhealthy, standing trees.

FAMILY 15: *Lyctidae*—POWDER-POST BEETLES

Small elongate beetles. Antennae ending in a 2-jointed club. Larvae feed on sap-wood of seasoned timber from broad-leaved trees, but not coniferous timber. This family includes the destructive powder-post beetles.

FAMILY 16: *Buprestidae*

Elongate beetles more or less pointed at hind end. Antennae short and serrate. Tarsi 5-jointed. Adults often brightly coloured with metallic hues. Forest-dwelling insects. Larvae are wood-borers with prothorax swollen and are often spoken of as 'flat-headed' borers.

FAMILY 17: *Elateridae*—CLICK BEETLES

Elongate beetles, mostly black or brown. Antennae threadlike or pectinate or serrate. Hind angles of prothorax produced into points. A process projecting on underside of prothorax which fits into cavity on next joint and is used in righting the insect with a jerk when it is placed on its back. Some of the larvae are found in soft wood, others in the soil, where they feed on roots. These beetles range in size from small to quite large.

FAMILY 18: *Tenebrionidae*

A very large family of dull-coloured beetles, mostly of moderate size. Tarsi of front two pairs of legs 5-jointed, hind tarsi 4-jointed. Antennae simple, ending in a slight club in some species. Some are unable to fly, others are strong fliers. This family includes the well-known meal-worm beetles, the toktokkie and the confused flour beetle.

FAMILY 19: *Meloïdae*—BLISTER BEETLES AND OIL BEETLES

Soft-bodied beetles of moderate to large size. Contain the drug cantharidin. Antennae simple. Tarsi of first two pairs of legs 5-jointed, of hind legs 4-jointed. As far as is known all are parasitic in their young stages and have remarkable life histories. Includes the common C. M. R. beetles that are found feeding on flowers.

FAMILY 20: *Bruchidae*—PEA AND BEAN WEEVILS

Small beetles that breed in the seeds of leguminous plants. Head with a short, blunt snout. Elytra short, leaving the tip of the abdomen exposed. Tarsi 4-jointed. Antennae simple or pectinate or serrate. Includes the well known pea, cowpea and bean weevils.

FAMILY 21: *Chrysomelidae*—LEAF-EATING BEETLES

A very large family of moderate-sized beetles, mostly convex and rounded and some brightly coloured. Antennae simple. Tarsi 4-jointed. Larvae mostly short, thick fleshy grubs that feed on the leaves of plants. Includes a number of pests.

FAMILY 22: *Cerambycidae*—LONG-HORN BEETLES

A large family of elongate beetles, some very large, with long antennae. Tarsi 4-jointed. The larvae are fat, legless grubs that burrow in timber, mostly in dead and dying trees and in fallen logs. Some feed on the roots or pith of herbaceous plants.

FAMILY 23: *Curculionidae*—WEEVILS

The largest family of them all. Small to moderate-sized beetles with the front of the head prolonged to form a pronounced rostrum or snout. Antennae elbowed. Tarsi 4-jointed. Larvae are legless grubs, mostly internal feeders or below the soil, and the numerous species attack every part of the plants, from the roots to the seeds.

FAMILY 24: *Scolytidae* (*Ipidae*)—BARK BEETLES AND AMBROSIA BEETLES

Small, cylindrical beetles, mostly wood-borers, but some attack the softer tissues of herbaceous plants. The antennae are clubbed at the tip. Tarsi 4-jointed. The bark beetles burrow in the bark and between the bark and the wood, forming characteristic tunnels with branches and making numerous small exit holes. The ambrosia beetles feed on fungus grown in their tunnels.

FAMILY 25: *Lucanidae*—STAG BEETLES

Beetles with large jaws, very large in the males in some species. Antennae elbowed and ending in a slight club. This family is not well represented in Africa. The larvae are wood-borers, as far as is known.

FAMILY 26: *Scarabaeidae*—DUNG BEETLES AND THEIR KIN

A very large family of beetles, ranging in size from small to very large. Antennae short and ending in a fan of three or more joints that can be folded one over the other. Tarsi 5-jointed. Larvae are mostly white grubs with six legs and are found in dung, decaying vegetation and in the soil. This family is very well represented in Africa and includes the well known dung beetles, chafers, fruit and flower beetles.

(Several small and comparatively unimportant families are omitted from the above list.)

PLATE 53

(*a*) THE MUD WASP, *Sceliphron spirifex*, female at her nest

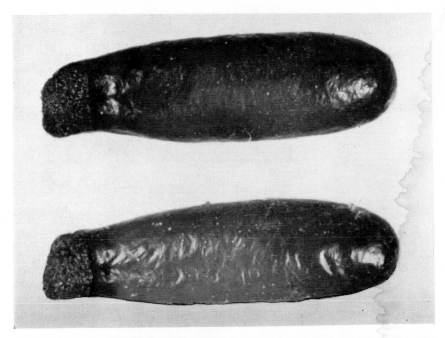

(*b*) Two cocoons of the Mud Wasp, *Sceliphron spirifex*. They are made of silk lined with a thin parchment-like layer of dried excrement; the dark mass at the bottom is also excrement passed by the larvae before pupating

PLATE 54

(a) THE YELLOW BEE PIRATE, *Philanthus diadema*, female, with a Honey Bee she has just captured

(b) THE WATSONIA WASP, *Dasyproctus capensis* female at the entrance to her nest

CHAPTER XVIII

FLIES

The Diptera

Flies have only one pair of wings, hence their scientific name, *Diptera*, which means "two-winged". The second pair of wings found in other insects are represented in the flies by a pair of tiny organs called balancers, or halteres, that look like the tops of pins and project, one on each side, just behind the bases of the front wings. These halteres, although very small, are complex bodies which are delicate sense organs but their exact function is not known. They have tiny muscles at the base and can vibrate rapidly, like the wings.

The mouthparts are adapted for sucking, not biting, and they usually form a proboscis which, in the blood-sucking species, can pierce the skin. The metamorphosis is complete, the larvae of most flies being blind, legless maggots with a very small head and reduced mouthparts.

This is an enormous order of insects, with more than 50,000 described and named species and many more that still have to be dealt with. Many of them are of great economic importance because they are pests of crops, parasites of domestic animals and transmitters of disease. They are not popular with collectors because of their lack of beauty and their unpleasant ways, yet they are of considerable interest and offer a promising field of study to any enthusiast who cares to take them up. We have still a great deal to learn about the innumerable species of flies found in Africa.

Crane Flies

The slender long-legged flies often called "daddy-long-legs" that sometimes come into the house and fly clumsily at the window panes are among the simplest of flies as regards bodily structure and are placed in a family called the *Tipulidae*. They have long threadlike antennae of six or more joints and very long, fragile legs that are easily lost. They are to be seen on the wing during the rainy season and are usually found in damp places because their larvae live in moist ground or in marshy spots or in water.

The adults vary in size from that of a small mosquito to large flies with a wing-spread of three inches or more. They are dull coloured, mostly brown or blackish, and a few species are known that are wingless. The male may be distinguished from the female by the blunt swollen tip of his abdomen: hers is long and tapering. Very little is known about the life histories of our native crane flies, but they probably differ little from those of their European relatives. The larvae are usually grey, tough-skinned and elongate, with a pair of spiracles at the hind end surrounded by short processes. They feed on the roots of grasses and other plants, on decaying vegetation, on

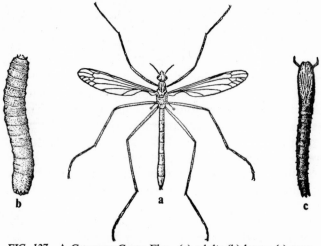

FIG. 127—A Common Crane Fly: (a) adult; (b) larva; (c) pupa.

mosses, and some of the aquatic species are predacious, feeding on small worms and other creatures dwelling in the marshes and ponds where they are found. The pupae are also elongate and look rather like the pupae of moths, but they have a pair of horns or tubes at the front end by means of which they breathe.

Moth Flies

Tiny mothlike flies, with broad, hairy wings that meet like a roof over their bodies, may often be seen in the house, particularly in the kitchen and bathroom, because they like the dampness at the sink and basin. They are feeble fliers and attract little attention because of their small size. These flies belong to the family known as *Psychodidae* and are often called moth flies, or sand flies. Some of them are blood suckers and they may cause considerable irritation, as they can creep through ordinary mosquito nets with ease and, to some people at least, their bites are more irritating than those of mosquitoes as they cause small red swellings which may persist for days. Only the females suck blood and they commonly choose the ankles of their victims as the place of attack. The "pappataci'" or three-day fever, that is prevalent in Southern Europe and North Africa, is transmitted by blood-sucking sand flies.

The female lays her minute eggs in batches in cracks and crevices in the ground, where it is damp and where there is decaying animal and vegetable matter, beneath the refuse bin, beside the kitchen drain,

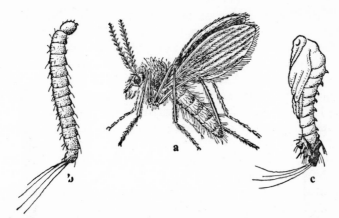

FIG. 128—A Sand Fly, *Phlebotomus* species: (a) adult; (b) larva; (c) pupa. The fly is about one tenth of an inch long

at the outlet of the septic tank, and similar places. The larvae look like miniature caterpillars and have four long bristles on the hind end. They are fully grown in about a month and then pupate in the soil. About ten days later the adults emerge. A number of different species are found in Africa but they have been little studied. The blood-sucking species, with long probosces and holding their wings at an angle of forty-five degrees above their backs, are called sand flies, apparently because of their sandy colour, while the species that do not suck blood have short probosces and hold their wings rooflike over the body; they are grey and are usually spoken of as moth flies.

Mosquitoes

All mosquitoes breed in water. A common belief in South Africa that they can breed in pepper-trees and gum-trees is wrong, unless the trees happen to be hollow and to contain accumulations of rain water. Furthermore, mosquitoes do not fly far from their breeding places; a range of half a mile to a mile is about their limit, as a rule, and many of them do not fly more than two or three hundred yards from the places where they were bred. They are not even carried long distances by wind, because they are such frail creatures that they take shelter and do not venture forth when a strong wind is blowing.

The common household mosquitoes, such as *Culex pipiens* and *Culex quinquefasciatus*, will breed in almost any accumulation of stagnant water. Rain-barrels, cisterns, cesspools, tin cans, pots, blocked-up gutters, anything, in fact, that will hold water for a few weeks will serve these pests as breeding places. It is only the female mosquito that sucks blood. It is said that she requires a feed of blood before she can mature her eggs. This may be true of many species, but it is certainly not true of them all, for certain kinds have been bred through several generations in the laboratory without the females receiving any blood at all. A male mosquito cannot suck blood because his mouthparts are only imperfectly developed and they are incapable of piercing the human skin; his food consists of the nectar of flowers and the juices of ripe fruits, food which the female will also take when she cannot get blood. The male's antennae are feathery, like beautiful little plumes ornamenting his head, whilst the female's antennae are threadlike and armed with only short hairs that are scarcely visible to the naked eye. This difference in the antennae offers an easy means of distinguishing the sexes.

The proboscis consists of an elongated lower lip which is deeply grooved along the upper side. Six slender lancets lie in the groove and are the weapons by means of which she pierces the skin of her victim and sucks the blood. The lancets are the highly modified mandibles, maxillae and two other mouthparts known as the hypopharynx and labrum-epipharynx. The comparatively thick lower lip, or labium, which constitutes the bulk of the proboscis, does not enter the wound; it is bent back out of the way as the lancets are thrust deeper and deeper into the flesh. Saliva is injected into the wound along a very fine, narrow channel in the hypopharynx and this sets up irritation and produces a little local inflammation that draws a plentiful blood supply to the spot; it is also the means by which disease organisms are introduced by those mosquitoes that transmit malaria, yellow fever, dengue fever, and filariasis. Because of the widespread misery, suffering and death caused by these diseases, mosquitoes must be regarded as the greatest insect enemies of the human race.

The mosquitoes that commonly attack human beings may be divided into two types, the culicines (from the name of the principal genus of the group, *Culex*) and the anophelines (from the principal genus, *Anopheles*), and they can be readily distinguished one from the other in all stages. Mosquitoes have scales, or flattened hairs, on their bodies and wings, much like those found in butterflies and moths; the moth flies, *Psychodidae*, are the only other flies that have these scales. The scales on the wings of a culicine mosquito are all of the same greyish tint, whereas many anophelines have patches of black scales

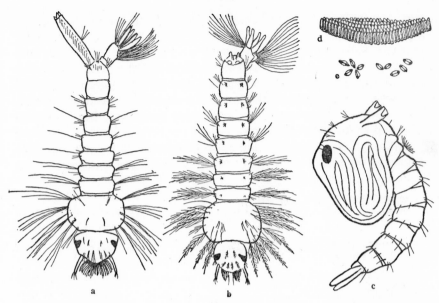

FIG. 129—Mosquitoes: (a) culicine larva; (b) anopheline larva; (c) pupa; (d) culicine
                      egg-raft; (e) anopheline eggs.

among the grey ones; these anophelines, therefore, have black spots on
their wings. On the head of the adult mosquito there is a pair of palps
projecting on each side of the proboscis. These palps are as long as
the proboscis in all male mosquitoes, but they are much shorter in
female culicines. Female anophelines, on the other hand, have palps
as long as those of the male. Culicine mosquitoes, when at rest, hold
their bodies parallel with the surface upon which they are resting,
while anopheline mosquitoes rest with the body at an angle of about
45 degrees with the surface. Thus the spotted wings, the long palps of
the females and the resting attitude offer easy means of distinguishing
the two types.

In a general way the life histories of all mosquitoes are much
alike, but there is considerable variation in details. Culicine females
mostly lay their oval eggs glued together in the form of miniature
rafts. These grey rafts, something like caraway seeds, may be found
floating on stagnant water and they are so formed that they cannot
be upset or submerged. A few culicines and all anophelines lay their
eggs singly, not joined together, and the eggs of anophelines may be
recognised by the tiny air-floats, one on each side. A few species lay
eggs that sink and some deposit their eggs in dry hollows where they
lie dormant until the rains fill the hollows and form pools.

The eggs of mosquitoes never hatch except in the presence of

water. The larvae are always aquatic and are the well-known "wrigglers"'
They have bunches of long bristly hairs on the body, instead of legs,
and these serve to keep them steady in the water. The eyes and
antennae are well developed and on each side of the mouth there is a
brush of stiff hairs, the mouth brushes, that serve to sweep the microscopic organisms that form the food of most larvae into their mouths.
Some species have predacious larvae that feed on other mosquito
larvae and small water creatures.

Although aquatic, the larvae breathe air and each has two
spiracles at the hind end of the body. In culicine larvae these spiracles

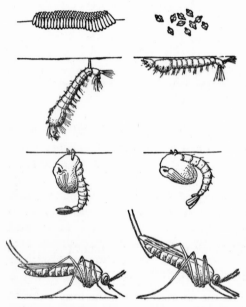

FIG. 130—Mosquitoes, culicines on
left, anophelines on right. Eggs of
culicines laid in rafts or egg-boats or
singly, but never provided with air-
sacs. Eggs of anophelines laid singly
and provided with air-sacs.

Culicine larvae have distinct breathing
tube or siphon, and hang at angle from
surface. Anopheline larvae have no
long breathing tube and lie just under
surface and parallel with it. Culicine
pupae usually have longish breathing
trumpets and hang nearly straight
down from surface. Anopheline pupae
usually have shortish breathing trumpets and do not hang straight down.
Culicine adults rest parallel with surface, have unspotted wings and short
palps in females. Anopheline adults
rest at an angle with the surface, have
spotted wings and long palps in
females.

are lodged at the tip of a prominent horn or breathing tube, which is
very short or absent altogether in anopheline larvae. In addition
there are flattened, leaflike tracheal gills on the last segment of the
abdomen so that the larvae can survive for some time below water,
but they must come to the surface from time to time to fill their
tracheae with air through the respiratory horn. The body of the larva
is slightly heavier than water so that it sinks slowly towards the bottom
and has to rise to the surface by jerky movements of its abdomen
from side to side. It can hang suspended from the surface film by
opening the little pointed plates at the tip of its respiratory horn which
form a little star at the surface but which close over the spiracles when
the larva goes below. Anopheline larvae have star-shaped hairs along

the back which also serve to hold them up when resting at the surface. Culicine larvae always rest at the surface with the body hanging down at an angle but anopheline larvae rest parallel with the surface.

The larvae cast their skin four times and take from a few days to two or three weeks to reach full size, the time depending on the temperature and the amount of food available. After the fourth moult they change into comma-shaped pupae. The "head" of the pupa is really the combined head and thorax and the curved portion is the abdomen. Unlike the larva, the pupa is lighter than water and it rises to the surface as soon as it stops swimming. Instead of having spiracles at the hind end of the abdomen, at the tip of a respiratory horn, the pupa has two breathing trumpets on the back of its thorax, so that, as it rises to the surface, these automatically pierce the surface film and the little creature can breathe. The pupae of most insects are inactive, but mosquito pupae can swim about by vigorously jerking their abdomens; they cannot feed. The breathing trumpet of culicine pupae are usually long and narrow from the side view, while those of anopheline pupae are short and broad. The pupal stage may last only a few hours in the case of those species that breed in rain pools liable to dry up quickly, while in other cases it may last two days to a week or more. The adults emerge rapidly from the floating pupae, through a longitudinal slit in the back of the thorax. They rest for a few moments, using the old pupal skins as boats and then fly off.

Most anophelines breed in natural accumulations of water, such as swamps, vleis, edges of streams and grassy ditches. They are not to be found, as a rule, breeding in blocked drains and gutters, tanks, and pots and tins round human dwellings, as culicine mosquitoes are. Although a number of different species of *Anopheles* are found in Africa, common and widely spread from the Cape to Cairo, only a few of these are known to be carriers of malaria. The rest are comparatively harmless, either because the malaria germs cannot survive and multiply in the insects, or because they do not enter dwellings and attack human beings but prefer the blood of animals. The commonest and worst transmitters of malaria in Africa are *Anopheles funestus* and *Anopheles gambiae*.

Anopheles funestus breeds in slow-flowing streams and the larvae may be found along the edges of shallow pools where the grass and reeds afford shade and where there is little or no actual movement in the water. It is, therefore, found where there are permanent streams and is present in greater or less abundance throughout the year. As it enters houses freely and seems to prefer human blood, it is mainly responsible for the endemic malaria in regions where it is found.

Anopheles gambiae, on the other hand, breeds in shallow temporary pools that are fully exposed to the sunlight. When the rainfall is heavy and there are many pools about on the veld this species can breed up rapidly and spread widely, and is, therefore, largely responsible

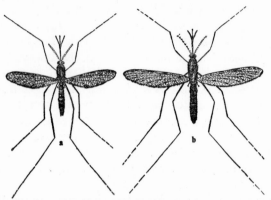

FIG. 131—The two worst Malaria Carriers in Africa: (a) *Anopheles gambiae*, (b) *Anopheles funestus*.

for epidemic outbreaks of the disease. Although *gambiae* enters houses and feeds on human blood it does not, as a rule, remain in a dwelling after it has finished feeding, but seeks a damp, dark sheltered spot outside for its resting place during the day. Some years ago *gambiae* was carried accidentally from Africa to Brazil and there it established itself and multiplied rapidly, causing one of the worst and most widespread outbreaks of malaria ever known in that country. A determined campaign and the expenditure of large sums of money resulted in the extermination of the pest before it got entirely out of hand.

The yellow fever mosquito, *Aedes aegypti* (also referred to in literature as *Stegomyia fasciata* and *Aedes argenteus*) has been widely spread throughout the world by man's commerce and is found in all tropical and sub-tropical regions to-day. Its original home is believed to be West Africa. This small black mosquito, conspicuously marked with silvery white bands on its legs and abdomen and with a white lyre-shaped design on its thorax, is perhaps the most thoroughly domesticated species of them all, as it is seldom found except in the vicinity of houses and it shows a decided preference for human blood. It hides in the rooms and attacks stealthily, usually by day, crawling under the clothing and biting silently and without warning. It breeds in almost any accumulation of water in and about the house, in water barrels, tanks, tin cans, blocked roof gutters, vases and so on. As this mosquito is the principal carrier of the deadly yellow fever, and as it is common in many parts of the world where the disease does not

PLATE 55

(a) THE FLY-HUNTING WASP, *Bembex capicola*, female

(b) Larva on right, cocoon on left of *Bembex capicola*

PLATE 56

Wooden stand, with glass tubes in which several species of solitary bees nested

occur, there is a constant danger that, in these days of rapid travel, visitors may bring in the virus with them and cause an outbreak of the disease. That is why people going to tropical and sub-tropical parts to-day have to have the yellow fever inoculation. The disease is endemic in West Africa as well as in the warmer parts of the Americas, and a constant watch has to be maintained against the possibility of its spread.

The yellow fever mosquito is also mainly responsible for the spread of dengue or break-bone fever. Sudden outbreaks of this disease may occur in any part of the world where the mosquitoes are

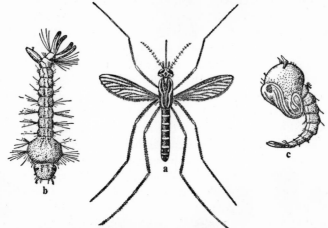

FIG. 132—The Yellow Fever Mosquito, *Aëdes aegypti:*   (a) adult female; (b) larva; (c) pupa.

found, spreading rapidly among the population and then disappearing as swiftly and mysteriously as they came. Although painful, the disease is very seldom fatal.

The disease known as filariasis, or elephantiasis in its aggravated form, is also transmitted by mosquitoes. The tiny thread worms are imbibed by the mosquito when feeding on an infected person and they go through certain developmental stages inside the mosquito's body. Later the worms make their way into the mosquito's proboscis and from here they get into other persons when the mosquito bites them. The tropical house mosquito, *Culex quinquefasciatus*, and the yellow fever mosquito are the principal agents in the spread of this disease, but it is known that several other species are also able to transmit it. Filariasis occurs in some of the warmer parts of Africa as well as in other tropical regions of the world. One of the most remarkable and puzzling features about the disease is the periodicity of the minute worms in the blood: they appear in swarms in the superficial blood

GG

vessels, just beneath the skin of infected persons at night, between 10 p.m. and 4 a.m., but disappear almost completely during the day, making their way into the deeper blood vessels inside the body. Thus, at the time when the mosquitoes are feeding, the parasites are in the position where they can get into the insect for the next stage in their development.

In addition to the above diseases, certain kinds of mosquitoes are the vectors of rift valley fever, horse sickness and blue-tongue of sheep.

Midges

On a still day, just before sunset, swarms of gnats or midges may often be seen flying above water. They are not mosquitoes, although superficially they look very much like them. They are harmless flies with no mouthparts capable of piercing the human skin; in fact, they do not feed at all in the adult state and their stomachs are filled with air. These midges belong to the family known as the *Chironomidae*.

If a net is swept through a swarm of these midges and the captured specimens are examined they will be found to be all, or nearly all, males. Like the mosquitoes, the males can easily be distinguished by their feathery feelers; the females have threadlike antennae with only short hairs on them. It is difficult to understand why the males assemble in these swarms and indulge in a dancing flight above the surface of the pool for hours at a time. It is said that the females which are ready to mate are attracted to the swarm and they dash into the midst of the dancing males, secure a partner and then leave.

Midges are often attracted into the house and may be seen on the window panes, usually to be mistaken for mosquitoes. A glance is enough, however, to distinguish them from their blood-sucking

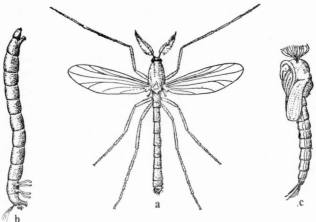

FIG. 133—A Common Midge, *Chironomus species:* (a) adult male; (b) larva; (c) pupa

relatives. A midge has not got a long proboscis on the front of its head, and it rests with front legs raised from the surface, whereas a mosquito always raises its hind legs. Furthermore, there are no scales on a midge's wings.

The female lays her eggs in stagnant water, in pools, barrels, ditches, blocked-up drains, and so on—the dirtier the water the more attractive it is to her. The eggs are laid in strings, several hundred being enclosed in a sausage-shaped rope of jelly, about an inch in length. These strings of eggs may be found attached by short, slender stalks to pieces of stick or dead leaves floating in the water. The egg-masses are large when compared with the size of the insects that laid them, but the greater part of the bulk is made up of the jelly surrounding the eggs and this, when first laid, consists only of a thin coating and it swells up enormously in the water, serving as a protective covering for the eggs.

The larva of the common midge is the well-known blood worm that can be found at any time of the year in the mud at the bottom of ponds and pools. The red colouring matter in the blood of the worm is the same as the colouring matter in our own blood, haemoglobin, but whereas the haemoglobin in human blood is contained in corpuscles, and not in the fluid of the blood, the fluid of the worm's blood is dyed with the substance, and not the corpuscles. In other words, the haemoglobin is dissolved in the larva's blood, much in the same way as the dye is dissolved in red ink. Most insects have colourless or bluish blood that contains copper, whereas haemoglobin contains iron. It is thought that the larva of the midge is a rare exception because it lives in stagnant water where oxygen is difficult to obtain; an efficient oxygen-carrier such as haemoglobin is, therefore, essential. The blood worm has two pairs of slender tubes on its hind end which serve as gills; they are filled with blood and serve to extract the dissolved air from the water.

The worm spins a flimsy tube for itself on the mud at the bottom of the pool. The silk for this tube comes from its salivary glands and particles of mud and decaying vegetation are glued to it. The larva remains inside this tube for the greater part of its time, moving its body with a rhythmical wavelike motion that causes water to flow through the tube and over its gills. It feeds on organic matter in the mud and on decaying vegetation. Sometimes it will leave the tube and swim towards the surface with a lashing movement of the body, twisting itself into figures of eight. The occasional journeys to the surface seem to be made in search of air. It does not trouble to return to its original home, but makes a new tube for itself wherever it happens to sink back upon the mud again.

When it is fully grown the larva is nearly an inch long and changes to a pupa inside the tube. It is still very slender and the head, legs and wings of the adult can be seen through the skin. Instead of four gills on its tail, its breathing organ now consists of dense tufts of threads on its thorax. When the adult is ready to emerge the pupa wriggles out of the tube and floats to the surface; it is lighter than water because its stomach is filled with air extracted by the gills from the water. At the surface the skin splits down the back and the fly emerges in the course of a minute or two, leaving the empty pupa case floating on the water. The life of the adult is limited to a few days as it cannot take any food.

The larvae of some species of *Chironomidae* may be found along the sea-shore, amid sea-weeds and in rock pools; others live in the sap beneath the bark of trees or in decaying organic matter; the larvae of some of those found in fresh water and that remain near the surface are green instead of red.

Gall Midges

Gall midges are tiny, delicate flies with long, feathery antennae and very few veins on their wings. The flies themselves are seldom noticed but their work on various kinds of plants is often conspicuous. For example, the common cone-bearing Cliffortia, *Cliffortia strobilifera*, is a shrub growing in damp places in the south-west Cape and, as its name implies, it bears numerous small cones, about three quarters of an inch long, green when young but grey when mature. These cones might easily be mistaken for the fruits of the plant, but they have nothing at all to do with the reproduction of the plant; they are abnormal growths caused by the presence of gall midges.

The female fly lays her pink eggs inside the young buds of the plant, just as they begin to develop at the bases of the leaves. The egg hatches into a legless maggot that feeds on the tender tissues of the bud and the irritation set up by the larva causes the bud to develop abnormally into a cone, instead of lengthening into a normal side branch. If one of the cones is pulled to pieces the pink larva will be found lodged at the base. Only one grub will be found inside a cone and it is a very small creature to cause such a large growth. Just behind its head, on the underside of its body, it has a curious Y-shaped projection of hard chitin; this is called the spatula or "breast-bone" and its function is unknown. It has been suggested that it is used by the insect to rasp the tissues when feeding.

When it is fully grown the larva spins a white silken cocoon and then changes into a pupa. A fortnight later the adult emerges from the cone.

There are many different species of gall midges found in this country but so far they have not been studied. Each species forms its own particular type of malformed growth on the fruits, flowers, stems and leaves of different kinds of plants. Perhaps the most interesting feature about the gall midges is the occurrence of a strange type of reproduction among certain species. There is a kind of gall midge

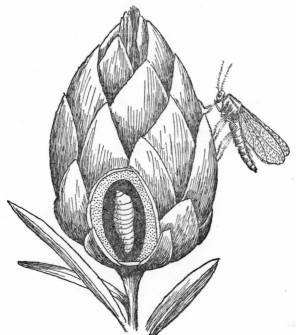

FIG. 134—Gall of a Gall Midge on *Cliffortia strobilifera*

found in Europe in which the female produces only four or five eggs. These are so large, when compared with the size of the insect itself, that they occupy practically the whole of her abdomen. This is a very small number of eggs for an insect and, if reproduction were by means of eggs only, the species would probably die out, as it has many natural enemies.

To make up for the lack of fecundity on the part of the adult female, the larvae are able to reproduce their kind. Simple ovaries form inside the body of the larva, one on each side of its body and each one containing sixteen eggs. These eggs develop without being fertilised; they hatch inside the larva's body and the young feed on the tissues of their parent, eventually killing it and eating their way out of the corpse. Each larva must perforce die in giving birth to its off-spring. All the eggs in the ovaries do not, as a rule, develop and the larva may produce from seven to thirty young.

This type of reproduction goes on for several generations and so from the four or five eggs laid by the original female a large number of larvae may develop. Sooner or later the larvae fail to produce eggs but grow to full size in the ordinary way and change into pupae. From these, males and females emerge which start the strange cycle all over again. This extraordinary mode of reproduction from immature individuals is called paedogenesis, a name which means 'reproduction from a child'. Besides certain of the gall midges, there are a few other kinds of flies belonging to the *Chironomidae* which also exhibit this phenomenon, as well as some jelly-fish and some parasitic worms. So far no case of paedogenesis is known among African gall midges, but it is quite likely that there are species among which it occurs.

The gall midges form a family known as the *Cecidomyidae*. Most of them live in galls during the larval stage but some are predacious and live on other insects, while a few live in excrement and decaying vegetation.

Fungus Gnats

The fungus gnats form another family of small flies that look something like mosquitoes or midges. They are found in damp, shady places in wooded kloofs, in cellars and sheds and in the neighbourhood of manure heaps. The larvae are slender worms, grey in colour with a small black head and they may often be found living gregariously in fungi, in moist, decaying wood and in rotting vegetation and manure. They give off much slime as they move about and so form a slimy web in their food in which they wriggle actively when disturbed. The larvae of some species have the strange habit of migrating when fully grown in a dense crowd of several thousand individuals that form a writhing string, like a grey snake, which may be several feet long and two or three inches wide. These have been dubbed "snake worms" in the United States. The larvae and pupae of some species are brightly luminous, giving off a much brighter light than the glow-worm and it is said the luminescence comes from the malpighian tubes. These flies form the family known as the *Mycetophilidae* and although they are quite numerous in suitable places in Africa they have not been studied here in any detail.

Blood-sucking Midges

A walk over mountain slopes in the spring and early summer, in the neighbourhood of shallow, swift-flowing streams, may be made v ery unpleasant by the irritating attentions of clouds of small midges. Th ese little insects fly around the face and settle particularly on those parts of the skin that are moist with perspiration. Their bites vary in their effects on different people; they raise small red weals on the skin of some and cause an intolerable itching, while other people hardly

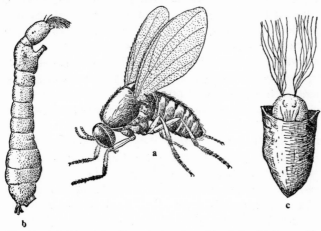

FIG. 135—The Fowl Midge, *Simulium nigritarsis:* (a) adult; (b) larva; (c) pupa in its case. The fly is only about one tenth inch long and grey in colour.

notice them. These midges are all females because, as in the case of mosquitoes, only the females are blood-suckers. The males are rarely seen; in fact, to obtain them it is usually necessary to rear them from the immature stages. They belong to a family of small flies widely spread over the world, known as the *Simuliidae*, and most of them are only about one tenth of an inch long and black or grey in colour.

The black-footed Simulium, *Simulium nigritarsis*, is very common at the Cape in spring. The female, when about to lay her eggs, seeks out a shallow, swift stream and deliberately crawls down the side of a stone or other object into the water. Her body is enclosed in a bubble of air when she does this, the air being entangled in the hairs that clothe her body. The eggs are very small, yellow and glued together in a flat mass which may be found adhering to the underside of stones and twigs and leaves in the water.

After ten days or a fortnight the eggs hatch and give rise to tiny worms shaped something like Indian clubs, with the hind part of the body swollen. There is a sucker at the tail end by means of which the larva can adhere firmly to a stone, thus preventing the turbulent mountain torrent from carrying it away. In front, just behind the small head, there is a projection which consists of the creature's only pair of legs fused together. This double leg is armed with spines and the larva can crawl over the rock like a looper caterpillar fixing the spines in front and then letting go with its sucker and bringing the hind end of the body forward, bending its body into a loop as it does so. Usually, however, the larva is content to remain fixed by its sucker to a stone just beneath the surface of the water where the current is swiftest. On its head it has two prominent brushes, each bearing a fringe of about fifty long, dark bristles. By means of these brushes it catches the micro-organisms that form its food. Jutting from the anal aperture are three or four short tubes, like small sausages: these are the gills by means of which it breathes. This breathing apparatus is only efficient in highly aerated streams and so the larvae soon die if they are put into a jar of water; they can be reared only in running water.

When the larva is fully grown it is nearly half an inch long and dark grey in colour. It spins a cocoon of brown silk attached firmly to a stone or other object beneath the water. The cocoon is cone-shaped, open at the top, and inside this shelter the larva changes to a pupa. It now looks something like a tiny pink moth chrysalis, with two tufts of long threads jutting out from the thorax. These tufts are the gills and they protrude from the cocoon and wave about in the water.

The adult fly emerges from the pupa in a remarkable manner. The danger it has to overcome is that of being swept away in the swift current when it makes the change from the helpless water-dwelling pupa to the six-legged, two-winged fly adapted for a life in the air. When it is ready to emerge air is collected from the water by the two gills and secreted round the body of the adult, inside the skin of the pupa. Finally the pupal skin splits and the adult is shot up to the surface, carried by the bubble of air.

The black-footed Simulium may be a serious pest of poultry kept in runs not far from a stream where they breed, as they attack the birds at night and suck their blood. In Central Africa, from Uganda to the west coast, there is a common species well named *Simulium damnosum*, as it is the carrier of a parasitic worm that causes unpleasant cysts to form beneath the skin of infected persons. The cysts vary in size from that of a pea to a pigeon's egg and they contain large numbers of the tiny worms. The young worms produced by the female burrow in all directions in the skin and a Simulium biting such a person readily becomes infected and capable of carrying the parasites to other persons. Natives living in the neighbourhood of streams where the flies breed are often badly infested.

Worm Lions

There are only about a dozen species of worm-lions known in the whole world. Six of these are found in South Africa, three in the

PLATE 57

(a) THE WATSONIA WASP, *Dasyproctus capensis*, female, surrounded by the flies she has captured to stock one cell of her nest. Note her egg on the fly on the left of the bottom row.

(b) Some of the glass tubes from the stand shown on Plate 56. Tube No. 105 contains a nest of the CARDER BEE, *Anthidium junodi*; Tube No. 8 contains a nest of the LEAFCUTTER BEE, *Megachile venusta*; Tube No. 64 contains a nest of the MEMBRANE BEE, *Nothylaeus heraldicus*; Tube No. 97 is enclosed in a length of bamboo tube, to keep the contents in darkness in the laboratory.

PLATE 58

(a) A LEAFCUTTER BEE, *Megachile venusta*, atthe entrance to her nest

(b) Two Eucalpytus leaves, with pieces cut out by a Leafcutter Bee

Mediterranean region and two in America. Where they occur, they are quite common if one knows where to look for them. The pit made by the worm-lion is so similar to that made by the well-known ant-lions that it is impossible to distinguish one from the other unless you dig out the owners. It is about an inch to an inch and a half across at the top and half to three quarters of an inch deep and is always made in fine sand or dry, dusty soil.

The worm-lion dislikes a damp environment; you will never, therefore, find its pit in wet soil. For preference it chooses the loose, dusty soil beneath an overhanging rock or on the lee side of a dense bush or hedge, where it is protected from the rain. If you come across some of these pits you can easily capture the inhabitants by digging a little of the soil from the bottom of the pits and spreading it on a piece of paper. The worm-lion is about half an inch long, grey, blind and legless, with the hind end of the body broader than the head end. It has a small pore for a mouth, armed with two black hooks.

When first removed from its home it lies still and rigid, coiled in the shape of an 'S', and always on its back, for this strange creature lives, moves and has its being in the reverse of the normal position. After a time it comes to life and attempts to escape by burrowing into the soil. When digging a new pit for itself the larva lies on its back just beneath the surface of the soil and continually jerks its head up as it moves slowly round in a circle, throwing out the sand so that a circular groove is formed. As it moves round and round the circle becomes smaller, and its head jerks tirelessly all the time, the hole becoming deeper until finally the larva is lodged at the bottom of the conical pit. When it is safely installed in its home the larva lies motion-less at the bottom of the pit, for days if necessary, with its body completely concealed or with the head and the first two or three segments uncovered. If an insect, such as an ant or small beetle, stumbles into the pit the worm-lion at once springs into activity. Its head jerks up, striking blindly and trying to coil round the victim. Several attempts may be needed before it manages to get a grip and drive home the two pointed hooks in its mouth, injecting poisonous saliva as it does so.

As soon as this happens the victim dies and is pulled below the surface, where it is devoured. As is the case with the ant-lion (see page 133) there is no connection between the worm-lion's stomach and its intestine, so that it does not excrete waste matter in the ordinary way. A dark mass can be seen near the hind end of its body; this is the waste matter accumulated at the base of the stomach and it is only got rid of just before the full-grown larva changes into a pupa. The length of time the larva takes to reach full size depends on its

HH

luck in obtaining food. If victims are scarce it may take a year or more to grow up, but it reaches maturity much more quickly if food is abundant.

When it is fully grown the larva stops feeding and allows its pit to fall into disrepair. Buried about an inch beneath the surface, it makes a rough sort of tubular cocoon coated with sand grains and there it changes to a pupa. After two or three weeks the pupa wriggles to the surface and the adult fly emerges. It is slender, long-legged, nearly half an inch long, with smoky brown wings. Its body is smooth and shiny, brown and yellow, and its head bears two large eyes and a long beak. The common species in South Africa is known to science as *Lampromyia brevirostris*. It is not known what the flies feed on. They are not found on flowers and they refuse to feed in captivity on honey or sugar and water and they seem to be too feeble to capture other insects and suck their juices, despite their fierce-looking beaks. The females seek out suitable spots where the soil is dry and deposit their eggs there so that the larvae, when they hatch, find themselves in a favourable environment.

Worm-lions belong to the family of flies known as the *Leptidae*, slender, smooth flies of moderate size. Their larvae are predacious; some live in water, others in rotten logs and still others in damp soil and leaf mould. The worm-lions are exceptional in their habits and are the only fly larvae that dig pits for the capture of their prey.

Horse Flies

Horse flies, or blind flies as they are often wrongly called, belong to the large and important family of moderate to large-sized flies known as *Tabanidae*. They are active on warm, sunny days and the females are well-known as irritating blood-suckers, but the males subsist mostly on nectar and are harmless. The mottled horse fly, *Haematopota ocellata*, is very common and may be taken as our example of the group.

In the male the eyes are so large that they occupy the greater part of the head, meeting in the middle line on top. They are hairy and shine with beautiful iridescent colours in the living insect. The facets or lenses on the upper part of each eye are larger than those on the lower half, as they are in the *Simuliidae* and some other flies, but it is not known why this should be. The eyes of the female are also large and beautifully coloured but they do not meet in the middle line of the head, nor are they hairy.

The blood-sucking habit makes the female horse flies potential carriers of disease-causing organisms, but few of them have so far been convicted of this. In West Africa certain species are the carriers

of a parasitic worm, called loa-loa. These minute thread worms live
in the tissues of human beings and, when the eggs hatch, the tiny worms
are set free in the blood. A horse fly sucking the blood of an infected
person is infected in its turn and the worms go through certain developmental stages in the fly's muscles. Eventually the parasites make their
way into the mouthparts of the fly and enter the wound in the skin of
the next person attacked.

Some horse flies have very long beaks that project in front of the
head and are more than twice as long as the body. The males use

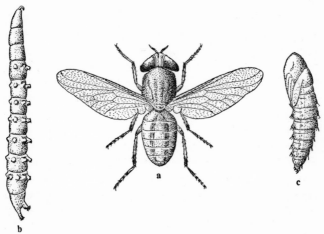

FIG. 136—The Banded Horse Fly, *Tabanus kingi:* (a) adult female; (b) larva; (c) pupa

their long proboscs for sipping nectar from deep flowers whilst
hovering on the wing. The female, on the other hand, bends her long
proboscis to one side when sucking blood and inserts only the short,
stabbing lancets. Like that of the mosquito, the long lower lip is
grooved along the upper side and the six lancets that make the wound
lie in this groove. If one of these flies is caught and the tip of the
proboscis bent down, the cutting mouthparts will be displaced from
the groove and it will be seen that they are only about one third as
long as the whole proboscis. These long-tongued horse flies belong to
the genus *Pangonia*.

Horse flies breed in water or damp soil. The female lays her eggs
in masses on the leaves of water plants or on grass, twigs or stones
close to the water. The larvae drop into the water when they hatch or
they burrow into the damp soil at the water's edge. Little is known
about the details of the life histories of the various species. The larva
is predacious, with a small head armed with sharp, curved jaws. It
feeds on the juices of water insects, small tadpoles and worms, which

it spears with its sharp jaws. It is said that some of the larger kinds can inflict a painful bite.

When the larva is fully grown it forms a cell just beneath the surface of the soil and there changes into a pupa. The pupa looks like a small moth chrysalis and it can be recognised by the two spiracles on its back, shaped like small ears. The abdomen is armed with rows of spines. The larval stage is long but the pupal stage lasts only two or three weeks.

Robber Flies

The family of flies known as robber flies, *Asilidae*, includes a large number of species with many representatives in Africa. They are bristly flies with powerful legs and elongated bodies, grey or brown and varying from about half an inch to an inch and a half in length. A prominent tuft of long, stiff bristles on the front of the head is characteristic of them. The popular name of these flies is not quite accurate as they are not robbers, but assassins that slay and devour.

Robber flies are among the keenest sighted of insects and they seem to be quite fearless as they will attack insects much larger than themselves, regardless of whether they are armed with stings or not. Flies, bees, wasps, beetles, dragon-flies, butterflies, plant bugs, all are liable to fall victims to these fierce hunters. The strong legs, armed with bristles, stout claws and pads form efficient grasping organs when the fly swoops down on its victim like a miniature hawk and stabs it with the sharp proboscis that juts out in front of its head. It is not known whether the robber fly injects poison when it strikes but it is probable that saliva is introduced into the wound and kills the prey in a few seconds.

Very little is known about the life histories of our robber flies but they are probably similar to those of overseas members of this large and widely spread family. The larva is a cylindrical maggot, dark grey in colour, with a small pointed head armed with a pair of sharp, curved jaws. It is predacious and generally found in soil or in leaf-mould. There are certain robber flies in Africa, *Hyperechia* species, that closely resemble carpenter bees in appearance and the larvae of these flies are found in burrows in dead wood close to the burrows of the bees, and it is thought that they prey upon the larvae of the bees.

Bee Flies

The bee flies, *Bombyliidae*, form a large family, with numerous species in Africa. Many of them are short, plump, hairy insects that look very much like bees, except that they have only one pair of wings, while others are elongate and resemble robber flies, hover flies and

wasps. They are of moderate or large size and most of them have a
long, slender proboscis projecting in front of the head. The adult
flies all feed on nectar and pollen and they may be found hovering
among the flowers on hot, sunny days. Often they may be seen settled
on the ground or on stones in the blazing sunshine, taking short,
hovering flights from time to time and returning again and again to
the same spot. As they cannot tolerate cold and wet and as they
depend on flowers for their food, they are abundant in the drier
regions when the flowers are out and are not common on grass veld
or in damp areas.

The life histories of only a few *Bombyliidae* are known and our
knowledge of even these is incomplete. They are all parasitic in the
larval stage, living on the eggs, larvae and pupae of other insects. At
least two species of bee flies, of the large genus *Systoechus*, are known
to parasitise the eggs of the brown locust and it is probable that other
members of this group prey upon the eggs of other kinds of grasshoppers and locusts. The female lays her eggs in the ground near or

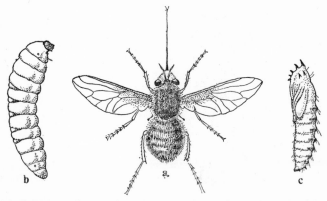

FIG. 137—A Destroyer of Locusts' Eggs, *Systoechus scabrirostris:*   (a) adult; (b) larva;
(c) pupa. The fly is black with brownish yellow hairs and about one inch long, including
the proboscis.

inside the egg-pods and the larvae, when they first hatch, are active
little creatures very much like the triungulins of the oil beetles (see
page 241), with six bristles instead of legs and a pair of long bristles on
the tail end. They seek out the locusts' eggs buried in the soil and
establish themselves in their midst.

Before it starts feeding, the young larva casts its skin and under-
goes a marked change of form, becoming a fat legless grub. It devours
the eggs and grows to a length of about half an inch by the time it is
ready to pupate. Then it burrows into the soil beside the egg-pod,
hollows out a cell for itself and changes into a pupa which is armed

with stout spines on its head and rows of stiff bristles on the abdominal segments. It uses these spines and bristles to make its way up through the soil to the surface when the adult is ready to emerge. Often large numbers of the locusts' eggs are destroyed by these parasites, which thus play a part in keeping down the numbers of this pest.

Other species of bee flies are known to prey upon tsetse flies, the caterpillars of certain moths, and the larvae of solitary bees and wasps, but precise details concerning their life histories are lacking.

Hover Flies

Hover flies, *Syrphidae*, form a large family of flies of varied habits and most are brightly coloured, striped, spotted or banded with yellow on a blue or black background. Frequently they may be seen poised in the air with rapidly vibrating wings and from this habit they get their popular name of hover flies. They visit flowers for the sake of the nectar and pollen and may be mistaken for bees or wasps, but can be readily distinguished by their single pair of wings. One of the largest,

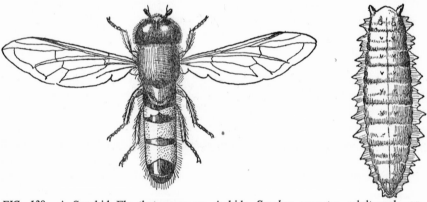

FIG. 138.—A Syrphid Fly that preys on Aphids, *Syrphus cognatus*, adult male on left, larva on the right.

commonest and best known members of the family is the drone fly, so called because it closely resembles a drone bee in appearance. This fly, *Eristalis tenax*, as well as some close relatives belonging to the same genus, often comes into houses and buzzes against the window panes.

The female lays her oval white eggs in small clusters at the edge of stagnant pools of dirty water, usually in a slight hollow in the mud where the eggs are sheltered from the direct rays of the sun. Any accumulation of foul water suits her: a blocked-up drain, a pool containing decaying vegetation and animal remains, the tub in which the gardener is preparing liquid manure, a puddle behind the stable in which horses or cows are kept. The eggs hatch into grey maggots, each with a slender tail, and they drop or creep into the water and feed on decaying organic matter, bacteria and protozoa.

Although the rat-tailed maggot, as the larva of the drone fly is called, lives in water it is an air-breather and will quickly drown if it cannot gain access to air. It has two spiracles at the tip of its tail and these lead to two slender tracheae that pass down the tail into the body. The tail is telescopic and, as it creeps about on the mud at the bottom of the pool, the larva elevates its tail so that the tip just projects above the surface. The tail can be extended until it is a slender thread three or four inches long, but if the larva goes into water deeper than this it must come to the surface from time to time to get air.

The larva has an elaborate filter in its pharynx, consisting of nine stiff Y-shaped plates, parallel with one another and with the arms of the Y shredded so that they form an efficient strainer which retains particles of food as the water passes between them. A pump in the insect's pharynx keeps the water moving in and out and thus this tiny maggot may be said to feed much in the same way as the gigantic baleen whales.

When the larva is fully grown it leaves the water and buries itself in the damp soil besides the pool. Here it changes into a brown pupa, easily recognised by its stump of a tail, and two or three weeks later the adult fly emerges. It is thought that the close resemblance of a drone fly to a honey-bee gave rise to the curious belief of ancient times that swarms of bees could be produced from the rotting carcase of a horse or ox. Many ancient writers repeat this story, from Ovid and Virgil. It is probable that some observant persons long ago noticed drone flies hovering over a dead, putrescent animal and later saw numbers of the flies emerging from the neighbourhood of the filthy liquid under the corpse and assumed they were bees. It has been suggested, too, that Samson's famous riddle, "Out of the eater came forth meat, and out of the strong came forth sweetness," was also due to the fact that he mistook drone flies hovering over the dead lion for bees.

The larvae of many hover flies are predacious and live on aphids, and they play an important part in keeping down the numbers of these pests. These hover flies are mostly slender and marked with yellow on brown or black. The female lays her small oval white eggs among the aphids on the infested plants. The larvae are sluglike, often marked with green or brown, pointed at the front end and with two spiracles on a small, dark coloured prominence at the hind end. They creep over the leaves and twigs, spearing the aphids and sucking their juices. When they are fully grown they fix themselves in sheltered spots on the plant, change into oval pupae, and a few days later the adults emerge. A little searching during the spring and summer months will generally reveal the presence of eggs, larvae and pupae of these flies on plants which are badly infested with aphids.

The larvae of still other species of hover flies, *Microdon* species, may be found in ant's nests. They are small, oval, white and flattened and they can only move about very slowly. The ants tolerate the

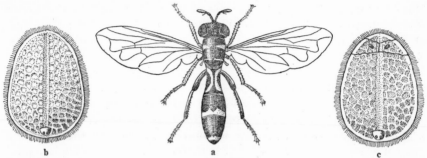

FIG. 139—The Ants' Nest Scavenger, *Microdon illucens:* (a) adult; (b) larva, a scavenger in ants' nests; (b) pupa. The fly is about one third inch long and black and yellow.

presence of these larvae in their nests because they apparently do no harm, but are scavengers, feeding on dead and dying ant larvae and pupae and on any waste organic matter in the nest. The larvae pupate inside the nest and the adults make their way out into the open air after they emerge.

Fruit Flies

The common or Mediterranean fruit fly, *Ceratitis capitata*, the Natal fruit fly, *Pardalaspis cosyra*, and the Rhodesian fruit fly, *Pardalaspis quinaria*, are very well known because of the harm they do to ripe fruits of all kinds. They are pretty little insects, slightly smaller than the house fly, with striking colours and wings mottled with smoky markings. They may be seen in the orchards, resting on the leaves of the trees, with wings held in a characteristic fashion, running to and fro and taking short flights. The life history of all of them is similar.

The female has a sharp ovipositor by means of which she pierces the skin of the ripening fruit and deposits her oval white eggs in small groups just below the surface. The larvae that hatch from the eggs burrow through the pulp, causing soft patches which soon decay. When fully grown they are about a quarter of an inch long, typical fly maggots with pointed head end and blunt hind end on which two spiracles are lodged. If removed from the fruit and placed on a hard

PLATE 59

(*a*) The common CARPENTER BEE, *Mesotrichia caffra*, female above, male below

(*b*) A female CARPENTER BEE, *Mesotrichia caffra*, at the entrance to her nest

PLATE 60

(a) A TOKTOKKIE BEETLE, *Psammodes reichei*

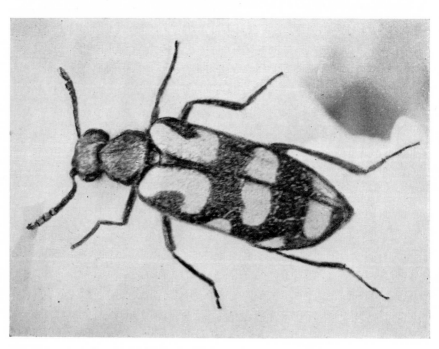

(b) C. M. R. BEETLE, *Ceroctis capensis*

flat, surface they will try to progress by wriggling for a time and then, one after another, they will be seen to bend into a circle, bringing their pointed mouthparts into contact with the hind spiracles; after a short pause they will straighten with a jerk that causes them to leap an inch or so through the air.

The full-grown larvae leave the fruit and drop to the ground where they bury themselves as quickly as possible. On hard soil, in hot sunlight, they jump erratically in the manner just described in order to reach a suitable spot for burrowing as quickly as possible. Safely lodged in a cell beneath the surface the maggot shortens and thickens, its skin hardens and forms a puparium inside which the pupa is formed. A few days later the adults emerge. There are several generations a year, as long as there is fruit ripening in the orchard. The adults hibernate during the winter; in badly infested orchards numbers of the flies may often be found clustered together in sheltered spots on the trees.

Besides the three species already mentioned, there are a large number of fruit flies found in Africa, belonging to the family *Trypetidae*. The larvae of all of them feed on plants. Many of them are found in fruits and seeds of various kinds of native plants; some feed in the flower heads of the Compositae; other burrow in stems and buds, while still others form galls. The pumpkin fly, *Dacus vertebratus*,

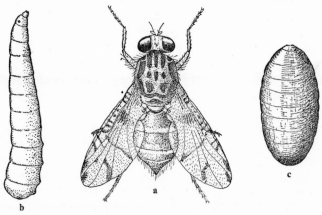

FIG. 140—The Common Fruit Fly, *Ceratitis capitata:*   (a) adult female; (b) larva; (c) puparium.

is a slender, reddish brown fly which breeds in cucumbers, marrows, water-melons and pumpkins and which frequently does considerable harm. The olive fly, *Dacus oleae*, is a closely allied and very similar insect that breeds in wild and cultivated olives. The tomato fly, *Trida-*

II

cus pectoralis, often does much damage to tomatoes in the warmer parts of the country.

Vinegar Flies

If some over-ripe fermenting fruit is left exposed on a dish a number of small flies will soon be attracted to it. They are only about one eighth of an inch long, pale brown in colour, with red eyes, and they will be seen hovering about the dish and feeding on the juice. Tests have shown that these flies prefer a juice that contains about 20 per cent. of alcohol and a little acetic acid. That is why the rotting, fermenting fruit attracts them. They swarm around wine-vats, wine-presses and vinegar factories. Often one or more of them may come hovering in front of the mouth of a man who has just taken an alcoholic drink.

A careful search on the bruised, wet surface of the fruit, after it has been exposed to the flies for a day or so, will reveal the very small oval white eggs, each with two filaments on it like a pair of slender horns. It is suggested that these filaments are breathing organs which enable the embryo inside the egg to obtain air even when it is submerged in liquid, as is often the case. The egg hatches in one or two days into a blind, white legless maggot which wriggles its way among the rotten fruit, feeding on the fermented juice. It has a pair of spiracles on its hind end which are lodged on a fingerlike process which can be thrust in and out. It reaches full size in a few days and then seeks out a spot that is more or less dry and solid, where it can change into a pupa. Like the larvae of all the higher flies, it does not cast its skin when it pupates, but the last larval skin hardens to form an outer case, called the puparium, protecting the soft pupa inside. A few days later the adult emerges by pushing open a sort of triangular lid on the front end of the puparium.

There are a number of species of these flies, forming the family *Drosophilidae*, which are found in Africa as well as other parts of the world. Some of them are so abundant that they are a nuisance when grapes are being pressed and when fruit is being harvested and packed. They are only interested in the fruit after it has been damaged and has begun to ferment; they do not attack fruit on the trees. In addition to those which are found in fermenting fruit, there are other species which breed in animal excrement, and still others which lay their eggs on the leaves of various kinds of plants, and the tiny maggots burrow between the upper and lower surfaces of the leaves.

Because they are easily reared in large numbers in the laboratory and because there are many generations a year, vinegar flies have been largely used as subjects in the study of heredity. It has proved an admirable subject for such studies because it produces a number of variations in the breeding jars, such as in the size and shape of the wings, the colour of the body, the number and arrangement of the bristles, the colour of the eyes, and so on. These variations and the manner in which they are inherited have been carefully studied and the results obtained have thrown a flood of light on some of the problems of heredity. It may be said that the little vinegar flies have added more to our knowledge in this respect than any other creatures.

The Lesser House Fly

The lesser house fly, *Fannia canicularis*, is very common and widely spread. In spring and in autumn the males of this species may often be seen in houses, hovering below electric lights and chasing one another in short flights, but always returning to their favoured spot

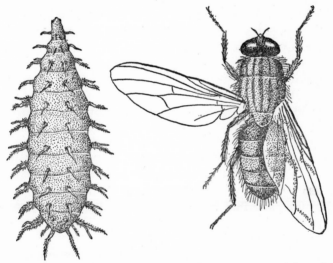

FIG. 141—The Lesser House Fly, *Fannia canicularis*. Larva on left, male on right.

just below the fittings hanging from the ceiling. The females do not behave in this way and they are not often found in houses. These flies may be mistaken for the common house fly but they can be recognised by their smaller size and by the venation on their wings: the two main veins reaching the tip of the wing do not meet at a point, but are separated at the ends.

The female lesser house fly lays her eggs in batches in decaying vegetable matter as a rule, but she may also oviposit in excrement, in soil soiled with urine, in fungi or in rotting wood. The larva can be recognised by the long, fleshy processes on its body. It is of a dark grey colour, somewhat flattened, and about a quarter of an inch long. As it becomes covered with debris that clings to the fleshy processes and as it moves slowly, it is not easy to find. When fully grown it buries itself in the soil and there pupates. The last larval skin, hardened and contracted, forms the puparium.

The latrine fly, *Fannia scalaris*, is very similar to the lesser house fly, but it is darker in colour and it does not come into houses so freely. The female lays her eggs in decaying animal and vegetable matter and in excrement and the flies may be bred in large numbers from buckets in privies if they are not emptied often enough. The larva is very like that of the lesser house fly but the fleshy processes on its body are branched and have a feathery appearance.

The above two species belong to the large family of small garbage flies of a greyish or black colour, known as *Anthomyidae*. There are many species found in this country but, apart from the cosmopolitan lesser house fly and latrine fly, little is known about their habits and life histories. The larvae of some species are parasitic on birds, while others are pests of certain crops.

The House Fly and Its Kin

The house fly, *Musca domestica*, is the commonest and most widely spread of all household pests. It is a potential carrier of such diseases as typhoid, dysentery and infantile diarrhoea and it is suspected also of being one of the vectors of infantile paralysis. Because the insect breeds in filth and feeds on filth it is a danger to health and its presence in and around the home should not be tolerated.

There are other kinds of flies that come into the house and that closely resemble this pest but the true house fly can be recognised by the following combination of characters: it has a fleshy proboscis beneath its head, four dark stripes on its thorax, and the two veins on the wing that go to the tip meet at a point, enclosing a large cell. The male can be distinguished from the female by his larger eyes: his eyes almost meet on top of the head while hers are separated by a space of about one third of the width of the head.

The house fly cannot swallow solid food; it can only feed on liquids or easily soluble substances. In feeding on sugar, the insect picks up a grain in its proboscis, turns it round and round and at the same time dissolves the sugar by discharging saliva on to it, and then it sucks up the sweet solution through its proboscis. The flies will feed on any liquid excrement they can find, the contents of the latrine bucket, the cess pool, the foul drain, the sputum flecks, and so on, and from these places they will fly into the house and get on to the milk jug, the sugar basin and the jam jar.

Inside its body the fly has a large crop in which it can store food not required immediately. In feeding, the fly satisfies its hunger by taking up a certain amount of food into its stomach and it then proceeds to fill its crop, which branches off from the gullet, as a reserve supply to provide for future needs. Inside the house it finds food more to its liking and it empties its crop on to the sugar, milk, butter, or

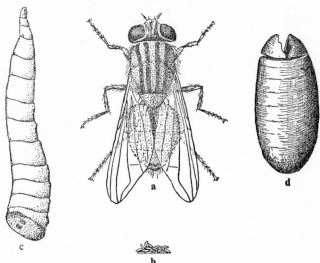

FIG. 142—The House Fly, *Musca domestica:* (a) adult female; (b) eggs; (c) larva, (d) puparium.

jam, in order to make room for the tastier substance. Furthermore, the fly's feet, each with two sticky pads that enable it to crawl up the window pane, are always contaminated with bacteria, so it is not surprising that the house fly is a serious menace to public health.

The favourite breeding places of the house fly are fresh, fermenting heaps of horse or pig manure, but it will breed in almost any accumulation of garbage and rotting vegetable matter. The female seeks out a small cavity in the manure and deposits a batch of about one hundred to one hundred and twenty white eggs, oval in shape and about a twelfth of an inch long. The warmth generated by the fermentation causes the eggs to hatch within twenty-four hours. A female may lay four or five batches of eggs before her ovaries are exhausted, making a total of about five to six hundred altogether.

The larvae are white, legless maggots, with a pair of hooks in the mouth instead of jaws and two spiracles at the rear end. As soon as they are hatched, they burrow into the manure heap and seek out a spot where the conditions of moisture and warmth are congenial. They feed for about five days on the liquid and easily soluble portions of the manure. When fully grown they leave the interior of the heap and seek out sheltered spots round the edge, where they burrow into the soil or creep beneath stones, loose rubbish or bits of old sacking.

The larva now contracts and takes on an oval form, the skin hardens and turns first red and then brown. This hardened outer skin is the puparium; no moult takes place at this stage, as is the case with butterflies, moths, beetles and other insects, as well as the lower flies. The pupa of the fly is formed inside the puparium. After five days the adult is ready to emerge, but it is a soft, weakly creature quite unable to struggle with sufficient violence to break open the hard puparium. A bladder, called the ptilinum, bursts through a slit on the front of the insect's head and this pulsates, being thrust in and out as the blood is pumped into it. The ptilinum acts as a miniature battering ram, striking the top of the puparium until it is pushed off and the fly is able to creep out. The fly also uses this bladder to push its way up through the soil to the surface. Arrived in the open air, the ptilinum is slowly withdrawn and the slit in

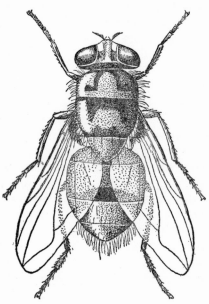

FIG. 143—The Green-tailed Sheep Blow Fly, *Chrysomyia chloropyga*, female

the head closes up; the blood is now forced into the wings and these expand and stiffen and the fly is able to fly away. This method of escaping from the puparium is not peculiar to the house fly; it is common to all the higher flies and they all have a characteristic scar on the front of the head which marks the position of the slit through which the ptilinum protruded.

The house fly belongs to the large and very important family known as the *Muscidae*. This family also includes the well known and common blow flies, so called on account of their habit of "blowing" meat, that is to say, laying their eggs on it. The blow flies include the extremely harmful sheep blow flies, of which three species do considerable damage to flocks in the Karoo. These are the green-tailed sheep blow fly, *Chrysomyia chloropyga*, the banded blow fly, *Chrysomyia albiceps*, and the green blow fly, *Lucilia sericata*. These sheep-maggot flies differ from ordinary flesh flies only in their habit of laying their eggs on live sheep as well as on meat. They are to be found in other parts of the country where no sheep are kept and there they breed entirely in carrion.

The green-tailed blow fly is a stoutly built fly, about four tenths of an inch long, metallic green and blue in colour, with a characteristic black mark on its thorax that makes it easy to recognise the species. The banded blow fly is green with dark bands across its body and it is a little smaller than the green-tailed fly. The green blow fly is bright metallic green without any bands or markings and it is about the same size as the green-tailed fly, only slightly more slender in build. All have a similar life history.

The female lays her small white eggs in some sheltered crevice in meat or in a freshly killed carcase on the veld or on the soiled wool of a living sheep, in batches of fifty to two hundred. The eggs hatch in twelve hours in hot weather but take three days or more in spring and autumn. The larvae are white legless maggots, pointed at the head end, very much like the larvae of the common house fly. As they creep over the meat they thrust their mouth-hooks in and out of the small pores that are their mouths and at the same time they eject copious saliva that moistens the meat and digests it. Thus digestion takes place outside the body of these insects and they form a sort of meat broth which they can suck up. A number of them feeding together will quickly dissolve the meat in their immediate neighbourhood, while the wool on the infected area of a sheep becomes wet and soiled and rots very rapidly. If the maggots are not destroyed or removed from the sheep they will eat away the skin and produce an ugly sore that attracts more flies to lay their eggs there and the animal may eventually be killed.

During the First World War many wounded men who had to be left lying helplessly in "no man's land" had their wounds infected with maggots of flesh flies. Surgeons noticed that such wounds often healed up more rapidly and cleanly than wounds not so infected. This led to the idea of treating deep-seated bone sores, known as osteomyelitis, with sterile maggots, but modern drugs have rendered this rather unpleasant mode of treatment unnecessary. The action of the fly larvae in helping to clean up an infection is easily understood when one remembers their method of feeding. Groping restlessly inside the wound with their pointed heads and pouring out their digestive juice, they dissolve away the dead and diseased tissue and kill the bacteria at the same time, thus acting as a powerful antiseptic.

The larvae may be fully grown in two days or they may take two or three weeks, depending on the temperature and the amount of food available. As soon as they have finished feeding, the maggots seek out a suitable spot where they may bury themselves in the soil or hide under the cover of a stone or some other dark, sheltered spot. Those bred on living sheep simply drop to the ground and hide. They change into puparia and the adults emerge in the manner already described for the house fly. The pupal stage lasts for a week in summer but larvae that reach full size in autumn spend the winter either as larvae in the soil or as puparia.

It should be remembered that the sheep blow flies normally breed in carrion and they play an important part in nature, bringing back the dead flesh into rapid circulation again among living things. Linnaeus declared that two flies can devour a dead horse more rapidly than a lion can, and he was referring to the flesh flies and their prodigious fecundity. The three species mentioned above only attack sheep when their wool is soiled, particularly in the region between the hind legs, or in spots where they have been wounded. The large bluebottle, *Chrysomyia marginalis*, which is so common all over the country, never attacks sheep but breeds only in meat.

The stable fly, *Stomoxys calcitrans*, is very common and widely spread, particularly on farms where animals are kept. It looks like the common house fly but can be recognised by the hard, black proboscis that projects in front of the head. This fly is a blood sucker and sometimes attacks human beings, thereby giving rise to the idea that the house fly is the culprit; but the house fly, with its soft, fleshy proboscis, is quite unable to pierce the skin and suck blood. The stable fly breeds principally in stable manure and refuse, but its larvae may also be found in decaying heaps of grass cuttings, sewage sludge, and so on.

Tsetse flies, *Glossina* species, are found only in Africa. There are a dozen different species and they are of the utmost importance as the vectors of nagana and sleeping sickness. Together with the malaria-carrying mosquitoes, they are mainly responsible for Africa remaining the unknown, unexplored dark continent for so long. The largest of the tsetse flies are little more than half an inch in length and the smallest are about the size of a house fly. They are very much alike in appearance and habits. The name "tsetse" is said to have been given them by natives in imitation of the buzzing sound made by these insects when they fly. They feed only on blood and they get most of their food from game animals, but they also attack human beings, domestic animals, crocodiles and other living creatures. Most of them like patches of forest and bush where there is warmth, damp and shade, so they are restricted to these areas, which are known as fly belts.

A tsetse fly can be recognised by its brown colour, by the manner in which it carries its wings folded like the blades of a pair of scissors

PLATE 61

(a) THE WRINKLED SCARAB, *Scarabaeus rugosus*, one beetle with its ball of dung, the other an uninvited guest

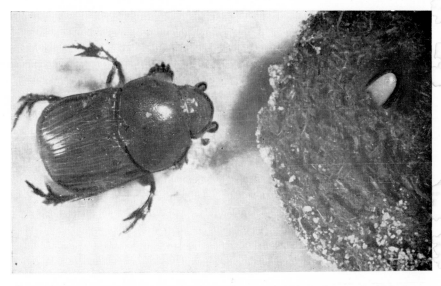

(b) THE BRONZE AND GREEN DUNG BEETLE, *Onitis aygulus*, with its large egg in the food mass

PLATE 62

(*a*) Larva of the Bronze and Green Dung Beetle, *Onitis aygulus*, in its cell

(*b*) A TROX BEETLE

when it is at rest, by the strong proboscis jutting out in front of the head, and by the arista (the stout bristle on each antennae) being feathered on one side only. The female does not lay eggs, nor has she any particular place where she breeds. Her eggs hatch one at a time inside her body. The larva is very much like that of the house fly,

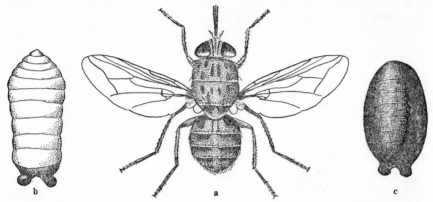

FIG. 144—The Tsetse Fly, *Glossina morsitans:* (a) adult; (b) larva; (c) puparium

except that it is shorter and broader and has two round, black swellings on the hind end of the body. It remains inside the female's body and is nourished by liquid food supplied to it by special glands. It is fully grown in about a fortnight and by that time the female's body is swollen with the large maggot inside. She seeks out a damp, shady spot and deposits the larva among dead leaves, beneath a fallen log, or beside a stone.

Soon after this another egg hatches inside her body and two or three weeks later she is ready to deposit another full-grown larva. So it goes on and the female may produce twenty or more larvae before she dies. As soon as a larva is dropped by a female it buries itself amid the dead leaves or in the soft, damp soil. Then its skin hardens and turns dark brown, to form the puparium. It is about a month before the adult emerges and it may live for four or five months.

There are large areas in Central Africa where it is impossible to keep domestic animals because of the tsetse flies and nagana. Many of the game animals on which the flies feed have the Trypanosoma parasites in their blood that cause nagana but the animals are immune and the germs do not seem to trouble them. But when these germs are transmitted to domestic animals by the flies such animals contract the disease and are killed. Sleeping sickness is a similar disease of human beings and in the past many thousands have died of it in parts of Africa.

JJ

Because the tsetse flies have no particular breeding places, the females just drop their larvae wherever they happen to be, these insects are very difficult to control. In some places the trees and bushes along the river banks and round the lakes have been chopped down. As a result there is no shade for the flies and they leave these cleared areas or die out. Attempts have been made to kill all of the game in some areas so that the flies are deprived of food, but it is by no means certain that the destruction of game animals will cause the flies to disappear: they may survive by feeding on the blood of smaller animals. The Harris tsetse fly trap catches large numbers of certain species of flies but it does not eradicate them altogether. In recent years the flies have been exterminated in Zululand by the use of D.D.T. dusted from aeroplanes and distributed by "bombs."

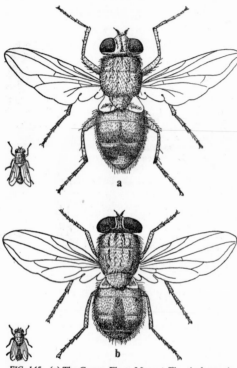

The tumbu fly, *Cordylobia anthropophaga*, is an unpleasant insect that is widely spread in the warmer regions of Africa, from Zululand right up to the Sudan. The female lays her eggs in sandy soil contaminated with urine or excreta, and sometimes on clothes hung up to dry and on bedclothes

FIG. 145—(a) The Congo Floor Maggot Fly, *Aucheromyia luteola;* (b) The Tumbu Fly, *Cordylobia anthropophaga.*

opened up to air. The tiny larvae from these eggs burrow into human skin when they come into contact with it and, unless removed, they develop in the flesh just below the skin and cause swellings like boils. If one of these swellings is closely examined a small opening will be seen, usually darker in colour than the rest of the lesion and with moisture round it. This is the hole through which the maggot obtains air. Babies are often attacked and it may be that the flies lay their eggs on the clothing, particularly in the region of the neck, while the child is lying in its cot. The natural hosts of these flies seem to be rats and other animals; cats, dogs and monkeys are also infected. If the larvae are not removed, they reach full size beneath the skin and then drop out on to the ground, where they bury themselves for pupation.

The Congo floor maggot, *Aucheromyia luteola*, is closely related to the tumbu fly and is also found widely spread throughout tropical and sub-tropical Africa. The female lays her eggs in the dust on the floor of native huts and the larvae which hatch from them hide in cracks and crevices during the day but creep out at night to feed on the blood of sleeping persons. The adult flies that develop from the Congo floor maggots are not blood-suckers, nor are the tumbu flies: only the larvae are harmful.

The termite guest fly, *Termitometopia skaifei*, is another member of this family that has a peculiar life history. The soft white larva of this fly, about half an inch long, is found in termite mounds at the

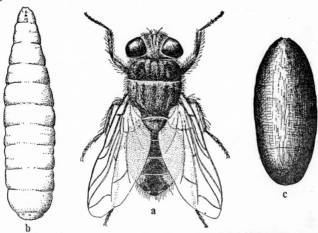

FIG. 146—The Termite Guest Fly, *Termitometopia skaifei:* (a) adult female; (b) larva; (c) puparium.

Cape during the summer months. It is fed and cared for by the termites, which seem to get from it a fatty exudation of which they are very fond. When it is fully grown in the autumn the larva burrows towards the outside of the mound, where it hollows out a cell for itself and pupates. The adult fly emerges in the following spring, is about the size of a blow-fly, dark grey in colour, and sluggish. Nothing is known about its egg-laying.

Warble Flies and Bot Flies

The warble and bot flies are stoutly built, hairy flies with vestigial mouthparts so that they cannot feed in the adult stage. They are all parasitic in the larval stage on mammals; the larvae found in the stomach and intestines are called bots, while those which live beneath the skin are known as warbles. Frequently when a buck is shot, large maggots are found just beneath the skin. Little is known about their life histories but they are obviously closely akin to the warbles of horses and cattle and we may reasonably assume that their ways are similar. The warble flies of cattle and horses, *Hypoderma bovis* and *Hypoderma lineatum,* lay their eggs singly on the hairs of the animals, chiefly about flanks and legs. The eggs hatch in a few days and the larvae bore their way into the skin and move about for several months through the body until they reach the gullet. Later they migrate again and finally make their way to just beneath the skin of the back, where they grow to full size, feeding on blood and serous exudations. When fully grown the maggots make their way out to the surface through holes they pierce in the skin and they fall to ground and bury themselves for pupation. It is very probable that the warbles

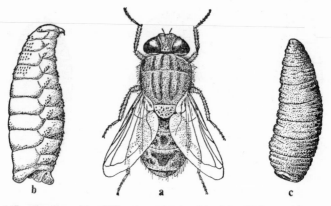

FIG. 147—The Sheep Nasal Fly, *Oestrus ovis:* (a) adult; (b) larva; (c) puparium.

commonly found on antelopes in this country have a similar life history.

The bot flies, *Gastrophilus* species, also lay their eggs on the hairs of horses, donkeys, mules and zebras, mostly on the fore quarters. The eggs hatch when they are moistened and rubbed by the animal licking itself and the young larvae are swallowed. They attach themselves to the walls of the stomach, where they feed on blood and grow into the well-known "bots". When fully grown they detach themselves and are carried through the intestine and finally ejected with the dung. They bury themselves in the soil for pupation.

The sheep nasal fly, *Oestrus ovis,* is a large fly, hairy and dull yellow or brown. The eggs hatch inside the body of the female and she deposits her tiny larvae in the nostrils of sheep and goats. They wriggle their way up into the nasal passage and attach themselves to the mucus membrane.   Here they grow slowly, taking eight or nine months to reach full size.   When fully grown they are stout, barrel-shaped maggots about an inch long and they loosen their hold inside the nose and wriggle out, or are sneezed out by the sheep and they fall to the ground, where they pupate.   There are a number of indigenous species of *Oestrus* that attack antelopes, bush pigs and other wild animals.

The above flies belong to a small family known as the *Oestridae* and they are all largish flies, often bee-like in appearance.

Tachinid Flies

Frequently small, oval white eggs may be seen attached to the sides of caterpillars.   If such caterpillars are kept and reared, burly, hairy flies will develop from them instead of butterflies or moths. These are parasitic flies belonging to the family *Tachinidae* and the larvae of them all are parasites of other insects, chiefly caterpillars, but they also attack beetles, grasshoppers and, to a lesser extent, members of other orders.

As a typical example of the family we may take the tachinid parasite, *Carcelia evolans*, of the wattle bagworm.   This is a dark grey fly marked with silver and it measures nearly half an inch in length. The female lays her oval white eggs on the front part of the wattle bagworm's body whilst it is feeding.   Although as many as five eggs may be found on one caterpillar only one fly can develop in a single bagworm.   The eggs hatch into tiny maggots very similar to those of the house fly and they burrow into the caterpillar's body where they

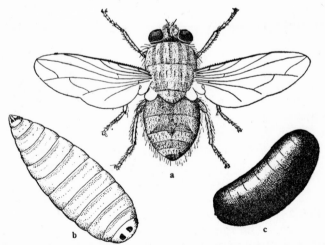

a

b   c

FIG. 148—The Tachinid Fly, *Carcelia evolans*, of the Wattle Bagworm: (*a*) adult female;
(*b*) larva; (*c*) puparium.

feed on the liquids and the fat body, at first avoiding the vital organs. One of the fly larvae gains a lead on the others in some way or other and the rest die. The survivor grows to a length of about half an inch and finally kills the caterpillar. The maggot leaves the dead body of its victim and may pupate inside the bag as it hangs on the tree or it may creep out and drop to the ground where it buries itself before pupation. There are two generations of these flies a year and they destroy large numbers of the bagworms.

Some tachinids lay a large number of very small eggs on the leaves of plants and caterpillars feeding on those leaves swallow the eggs. The eggs hatch inside the body of their host and the maggots burrow through the wall of the alimentary canal to get into the body cavity. In order to obtain air the parasite may pierce the skin of its host and place itself in such a position that the pair of spiracles on its hind end are at the small hole, or it may pierce one of the larger tracheae inside the body and thus make use of the caterpillar's own air supply. There are a large number of different species of tachinids and they are very common, playing an important part in keeping down the numbers of other insects.

The tachinid parasite of the honey bee, *Rondanio-oestrus apivorus*, is common and widely spread in Africa and it seems to be limited to this continent as it has so far not been recorded from any other part of the world. The adult flies may be found haunting bee hives at almost any time of the year, but they are commonest in summer. Only the females are to be seen at the hives. They are rather squat flies, grey with black markings and the same size as a house fly. If one of them

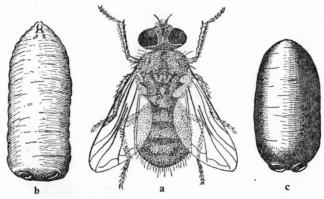

FIG. 149—The Tachinid Fly, *Rondaniooestrus apivorus*, of the Honey Bee: (*a*) adult female; (*b*) larva; (*c*) puparium.

is watched, it will be seen that she rests for a while, generally just above the entrance to the hive, with her head towards the entrance.

From time to time she flies up and mingles with the bees returning to the hive. Her movements are difficult to follow amid the busy throng, but she swoops down and just touches a bee as it is flying into the hive, and after having touched two or three in this way she settles once more on the side of the hive. Then she repeats the performance a few minutes later, and so it goes on. The bees that are touched by the fly do not hesitate in their flight but go straight into the hive as though nothing untoward had happened to them. The bees show no hostility to the flies, although hundreds of them are killed off by these harmless-looking parasites.

The fly does not lay eggs on the bees as she swoops on to them. Her eggs hatch inside her body and a large number of tiny maggots are packed like sardines in her oviduct. She deposits one of these newly-hatched maggots on the bee when she touches it. The tiny larva adheres to the bee because a little sticky fluid is exuded with it. It works its way between the segments of the bee's abdomen and burrows through the thin skin there into the bee's body. Here it lives on the fluids and, when it is fully grown, it occupies almost the whole of the bee's abdomen. It is a fat white maggot with two conspicuous black, circular plates on the hind end marking the site of the spiracles.

Despite the huge parasite it is carrying, the bee shows no signs of distress and works to the last. Death, when it comes, is very sudden. The parasitised bee drops to the ground, spins round furiously for a moment or two and then lies still. A few minutes later the larva breaks its way out of the dead bee's abdomen and proceeds at once to hide itself, in the soil if it is soft, or beneath a stone, amid dead leaves or other debris, where it pupates. About two months later the adult fly emerges. There are two generations of the flies a year, but the generations overlap and the flies seem to be comparatively long-lived, hence they can be found at the hives during the greater part of the year.

The Sheep Ked and its Kin

The sheep ked, *Melophagus ovinus*, is a wingless, blood-sucking fly that is found only on sheep. It is about a quarter of an inch long, dark brown in colour and covered with short hairs. Owing to its parasitic mode of life it has lost all trace of wings and it spreads from sheep to sheep by contact. One large egg at a time is produced in the ovaries of the female and this is not laid but is retained inside the body and nourished by the secretion of special glands until it is fully grown. The female deposits her fully-grown larva amid the wool and it is fixed in position by a sticky fluid which hardens rapidly. The skin of the larva hardens and turns brown to form a puparium and about three weeks later the adult ked emerges. The keds live for four or five months and a female may produce about a dozen young in this period. This insect is an important pest as it causes considerable irritation to the sheep and an animal may fall off in condition and rub and scratch itself so much that its fleece becomes ragged and the quality of the wool is lowered.

The ked belongs to a family of blood-sucking flies known as the *Hippoboscidae*. They are tough, flattened insects with leathery skin; some are wingless whilst others have a pair of well developed wings and are strong fliers. The horse fly, *Hippobosca rufipes*, is common in this country and may be seen around horses, irritating them by their bites and making them very restless. The ostrich fly, *Hippobosca struthionis*, is another well known member of this family and seems to limit its attentions to ostriches and other large birds. These squat red and black flies all reproduce their kind in the same way as the sheep ked, the maggots of the winged species usually burying themselves in the soil for pupation.

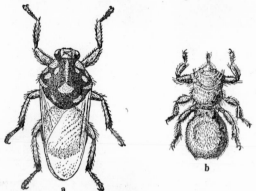

FIG. 150—(a) the Red-legged Horse Fly, *Hippobosca rufipes* ; (b) Sheep Ked, *Melophagus ovinus*.

The Bee Louse

The blind bee louse, *Braula coeca*, is well known to beekeepers as a tiny brown parasite found on bees, chiefly on the queens but also on workers and rarely on drones. In a badly infested hive the queen may have a dozen or more of these parasites on her back, but this is by no means common; usually only a few bees can be found with one or two of the parasites on them. The little creatures, only about an eighth of an inch long, cling tightly to their hosts but they can move about nimbly and leap from one bee to another; their claws are large and like curved combs and there are two sticky pads on each foot, thus it is difficult to remove one of them by force—often one or more of its legs will be left behind if it is pulled off the bee with a pair of forceps.

The female louse lays her flattened white eggs on the comb, where they are easily visible to the naked eye, round the edges of the cells and on the wax cappings. The eggs hatch out into tiny maggots that are obviously fly larvae, similar to those of the higher flies. The larvae feed on honey and pollen, burrowing along the cappings of the cells like miniature moles. When fully grown they change into puparia

PLATE 63

(*a*) **THE ZEBRA BEETLE,** *Stripsipher zebra.* It is about half an inch long.

(*b*) **THE LAWN BEETLE,** *Heteronychus arator.* It is about half an inch long.

PLATE 64

(*a*) A White Grub, root-eating larva of a Chafer Beetle

(*b*) THE GREEN PROTEA BEETLE, *Tetrastychus capensis. It is about an inch long.*

inside their tunnels and about a week later the adults emerge. It takes about three weeks from the hatching of the egg to the emergence of the adult.

The newly-emerged adult is white at first but it soon turns brown and wanders about until it can climb on to a bee. It cannot feed on the honey and pollen in the cells at this stage because it has only small sucking mouthparts; when it is hungry, it crawls down on to the front of the bee's head and tickles its host's mouthparts until the bee regurgitates a small drop of honey which the louse licks up. These

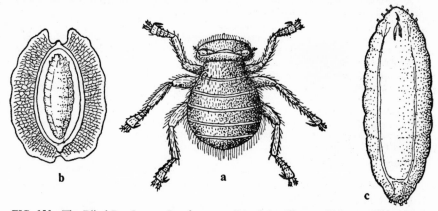

FIG. 151—The Blind Bee Louse, *Braula coeca*: (*a*) adult; (*b*) egg; (*c*) larva. The adult is brown and about one twelfth of an inch long.

parasites do little harm to their hosts. As far as is known there is only one species widely spread throughout the world and this is placed in a family all by itself, the *Braulidae*. Formerly it was believed that the life history of the bee louse was similar to that of the *Hippoboscidae*, so the *Braulidae* are placed next to this family, but later discoveries have shown that its life history is as described above and the exact position of this small family of peculiar, wingless flies is uncertain.

CLASSIFICATION

ORDER 19: *DIPTERA* (Flies)

Flies are two-winged insects, with the second pair of wings reduced to small sensory organs called halteres, or balancers. The mouthparts are suctorial. The tarsi are usually five-jointed. The metamorphosis is complete, the larvae being legless and blind, as a rule. A very large order of over 50,000 described species.

SUB-ORDER 1: *Orthorrhapha*
This sub-order includes the families of simpler flies in which the pupae are similar to those of beetles and butterflies and moths, and the antennae of the adults are more or less thread-like.

SERIES 1: *Nematocera*
Flies with threadlike antennae of many joints, longer than the head and thorax and the joints all alike.

KK

FAMILY 1: *Tipulidae*—CRANE FLIES
Slender, long-legged flies with long antennae of six or more joints. Larvae are elongated, grey or brown, with small head.

FAMILY 2: *Psychodidae*—MOTH FLIES OR SAND FLIES
Minute moth-like flies covered with long, coarse hairs, often mixed with scales. Larvae small grubs, with long bristles on the hind end, mostly aquatic or living in wet soil.

FAMILY 3: *Culicidae*—MOSQUITOES
Slender flies, mostly with an elongated proboscis. Antennae slender, plumose in males. Wings with scales along veins and round edges. Larvae and pupae are aquatic.

FAMILY 4: *Chironomidae*—MIDGES
Delicate flies that resemble mosquitoes but most of them lack the long proboscis. A few species are blood-sucking. Antennae slender, plumose in males. Larvae worm-like and live in water or damp soil.

FAMILY 5: *Cecidomyidae*—GALL MIDGES
Very small flies with long antennae adorned with whorls of hairs. Wings with few veins. Larvae live in galls on plants, or in excrement or decaying vegetable matter; a few are parasitic.

FAMILY 6: *Mycetophilidae*—FUNGUS GNATS
Small flies with long antennae, usually without whorls of hairs. Larvae worm-like with a small, dark head, living in fungi or in decaying vegetable matter.

FAMILY 7: *Simuliidae*
Small, stoutly built flies with broad wings with few veins on them. Males have large eyes meeting on top of head. Larvae wormlike, living in running water. The adults are blood-suckers.

SERIES 2: *Brachycera*
Flies with antennae shorter than the thorax, generally of only three joints, with the terminal joint elongated. Head of larvae small and incompletely developed.

FAMILY 8: *Leptidae*—WORM-LIONS AND OTHERS
Smooth, slender flies of moderate size, predacious on smaller insects. The larvae are wormlike and predacious, a few species form pits and are known as worm-lions.

FAMILY 9: *Tabanidae*—HORSE FLIES
Stoutly built flies with large eyes and a projecting proboscis adapted for piercing. Females are blood-suckers. Larvae are wormlike with small, retractile head, well developed antennae and strong mouth-hooks. They are carnivorous and found in damp situations.

FAMILY 10: *Asilidae*—ROBBER FLIES
Powerful, elongate, bristly flies, with a short, hard proboscis adapted for piercing. Moderate to large-sized, fierce hunters of other insects. The larvae are wormlike and live in soil, decaying wood or leaf mould and they are predacious or scavengers.

FAMILY 11: *Bombyliidae*—BEE FLIES
Very hairy flies, many resembling bees in appearance. Usually with a long, slender proboscis. Wings often with dark markings. Larvae are parasites on solitary bees and wasps, beetles, caterpillars and grasshoppers' eggs.

FAMILY 12: *Empidae*
Small bristly flies, something like small robber flies. Predacious on smaller insects, with a hard, horny proboscis adapted for piercing. Often dance in the air in swarms, like midges. Larvae are predacious.

FAMILY 13: *Dolichopodidae*
Small, bristly flies, metallic green or blue, with a short, fleshy proboscis, predacious upon smaller insects. Larvae found in damp situations and are predacious.

SUB-ORDER II: *Cyclorrhapha*
This sub-order includes the higher families of flies in which the larva does not cast its skin when fully grown, but the skin hardens and forms an outer case enclosing the pupa and is called a puparium. The adult breaks its way out of the puparium by means of a ptilinum, a bladder that emerges from a split in the head and serves as a

tiny battering ram. The adult fly retains the scar of the ptilinum on the front of its head after the bladder has been withdrawn. The antennae are short, three-jointed, with a strong bristle called the arista. The larva is a maggot with a vestigial head and usually with two pairs of spiracles, one at the head end and the other at the hind end.

FAMILY 13: *Syrphidae*—HOVER FLIES
Moderate to large-sized flies, often brightly coloured, smooth and shining. The larvae of many species prey upon aphides, others live in decaying organic material, some are scavengers in ants' nests and a few feed upon fungi and bulbs.

FAMILY 14: *Conopidae*
Moderate-sized flies, slender and smooth, look like small wasps, slow fliers, often seen at flowers. Larvae are parasites of adult bees and wasps, living in the abdomen of the host.

FAMILY 15: *Trypetidae*—FRUIT FLIES
Pretty little flies with mottled wings. Larvae are maggots found in various kinds of fruit; all are vegetarian; besides those living in fruit there are others that live in the flower heads of Compositae, that burrow in leaves or stems and that form galls on plants.

FAMILY 16: *Drosophilidae*—VINEGAR FLIES
Small flies with red eyes found in numbers wherever there is decaying, fermenting fruit, round wine vats, vinegar factories, and so on. The larvae are small white maggots that live in fermenting fruit; some are found in excrement and some burrow in the leaves of plants.

FAMILY 17: *Anthomyidae*
A large family of small to moderate-sized flies, resembling the house fly in general appearance. The larvae are vegetable feeders or live in decaying animal and vegetable matter; a few are carnivorous. The lesser house fly, *Fannia canicularis*, is the best known member of the family.

FAMILY 18: *Muscidae*
A very large and important family, including the house fly, blow flies and tsetse flies. The arista of the antenna is feathered to the tip, in some species on both sides, in others (such as the tsetse flies) on the top only. The habits and life histories of the members of this family are very varied, but the larvae are maggots that are essentially alike in their structure.

FAMILY 19: *Oestridae*—WARBLE FLIES AND BOT FLIES
Stoutly built, hairy flies with vestigial mouthparts. The antennae are short and more or less hidden in cavities in the front of the head. The eggs are laid on the hairy coat of animals and the larvae find their way into the stomach (bots) or beneath the skin (warbles).

FAMILY 20: *Sarcophagidae*—FLESH FLIES
Largish flies, grey as a rule, with striped thorax and marbled abdomen. The arista of the antenna is plumose only to the middle and the tip is bare. The larvae occur in carrion or are parasites of insects and other creatures, including worms, scorpions and spiders. The females of some species retain their eggs in their bodies until they hatch and they deposit the newly-hatched young.

FAMILY 21: *Tachinidae*
Stout-bodied, bristly flies, with the arista bare. The larvae are parasitic mainly on caterpillars, but some attack beetles, grasshoppers and other insects.

FAMILY 22: *Hippoboscidae*
Flattened insects with tough, leathery skin, with small head sunk into thorax, antennae small with only one joint, legs stout and armed with strong claws for clinging to hairs of host. Some are wingless. Blood-sucking parasites of mammals and birds. The larva is retained in the female's body until it is fully grown and then it is deposited and changes at once into a puparium.

FAMILY 23: *Braulidae*
Very small family including only blind bee louse, *Braula coeca*, a wingless parasite, clearly, from its development, a fly, but whose position in the order is uncertain.

(A number of families of flies that are not so frequently met with have been omitted from the above list.)

CHAPTER XIX

FLEAS

The Aphaniptera

Fleas form a small group sharply divided from all other insects because their bodies are flattened from side to side, and not dorso-ventrally, or from above downwards, as other insects are. They have no traces of wings but it is presumed that they originated long ago from winged ancestors and lost the power of flight because of their parasitic habits. In their development they show a slight affinity to the lower types of flies but, apart from this, they form an isolated group of doubtful affinities. More than five hundred species are known in the world and they are all blood-sucking parasites of birds and mammals. They are placed in an order by themselves called the *Aphaniptera*, or *Siphonaptera*.

Household Fleas

The fleas most commonly found in human dwellings are the dog flea, *Ctenocephalus canis*, the cat flea, *Ctenocephalus felis* and the human flea, *Pulex irritans*. The first two may be recognised, if examined under the lens, by the stout, dark brown bristles on the head and the prothorax, forming combs; these combs are absent in the human flea. They are all closely similar in their habits and life histories.

Both male and female fleas are voracious blood-suckers, and in this they differ from mosquitoes and horse flies, among which only the females feed on blood. When feeding, they inject saliva into the wound made by the sharp, lancet-like mouthparts and it is this saliva that causes the irritation and swelling. They are long-lived for such small insects; specimens have been kept alive in the laboratory for

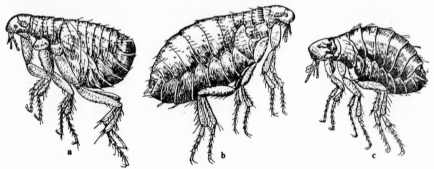

FIG. 152—Fleas: (*a*) the Human Flea, *Pulex irritans*, male; (*b*) the Dog Flea, *Ctenocephalus canis*, female; (*c*) the Fowl Flea, *Echidnophaga gallinacea*, female.

eighteen months and longer and it has been proved that, under suitable conditions of moisture and temperature, adult fleas can live for a year or longer without food.

The female deposits her small, oval white eggs, about the size of a pin's head, amid the fur of the animal on which she is feeding, or she may drop off and lay her eggs loosely on the ground. A woman who has been nursing a cat on her lap will, if she is observant, sometimes find fleas' eggs on her lap after the cat has jumped down. A dog, giving itself a vigorous shake inside the house, will often send a shower of eggs flying all round him. The dog's kennel or the favourite sleeping place of the cat usually has large numbers of eggs lying about in it, but they are so small they pass unnoticed.

The eggs hatch in about a week and give rise to small cylindrical larvae, without legs or eyes, pale yellow in colour. The little worms move about actively in the dirt and debris on the floor of the kennel, between the cracks of the floor-boards and in similar places. They feed on any bits of organic matter they can find, such as crumbs, hairs, epidermal scales, dried blood flecks, or excreta. They are not blood-suckers, but they will eagerly devour any bits of dried blood they can find. The adult fleas are such greedy feeders that they often expel undigested blood from their intestine whilst they are imbibing more through the mouth. The ejected blood clots on the hairs of the animal and finally drops off as tiny black lumps, and these form an important part of the food supply of the larvae.

When a larva is fully grown it spins a crude silken cocoon in some crack or crevice. At first the cocoon is white, but it soon gets coated with dust and becomes inconspicuous. Inside the cocoon the larva changes to a pupa, white at first but slowly turning brown. The length of life of the larva varies widely according to the food supply and the weather conditions. If food is abundant and the weather is moist and warm, the larva may be fully grown in a fortnight, but under adverse conditions it takes much longer to arrive at the pupal stage.

The adult flea emerges from the pupa in about a fortnight, but it does not leave the cocoon at once. It may lie dormant for weeks or months, if there are no suitable animals in the vicinity upon which it can leap for a feed. This accounts for the fact that people are often attacked by hordes of ravenous fleas when they first enter a house that has been empty for a long time. The fleas from the dog and cat and person of the previous occupant laid their eggs and these developed in the debris of the floor whilst the house stood empty. The adults from these larvae remained quiet in their cocoons until the vibrations of the footsteps of the newcomers, as well as the scent of their bodies, aroused them to activity.

Fleas are scarce in the dry parts of the country and this is due to the heat and aridity. These insects flourish best in a moderately warm, moist atmosphere. Besides plague, certain species of fleas have been proved to be the vectors of a relatively mild form of typhus fever which has its reservoir in rats. The common tapeworm of dogs which is found occasionally in man, is carried by the dog flea, *Ctenocephalus canis*. The eggs of the tapeworm are devoured by the larvae of the flea and they hatch inside the larvae and reach a certain stage of development in their bodies. If a flea with these immature worms inside it is swallowed by a dog, or a human being, the worms complete their development into tapeworms in their new hosts.

Rat Fleas

It is well known that rat fleas are the transmitters of plague. If statistics of plague outbreaks in this country since 1899, when the disease arrived here from India, are studied, it will be seen that the worst outbreaks have occurred in years when the rainfall has been exceptionally good. A wet summer means an abundance of fleas and

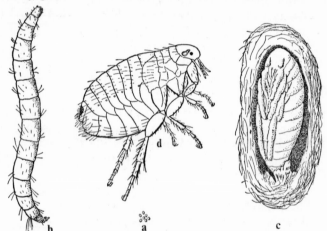

FIG. 153—The Rat Flea, *Xenopsylla cheopis:* (*a*) eggs; (*b*) larva; (*c*) pupa in cocoon; (*d*) adult female.

many fleas mean increased danger from plague. The disease is endemic in Africa as it has established itself among the veld rodents over a very wide area and it is practically impossible to wipe it out.

The common rat flea, *Xenopsylla cheopis*, has a world-wide distribution, having been carried by man's commerce to all the seaports, along with its normal hosts, the domestic rats. Its original home was probably the Mediterranean region and its host the black rat. It is essentially a flea of warm climates and it cannot establish itself permanently in countries with long cold, winters. This is the flea most commonly associated with outbreaks of plague but there are other species, such as X*enopsylla brasiliensis*, X. *eridos* and X. *erilli*, all of which are found on rodents in Africa, that may play an important part. The members of the genus X*enopsylla* are short, stout fleas that resemble the human flea in that they have no combs on the head or prothorax and they can, therefore, be readily distinguished from the common cat and dog fleas, which have these combs well developed.

Plague is usually transmitted from one animal to another by the fleas in a curious manner. After feeding on an infected animal, the digestive tract of a flea may become blocked with a solid mass of living germs and partially digested blood. Such a "blocked" flea cannot take any more food and it becomes ravenously hungry and thirsty. When the sick animal dies the flea leave its body and seeks out new hosts. A "blocked" flea getting on to another animal attempts to feed; it sucks up blood, but this cannot pass into its stomach because of the plug of germs, and it is regurgitated into the wound. In this way the flea acts as a living hypodermic syringe and infects its new host with the plague. Being unable to feed, the "blocked" fleas eventually die of starvation but, in their restless search for food they may infect a number of new hosts before death overtakes them.

An outbreak of plague among wild rodents on the veld is not very serious if they are remote from human dwellings and if there is no contact between them and the domestic rodents. But if they are near a farm or a village or town then the disease may spread first to domestic rats and mice and then to human beings. There are certain kinds of wild rodents that may act as a go-between, such as the striped mice and the multimammate mice, which enter homesteads and farm buildings and which also come into contact with the gerbilles and other rodents on the veld. These little animals may pick up infected fleas and bring them into the vicinity of our homes.

Rat fleas breed chiefly in the sleeping places of their hosts, and their life history is similar to that described above. The common rat flea, X*enopsylla cheopis*, can breed in large numbers amid the dust and debris in barns and stores where grain is kept and that are infested with rats. The larvae of this species seem to be able to find all the food they need in the dust on the floor and in the bags and do not need the dried blood flecks that form an important part of the food of other species. They may be transported long distances in the bags of grain.

Jigger Fleas

The jigger or chigger flea, *Tunga penetrans*, is a native of tropical America and was first introduced into West Africa about eighty years ago. Since then it has spread rapidly over nearly the whole of Africa. It is a small flea, only about one twenty-fifth of an inch long, without any combs, with comparatively slender legs and a long proboscis. The adults are similar in their habits to other fleas and they will feed on the blood of a wide range of hosts, but human beings and pigs seem to be their favourites, although cats, dogs and rats are also attacked.

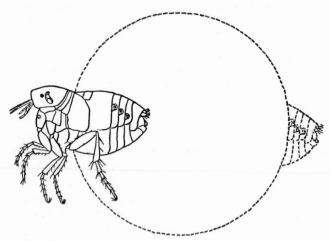

FIG. 154—The Jigger Flea, *Tunga penetrans*, female. The dotted lines show how her body swells as her eggs develop inside her.

The particular importance of this flea lies in the fact that the females, after they have been fertilised, but before their eggs develop, burrow into the skin of their hosts, especially in such tender spots as beneath the toe-nails and between the toes.

The flesh around the flea becomes inflamed and swollen and encloses the insect, with only a small hole leading to the exterior through which the tip of the flea's abdomen projects. As the eggs develop inside the female her body swells up to the size of a pea and then, in about a week, she expels her eggs through the hole, up to one hundred or more in number. Sometimes the whole insect is expelled by pressure on the inflamed tissues as the person walks. The eggs hatch on the ground—usually on the floor of native huts and houses and yards used by bare-footed people that are infected—and the larvae feed on organic debris and develop in the manner already described, taking about seventeen days to reach the adult state.

The wounds made by the burrowing females may become infected with bacteria and very painful. Sometimes the distended body of the insect is broken in the wound and the eggs released there and there may be severe ulceration and pus formation. Walking bare-footed in jigger-infested areas is almost certain to result in infestation. The best way to deal with the pest is to enlarge the hole with a sterile needle and to remove the insect whole, afterwards treating the wound with an antiseptic.

The fowl flea, or sticktight flea, *Echidnophaga gallinacea* is another member of the jigger flea family and it may occasionally attack human beings, particularly children who go into infested fowl runs. It is a small dark-coloured flea that attacks poultry in tropical and sub-tropical countries and it is widely spread in Africa. It has a long, proboscis by means of which it can cling to its host, like a tiny tick, and it is gregarious, collecting in dense masses on the heads of the fowls and sometimes in the ears of such mammals as dogs, cats, rats and other animals. The eggs fall to the ground and the larvae develop in the normal manner.

CLASSIFICATION

ORDER 20: *APHANIPTERA (Siphonaptera)*—FLEAS

Small, wingless, laterally compressed insects; adults all parasitic on warm-blooded animals. Eyes may be present or absent. The antennae are short, clubbed and rest in grooves on the side of the head. Mouthparts modified for piercing and sucking. The coxae of the legs large, tarsi five-jointed. Larvae are elongate, blind, and without legs.
Fleas are usually classified in three families:

FAMILY 1: *Pulicidae*

This family includes the majority of species and the human flea, *Pulex irritans*, and the rat fleas belong to it. Some have eyes, others are eyeless, some have combs on the head and prothorax and others lack these combs. The adults do not fix themselves on their hosts.

FAMILY 2: *Sarcopsyllidae*

This family includes the jigger fleas and sticktight fleas. The males have normal habits but the females adhere to their hosts or burrow into the skin. Their mouthparts are long and the thoracic segments are shortened. The legs are comparatively slender.

FAMILY 3: *Ceratopsyllidae*

These fleas are found only on bats and birds, and are of interest only to the specialist.

CHAPTER XX

WASPS

The Hymenoptera

Wasps, bees and ants form an enormous order of over sixty thousand different species, known as the *Hymenoptera*, or membranous-winged insects. They are extremely varied in their habits and life histories, but all the winged members of the group have two pairs of membranous wings, the hind pair smaller than the front pair and the two linked together by minute hooklets on the hind wings that fit into a fold in the front wing when the insect is in flight. The mouthparts are adapted for biting and often for lapping and sucking as well. The ovipositor of the female is adapted for sawing, piercing or stinging. The metamorphosis is complete, the larvae of the great majority of the order being legless, blind maggots.

Saw-flies

The most primitive members of this group are the insects known as saw-flies. They differ from all the others in that the abdomen is not separated from the thorax by a narrow constriction; the connection between the two is broad, and saw-flies lack the narrow waist that is so characteristic of the higher Hymenoptera. Also the ovipositor of the female is not modified to form a sting but is a double-bladed saw with which she bores holes in plant tissues for the reception of her eggs. The habits of these insects are simple and they do not exhibit the remarkable instincts of the higher wasps, bees and ants. The larvae feed on plants, some in galls, some burrowing in the stems, but the majority feeding on leaves like caterpillars.

A common species in South Africa is the pelargonium saw-fly, *Athalia pelargonii* The adult is about half an inch long, black and yellow; so far only the female has been found. The male is very rare or absent altogether, as is the case with many other species of saw-flies. When laying her eggs the female settles on the underside of a pelargonium leaf and, applying her saw to the surface, draws the blades alternately to and fro until she has made a slit in the leaf just large enough to receive an egg. The hole does not penetrate to the upper side of the leaf so that the egg, when deposited, is sheltered between the upper and lower skin of the leaf.

The egg swells up after it is laid until it is nearly three times as big as it was. It is not known what causes this, but the female injects a drop of liquid into the hole with the egg and this may have something to do with the increase in size. The egg hatches in about twelve days and the larva makes its way out of the chamber by biting a small round hole in the upper surface of the leaf. It feeds for three or four weeks, moulting five to seven times before it is fully grown. About three-quarters of an inch long, it looks very much like a small, green caterpillar, but it has twenty legs instead of the usual sixteen of a caterpillar. The pelargonium saw-fly larva has seven pairs of prolegs, as well as the six true legs on its thoracic segments, and its prolegs lack the tiny hooks that are found on the prolegs of a caterpillar. Furthermore, the saw-fly larva has only one eye on each side of its head, whereas a caterpillar has five or six.

The fully grown larva seeks out a sheltered spot on the plant or amid dead leaves at the base and spins a neat, silken cocoon, oval, about half an inch long and yellow in colour. After resting for several days, it pupates and ten days or so later the adult emerges. As the males are so rare, it is obvious that the majority, if not all, of the eggs of this species must develop parthenogenetically, without fertilisation.

The pear slug, *Caliroa cerasi*, is an introduced species of saw-fly that is common in the Western Province and the larvae of which in some years do severe damage to the foliage of pear, quince, and plum trees. The larva is a black, slimy worm, about half an inch long, that feeds on the upper surface of the leaves of the trees. When it is fully grown it leaves the tree and buries itself in the soil at the base, forming a hard, dark cocoon round itself and then pupating. The adult saw-fly is black and about a quarter of an inch long. There are two generations a year, the adults of the first generation appearing in spring and those of the second generation about mid-summer. The larvae from this second generation spend the winter beneath the soil in their cocoons.

Ensign Wasps

Parasitism is very common throughout nature and many people find this aspect of the study of the outdoor world very cruel and repellent, but it is essential because all living things tend to increase too fast and to outgrow their food resources. Parasitism plays an important part in maintaining the balance of nature. There are several families of Hymenoptera that are parasitic on other insects and that are the principal agents in keeping down their numbers. One of these is the *Evaniidae* and the members of it are sometimes called ensign wasps because of their curious habit of carrying the abdomen raised. This is because the slender base of the abdomen is joined to the thorax high up on the back, and not in a straight line, as is the case with other insects.

A common member of this family is *Gasteruption spilopus*, which parasitises certain kinds of solitary bees. It is a slender wasp, about half an inch long, reddish brown in colour, and the female has a long, thread-like ovipositor that is longer than the rest of the body, black with a white tip. She flies slowly and deliberately, with her abdomen in the air, closely investigating holes in walls, fencing posts, tree stumps and similar places where her victims make their nests. She preys upon primitive bees of the family *Prosopidae* (see page 342) and she needs for her purpose nests that contain freshly completed cells, containing the mixture of honey and pollen laboriously gathered by

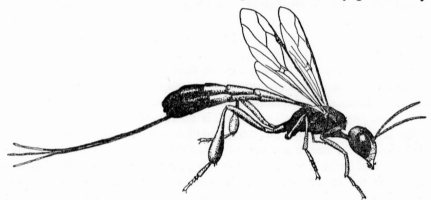

FIG. 155—The Parasite of Solitary Bees, *Gasteruption spilopus*, female. Note the curious position of the junction between thorax and abdomen.

the bees, each with an egg floating on top of the semi-liquid food. She seems to be able to tell when a hole contains a nest by her sense of smell and, having found such a nest, she at once plunges boldly inside to investigate. Should the owner of the nest be at home she backs out again, followed by the bee to drive her off, but there is no quarrel or fight. The parasite simply settles near the hole and waits until the bee leaves to hunt for food again. Then into the hole the wasp goes again and, after a short inspection, she comes out and backs into the hole once more, tail first.

Her ovipositor consists of three threads, side by side, the two outer ones forming a protective sheath for the slender tube in the middle. When she re-enters the hole backwards she holds the two halves of the sheath bent up out of the way over her back, and only the slender, tubular, central thread of the ovipositor is thrust down into the bee's cell. Her long, white egg passes down this capillary tube and is stuck on the side of the cell, just above the mass of honey and pollen. Then, her work at that nest completed, she leaves the hole and flies away, to repeat the process elsewhere.

The bee returns to her home, quite unaware of what has happened in her absence, and proceeds to build and stock more cells on top of the one that has been parasitised. Three days later the parasite's egg hatches. As the bee's egg takes eight days to hatch, the parasitic larva has a good start. It is a tiny maggot and it creeps down the side of the cell and makes its way across the sticky surface of the honey and pollen until it reaches the fat, sausage-shaped bee's egg lying on top of the food. Then it proceeds to devour the egg which is much bigger than itself. At the end of twenty-four hours the bee's egg has dis-appeared and the parasite is much bigger as a result of its huge meal. It now looks like a small, white flat-fish lying on top of the honey. After having got rid of its rival, it adopts a complete change of diet and feeds on the honey and pollen. This lasts for about a week, by which time the parasite is about a quarter of an inch long, only about half grown.

In the meantime, the bee's egg in the cell above has hatched and the bee larva is feeding on the meal provided by its mother. The parasite below now breaks into the cell above and feeds on the honey and pollen there, and, as soon as this is finished, it turns on the bee larva and kills and devours that as well. Thus the parasite destroys two cells in the bee's nest before it is fully grown and it changes its diet three times, first an egg, then honey and pollen, and finally a larva. In sixteen to eighteen days it is fully grown and it pupates inside the two ravaged cells.

All the while it is feeding the larva does not pass any excrement. Its stomach is a blind sac and does not communicate with the hind intestine, therefore the waste matter from its food accumulates in its stomach. When it is fully grown and has stopped feeding the stomach and the intestine join and all the excrement is passed out at once, the larva thus cleansing itself and turning white as a preparation for pupa-tion. By this remarkable provision of nature the larva in its confined quarters, in close contact with its food, does not soil its surroundings until its growth is complete. This is characteristic of nearly all the larvae of the higher Hymenoptera that live in cells amid their food.

There are two or three generations a year of these parasites. When the autumn arrives the parasitic grubs lying in their cells do not pupate. They pass through the winter months as larvae and do not pupate until the warmer weather arrives in spring. Then, when the solitary bees are active once more, the adult parasites emerge to carry on their work of helping to maintain the balance of nature. The male adult is easily distinguished from his mate as he does not have the long ovipositor on his abdomen.

Other species of this family are parasitic on the eggs of cock-roaches, some prey upon the larvae of long-horned beetles.

Ichneumon Wasps

The members of the very large family of parasites called the *Ichneumonidae* are often spoken of as ichneumon flies, but it is better to reserve the name "flies" for the two-winged Diptera and to speak of the Hymenoptera that are not bees or ants as "wasps"—parasitic wasps, solitary wasps, hunting wasps, social wasps.   Most of the

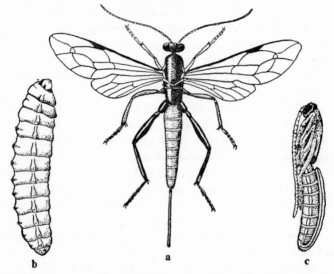

FIG. 156—The Ichneumon Parasite, *Philopsyche abdominalis*, of the Wattle Bagworm: (*a*) adult female; (*b*) mature larva; (*c*) pupa.

ichneumon wasps prey upon caterpillars, but some of the family are parasites of spiders, beetles, flies and wasps and bees. They are slender insects varying in size from very small to comparatively large wasps an inch or more in length. The majority are winged and the venation of the wings serves to distinguish them from closely related families, but some species are wingless. The females are armed with a slender, thread-like ovipositor.

The ichneumon parasite of the wattle bagworm, *Philopsyche abdominalis*, is common wherever its host is found and its plays an important part in keeping this pest in check. The adults vary in size but the males are usually about half an inch long and the females about three-quarters of an inch, including the ovipositor; the head, thorax and hind legs are black, the abdomen red, and the forelegs are yellowish white. The female, when attacking a bagworm, settles on the outside of the bag and thrusts her ovipositor through it and she lays her largish yellow egg inside, attached to the side of the bag.

The egg hatches in about three days and the larva feeds as an external parasite upon the bagworm. It can move about in the bag and it is aided in this by the short, sharp spines on its back, which catch in the silken sides of the bag and hold it securely in position whilst feeding. It has a pair of sharp mandibles by means of which it punctures the skin of its victim to get at the juices. When it is fully grown it pupates inside the bag, beside the shrivelled remains of the caterpillar. The larva does not spin a cocoon but roughly binds itself against the side of the bag by means of a few silken threads. In the female pupa the ovipositor can be seen curved over the back, but this appendage is always directed rearwards in the adult. In some seasons ten to twenty per cent. of the bagworms may be destroyed by this parasite and there are two generations a year.

The egg-sacs of the button spider, *Latrodectus indistinctus*, are parasitised by a small ichneumon, *Pezomachus latrodectiphagus*. The male is black and only about a fifth of an inch long and has two pairs of wings; the female is about the same size and looks very much like an ant as she is wingless, but she can be recognised by the ovipositor at the end of her abdomen. As many as seventeen of these parasites have been reared from one egg-sac of the spider; the egg-sac may contain about one hundred and seventy eggs, therefore it seems that each parasite needs about ten spider's eggs to bring it to maturity. The fully grown larvae of the parasite spin elongate cocoons inside the

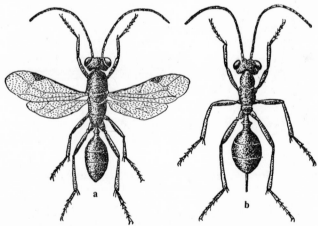

FIG. 157—The Parasite of the Button Spider, *Pezomachus latrodectiphagus:*   (*a*) male; (*b*) female.

egg-sac and pupate there and the adults emerge through small holes they make in the silken covering of the egg-sac. Several species of this genus, *Pezomachus*, with winged males and wingless females, are known to parasitise egg-sacs of spiders in other parts of the world but the above species is the only one so far recorded from Africa.

Of the many different species of ichneumons, the reddish brown, slender wasps, *Ophion* species, that are often attracted to lights at night, are parasites of cutworms. Others that attack the caterpillars of butterflies make striking cocoons, black and white, oval, and suspended by a thread near the dead body of the victim. The females of certain species that parasitise caddis worms enter the water in search of their prey and can remain below the surface for a long time. All the members of this large family show remarkable instincts in their ability to find their hosts and to provide for their offspring. Although they are parasites, many of them have to work hard in the distribution of their eggs; for example, the species that parasitise wood-boring insects have to locate their victims hidden in the timber and then they have to bore laboriously through the wood with their slender ovipositors in order to reach the larvae and lay their eggs on or in them; it is not known how they ascertain the exact position of the borers in their burrows.

Braconid Wasps

The parasitic wasps of the large family, *Braconidae*, are closely related to the ichneumons and differ from them mainly in the venation of the wings. Their hosts include caterpillars, fly larvae, beetle larvae, aphids and other insects. The species that prey upon aphids are

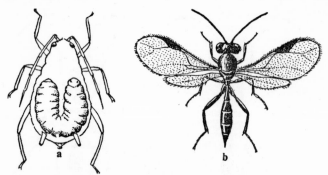

FIG. 158—The Aphis Parasite, *Aphidius testaceipes:*   (a) Larva in an aphis; (b) adult female.

very common and widely spread and the results of their work may be seen on almost any plant that is infested with plant lice. Numbers of the aphids will be seen that are swollen and that have a neat, round hole in the skin; these have been killed by the parasites and the holes are the exits made by the adults when leaving the dead bodies.

The female *Aphidius* lays her eggs within the bodies of the aphids, generally only one egg in one host. When attacking a victim she

V. DIMORPHISM AMONG SOUTH AFRICAN BUTTERFLIES. (Seasonal dimorphism on the left, sexual dimorphism on the right.) 1. *Precis archesia pelasgis*, the dry-season form; 2. *Precis archesia*, the wet-season form; 3. *Precis octavia natalensis*, the dry-season form; 4. *Precis octavia sesamus*, the wet-season form; 5. *Mylothris poppea ruepelli*, male; 6. *Mylothris poppea ruepelli*, female; 7. *Deudorix diocles*, male; 8. *Deudorix diocles*, female; 9. *Chloroselas pseudozerites*, male; 10. *Chloroselas pseudozerites*, female. All natural size.

stands just behind it and bends her abdomen forward, under her thorax, so that the tip projects in front of her head. Then, with a quick thrust of her ovipositor, she pierces the skin of the aphis and inserts her egg. She may lay three to four hundred eggs before she dies.

The egg hatches into a tiny, blind, white, legless maggot with an appendage on the hind end like a tail. This tail-like appendage is found in many parasitic larvae belonging to the Hymenoptera and it is thought to be respiratory in function; it disappears when the young larva moults and its tracheae are fully developed. The larva feeds for two days on the body fluids and fat-body of the aphis and then casts its skin. It is now a fat white maggot lodged near the hind end of the aphis and it feeds again for two days and then casts its skin once more. When it is a week old it is fully grown and the aphis dies. The parasite now cuts a small slit in the skin on the underside of the dead aphis and cements it, through this slit, to the leaf or stem with a little silk, so that the dead body, with the larva inside, cannot fall off or be blown away. The parasite pupates inside the swollen, hardened skin of the aphis and the adult emerges a few days later, cutting a neat, circular hole to do so.

The tiny parasites of the genus *Aphidius* play an important part in keeping down the numbers of aphids. Not only do they cause the premature death of the pests but they prevent them from multiplying so rapidly because the parasitised aphids produce few or no young. The *Aphidius* larvae are themselves kept in check by hyperparasites, by tiny wasps that lay their eggs in or on the parasitic larvae inside the aphids.

Anybody who has tried to rear moths and butterflies from caterpillars will know that the caterpillars frequently die before reaching maturity, killed by various kinds of parasites. Often the dead body of a caterpillar is surrounded by small white cocoons from which slender black wasps emerge. The commonest of the parasites that do this are members of the Braconid genus, *Apanteles*. One of these is an important parasite of the pine brown-tail moth, *Euproctis terminalis* (see page 181). At times numbers of the caterpillars of this moth may be found dead on the pines with small, dirty white cocoons heaped in a mass around them; these are the cocoons of *Apanteles euproctidis*, a tiny black wasp with red legs only about one-tenth of an inch long. Another species, *Apanteles halfordi*, attacks the caterpillars of the diamond-back moth (see page 148) and its small white cocoons may be found fastened to the cabbage leaves on which the caterpillars are feeding. A third species, *Apanteles ruficrus*, preys upon the army worm, and there are many others.

The karoo caterpillar parasite, *Chelonus texanus*, is a small wasp about three-eighths of an inch long and dark brown in colour. It was introduced into South Africa from America a few years ago to help in the control of the karoo caterpillar, *Loxostege frustalis*, that is in some seasons so destructive to the valuable sweet karoo bush *Pentzia*, one of the chief fodder plants of sheep in the Karoo. The female wasp lays her eggs in the eggs of the moth. Such parasitised moth eggs hatch normally and the caterpillars feed and grow as though nothing was the matter with them, and they pupate. The parasitic larvae feed and grow inside the caterpillars, one in each, and they pupate inside the pupal skin of their victims. In the entomological laboratories in Pretoria these parasites are bred in thousands in the caterpillars of the common meal moth, *Ephestia kuhniella* (see page 156) and the adults are then sent to the Karoo and released there to attack the karoo caterpillars. It is hoped that the wasp will become widely established and will keep down the numbers of the pest.

Fig Insects

There are many different species of wild figs found in Africa; some are forest giants, whilst others are smaller and grow on rocky mountain sides under harsh conditions. All of them bear fruits similar to the cultivated fig; they are thickened, hollow, juicy stems with a

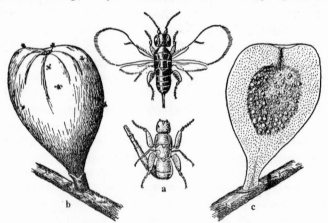

FIG. 159—The Capri Fig Insect, *Blastophaga psenes:* (*a*) Female above, male below; (*b*) fig with females on it, about natural size; (*c*) section of a fig, showing male, female and gall flowers.

large number of tiny flowers inside them. The only entrance to the fig is a narrow opening at the top, surrounded by a ring of small bracts. It is clear that insects such as bees and butterflies cannot possibly get inside the figs to pollinate them, nor can the wind carry pollen from one flower to another, because they are hidden in the deep cavity in the fig. The question therefore arises, how are the figs pollinated?

The answer is that they have associated with them certain peculiar insects, tiny wasps called fig insects that belong to the family *Agaonidae*. The males are wingless, brown and never leave the figs in which they were born and bred. The females are black and have four wings and are much more active than their mates. They are fertilised inside the figs soon after they emerge from the pupae. Then they creep out of the small opening at the top of the fig and, in doing so, they pass over the male flowers in the fig and get well dusted with pollen. The females fly to younger, smaller figs on the same or on neighbouring trees and creep into them. Thus the pollen is carried from one fruit to another and the female flowers in the young figs are pollinated. The female wasps lay their eggs in the ovaries of the female flowers and the larvae develop inside them to produce the next generation.

If some ripe figs from wild fig trees are collected and cut open it is usually quite easy to find the galls made by the larvae inside, each about the size of a large pin's head, and often the little brown males and the black, winged females may also be found in the cavity. Apparently most species of wild figs have their own species of fig insect associated with them and already many different species of fig insects have been described and named.

The best known of them is the Capri fig insect, *Blastophaga psenes*, which was introduced into California in 1899 from the Middle East to assist in the cultivation of Smyrna figs. Smyrna figs produce no pollen themselves and they must be pollinated with pollen from the Capri fig, which is inedible. The little fig insect does this work and it was only after the introduction of the insect that Smyrna figs could be successfully grown in California. The insect was brought from California to South Africa in 1908 and established in Capri figs growing at the Cape. For many years the Capri fig insects were distributed to fruit growers in the Union free of charge, to encourage the cultivation of Smyrna figs, but this has now been discontinued since it appears that this type of fig is not a commercial success under our conditions.

Chalcid Wasps

The very large superfamily of small wasps called the *Chalcidoidea* is comprised of several families, including the fig insects, *Agaonidae*, described above. They are mostly small black metallic insects with elbowed antennae and wings that are devoid of veins except the stout vein along the edge of the front wing. Nearly all of them are parasites, but there are some that feed on vegetable substances, in the stems of plants, in seeds (such as the lucerne chalcid) or in flowers (such as the fig insects). A few live in galls, such as those that are found on taaibos (*Rhus* species) and on wild species of Asparagus. Some of them are hyperparasites.

The woolly aphis parasite, *Aphelinus mali*, is a small chalcid that was introduced into South Africa in 1923 from the United States to help combat that major pest of the apple grower, the woolly aphis.

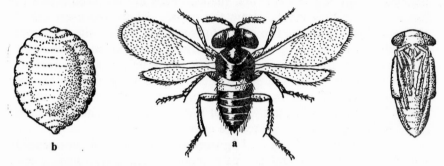

FIG. 160—The Woolly Aphis Parasite, *Aphelinus mali:* (a) Adult; (b) larva; (c) pupa.

It has become established and widely spread here as well as in other parts of Africa, and in other countries, and plays an important part in keeping this serious pest in check. The wasp is very small, smaller than the aphis itself, black with a pale band across the base of the abdomen. The female, when about to lay an egg in an aphis, first approaches it from behind, examines it with the tips of her antennae and then turns quickly and jabs it with her sharp ovipositor. If she succeeds in piercing the skin of her victim her tiny egg is deposited inside its body. This hatches into a typical parasitic larva, white, legless, blind, that feeds on the juices of its host. The parasitised aphis swells and turns black and eventually dies, and the larva pupates inside the dead body. About three weeks to a month after the egg was laid the adult wasp emerges through a round hole it bites in the skin of the dead aphis.

There are other species of chalcids that attack many different kinds of aphids and scale insects. A tiny chalcid wasp, *Mormoniella brevicornis*, is a parasite of blow flies in this country and helps to keep down their numbers. The adult is black and only about an eighth of an inch long and it may often be seen walking about among the larvae and puparia of blow flies under carcases on the veld. The female lays her eggs only in the puparia; she ignores the maggots, and she may lay as many as thirty or more minute eggs in one puparium. The parasitic larvae feed on the pupa inside the puparium and kill it and they pupate inside the case, beside the shrivelled remains of their host.

A few days later the adults emerge through a small round hole bitten in the side of the puparium.

Some of the smallest of all insects are egg parasites that belong to this group. The codling moth egg parasite, *Trichogrammatoidea lutea*, despite its lengthy name, is so small that four or five of them can come to maturity in one of the moth's eggs which is only about the size of a pin's head. This minute insect renders valuable service to the fruit grower by destroying large numbers of the eggs of the codling moth, as well as the eggs of such important pests as the American boll worm of cotton and other moths.

FIG. 161—The Egg Parasite of the Codling Moth, *Trichogrammatoidea lutea.* The insect is yellow and only about one thirty-second of an inch long—it is so small that six or seven of them may be bred from one codling moth's egg.

Another egg parasite, introduced from Australia some years ago and successfully established here, keeps in check the blue-gum snout beetle, a serious pest of gum trees that is also a native of Australia but that has found its way to Africa and spread widely.

Some members of this group exhibit the extraordinary phenomenon known as polyembryony, or the development of several individuals from one egg. One of the commonest examples of this is to be found in caterpillars (not yet identified) that burrow in the stems of shrubs belonging to the genus *Aspalathus*. Swellings are caused on the stems by the caterpillars working inside them and, if some of these are cut open, some of the caterpillars inside will be found to be parasitised. The parasitised caterpillar looks like a bundle of tiny white sausages, enclosed in the translucent skin that is all that is left of the caterpillar. A hundred or more tiny black chalcid wasps may emerge from such a caterpillar and all are of the same sex.

It is not known how the parasite attacks the Aspalathus borer but, from observations made on similar parasites in Europe, it is probable that the attack begins with the egg of the moth. The female wasp seeks out the egg of the moth attached to the stem of the Aspalathus plant, punctures it and deposits her own minute egg inside. The moth's egg develops normally and hatches, despite the presence of the parasite's egg. The latter then begins to grow inside the young caterpillar into a long string of what look like microscopic sausages. These separate and give rise to a number of larvae, all from the one original egg, that feed on the body fluids of the caterpillar and eventually kill it when it is nearly fully grown. Thus as many as fifty larvae or more may arise from the one egg and, if it has not been fer-

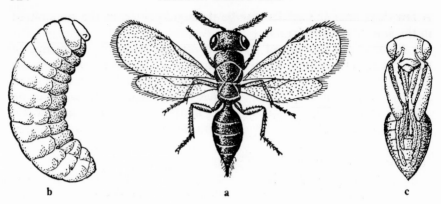

FIG. 162—The Lucerne Chalcid, *Bruchophagus funebris:*   (*a*) Adult female; (*b*) larva;
(*c*) pupa.

tilised, all will develop into males, whilst if the egg was fertilised all
will be females.

Sometimes the bloated skin of a cutworm may be found in the
garden, pierced with innumerable small holes like the lid of a pepper-
pot. Such a caterpillar has been killed by a polyembryonic parasite
and the holes in the skin are the exits made by the numerous progeny
from the parasite's egg or eggs. More than a thousand have been
counted from one caterpillar.

Velvet Ants

Small insects that look like ants, about a quarter of an inch long,
mostly with dark red thorax and black abdomen marked with white
spots or bands, may often be seen running about restlessly in the hot
sunshine. These are female wasps of the family *Mutillidae* and,
because of their velvety, antlike appearance they are often called
velvet ants, but they do not live in social communities and they are
only distantly related to the true ants. These females are armed with
a strong, curved sting and they can inflict a painful wound if handled
carelessly. The males are larger and stronger and have two pairs of
wings; their colouring is similar to that of the females, as a rule, but
in some species the two sexes differ markedly.

The female can stridulate by rubbing the narrow joints between
the thorax and abdomen together and it is said that a male will sometimes be attracted to the spot if a female is held down with a piece of
twig and caused to stridulate in protest. It is also said that the big,
strong males of some species literally abduct the females when about
to mate with them, picking them up off the ground and flying away
with them. All the mutillid wasps are parasitic on other bees and

wasps, and one or two species have been bred from the puparia of tsetse flies. The females run about tirelessly, seeking for nests of their victims that contain larvae, probably finding them by the sense of smell, as there is usually no sign of the nest at the surface. The details of their life history are imperfectly known but it seems that the eggs are laid on the larvae in the nests and the mutillid larvae feed as external parasites upon their hosts. The species shown in the illustration, *Dolichomutilla guineensis*, has been bred from the nests of the

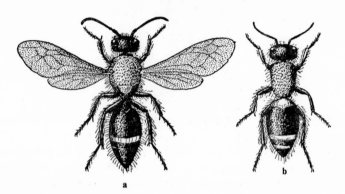

a

FIG. 163—The Mutillid Wasp, or "Velvet Ant," *Dolichomutilla guineensis*. Parasitic on solitary bees: (*a*) male; (*b*) female.

mud wasp, *Sceliphron spirifex* (see page 333). It is about half an inch long, red thorax and black abdomen with a white band. Like the rest of the mutillids, its thorax is so hard that it is difficult to get an entomological pin through it.

Scoliid Wasps

The family of solitary wasps known as the *Scoliidae* is well represented in Africa. They are mostly hairy insects, black and marked with bands of yellow or red, and they include some of the largest of wasps among their numbers, although some are small and slender. Both sexes are winged and frequently the female is much larger and stouter than the male. Members of this family may be recognised by the constriction which occurs between the first and second segment of the abdomen.

Scoliid wasps prey upon the larvae of beetles belonging to the scarab family, the females seeking out their victims in the soil and in heaps of decaying leaves and vegetable debris. Having found a suitable beetle larva, the wasp stings it and paralyses it, but a spark of life is left in the body so that it does not decay or dry up. She does not carry the larva away but leaves it lying just where she found it and she lays her egg on the ventral surface, just behind the legs. Then she goes off to find other beetle larvae upon which she can repeat the process.

The egg hatches into a white legless maggot that feeds as an external parasite upon the beetle larva, never shifting its position after

FIG. 164—A Scoliid Wasp, *Dielis quinquefasciata*, female

it has hatched. When it is fully grown it spins a dense, oval cocoon of silk beside the shrivelled skin of the beetle and pupates inside it.

Cuckoo Wasps

The cuckoo wasps, or ruby wasps, are small insects with stout bodies that are brilliantly coloured, metallic green and blue and red, and they form the family *Chrysididae*. They are parasitic on solitary bees and wasps; on bright, sunny days they may be seen actively running about, with quivering wings and antennae vibrating, on walls, stumps and on the ground where the nests of their hosts are to be found. It is very easy to recognise members of this family because of their characteristic colouring and appearance and because only three or four abdominal segments are visible from above. The upper side of the abdomen is rounded and densely pitted, whilst the underside is flat or concave; thus the insect can roll itself into a ball when it is alarmed, with the vulnerable underside protected, and only the hard, dorsal surface exposed.

The female seeks out the nests of other bees and wasps, particularly those of the mud wasps (see page 333). Having found one she waits until the owner is away and then she goes inside and lays her egg n the cell. Her larva feeds on the larva of the host insect or else on the food supply provided for it. When fully grown it spins a dense

PLATE 65

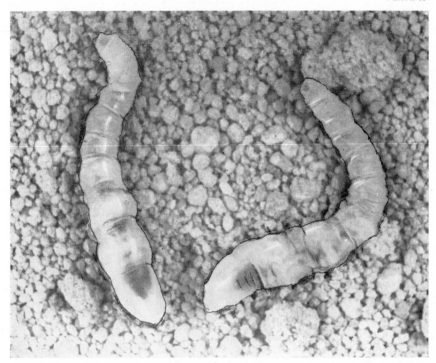

(*a*) "WORM-LIONS." Two larvae of the Fly, *Lampromyia brevirostris*. They are about half an inch long.

(*b*) A LONG-BEAK HORSE FLY, *Pangonia* species

PLATE 66

THE "WORM-LION" FLY, *Lampromyia brevirostris*. It is about half an inch long.

silken cocoon inside the cell, empties its alimentary canal of waste matter and then settles down for a long sleep until the following season, when it changes to a pupa and a fortnight or so later the adult emerges.

There are a large number of different species of cuckoo wasps found in this country but little is known about their habits and life histories. One of the commonest is the green cuckoo wasp, *Hexa-*

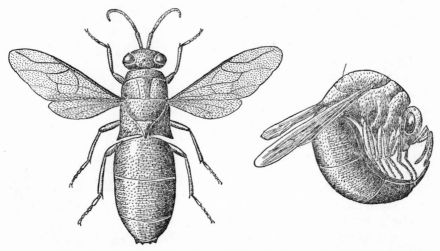

FIG. 165—The Cuckoo Wasp, *Hexachrysis lyncea*, female. It is about half an inch long and brilliant metallic green. On the right it is shown rolled up in a defensive attitude.

chrysis lyncea, that is about half an inch long and that preys upon the mason wasps. A smaller species, banded with green, blue and red, *Hexachrysis concinna*, parasitises leafcutter and carder bees.

Mason Wasps

The mason wasps of the family *Eumenidae* fold their fore-wings longitudinally when at rest, thereby reducing them to half their normal width, and this characteristic, shared with the social wasps, enables one to recognise them easily. These are slender-waisted wasps that nest in holes in the ground, in hollow stems, or build mud cells on twigs, stones and walls; the only nesting material they use in building their partitions and cells is clay moistened with saliva. They are mostly black or black and yellow and their prey consists of caterpillars.

One of the commonest and most widely spread species is the yellow and black mason wasp, *Eumenes caffer*, that is about an inch long, conspicuously marked with black on a yellow background. The

MM

female constructs beautiful little hemispherical cells of mud, with the circular opening at the top surrounded by a neatly curved rim. As soon as she has completed her cell she lays her egg inside, before bringing any provisions; this is the reverse of the usual practice, as most solitary bees and wasps lay their eggs after the cells have been stocked with food. The egg of this type of wasp is also peculiar in that it is suspended from the roof of the cell by a thread so that it is hanging in the air like a tiny sausage on a string. It is suggested that this is a provision for the protection of the young larva when it first hatches and starts to feed. The caterpillars stored in the nest by the mother are stung and partially paralysed, but they can still wriggle about and, if the newly-hatched larva lay in their midst, it might be crushed. For the first few days of its life it hangs from the thread, with its tail end still in the egg-shell; in this position it can reach its food but it is out of the way

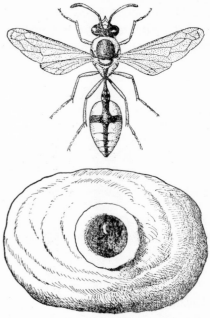

FIG. 166—The Mason Wasp, *Eumenes caffer*. Adult female above, the mud nest below, showing the egg inside hanging from a thread.

of the writhing caterpillars. When it is bigger and stronger it drops from the thread, as it is no longer in danger of being crushed.

The female stores a number of caterpillars in a cell, it may be a dozen or more, and after that she breaks down the rim round the entrance and plasters the whole cell with a protective coating of clay. Having completed this work she leaves the cell, never to bother about it again, and goes off to start another one elsewhere; she may complete ten or a dozen such cells before her life's work is finished.

The mason wasps of the genus *Eumenes* have a long, slender waist, but other members of the family, such as *Odynerus* species, have very short waists that are scarcely evident between the thorax and abdomen.

Social Wasps

The slender brown wasps, about an inch long, that make their paper nests beneath verandah roofs and are often spoken of as "hornets", are very well known in most parts of Africa. They are primitive social wasps of the genus *Belonogaster*, and there are several species of them, one of the commonest and most widely spread being *Belonogaster junceus*.

A fertilised female commences her nest by making a tough stalk of fibrous material under the shelter of a roof or an over-hanging stone or bank, or some similar spot. On this she constructs her first cell of papery material, hanging with the opening downwards, and she adds other cells round it in concentric circles as her building proceeds. Frequently she is joined by one or more females who assist in the labour of nest-building and a small colony is formed. The females lay their eggs in the bottom of the cells as soon as they are deep enough and, when the larvae hatch, they are fed with pellets of chewed caterpillars, brought to them as needed by the females.

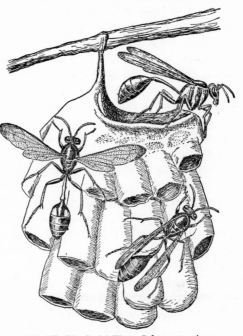

When a larva is fully grown the cell in which it lies is capped with papery material and it pupates inside. They develop into sexual individuals, males and females; there are no sterile workers among these wasps. The daughters stay with their mothers and assist with the nesting. There may be a certain division of labour, as it seems that the older females devote themselves to egg-laying whilst the younger hunt for food.

FIG. 167—The Social Wasp, *Belonogaster junceus,* on nest, about natural size

The males remain on the nest but they do no work and are fed by the females. The nests never grow very large, mostly consisting of about fifty cells, although sometimes larger nests of one or two hundred cells may be found. When a nest has reached this stage small groups of females leave it to found new nests elsewhere.

The smaller social wasps, *Polistes* species, are also very common and widely spread in Africa. These wasps build their paper nests, consisting of a single comb with the openings of the cells pointing downwards, suspended by a central stalk in a sheltered spot, on the twig of a bush, or on the underside of an over-hanging rock, beneath a roof, and so on. The nest is usually started by a single female, the queen, working alone, and she feeds her young on pellets of chewed insects. Her offspring may be fully developed females, like herself, or they may be workers, capable of laying only unfertilised eggs that develop into males.

A very interesting point about these social wasps is the relationship between the larvae and the females that feed them. The hungry larvae protrude their heads from their cells, with open mouths, like young nestling birds. It is said that they may even, when very hungry, scratch the sides of their cells to attract the attention of their nurses. When a larva is touched, a drop of clear liquid trickles from its mouth and this is eagerly lapped up by the female that is attending it. The liquid is saliva and is sweet and it is obvious that the adult wasps like it very much, therefore it may be said that in the wasp world the babies dribble copiously and the nurses lap up the liquid with avidity. All the adult wasps, males as well as females, are extremely eager for this salivary secretion and they can easily be observed on a *Belonogaster* nest soliciting the young to give them a drink. It is said that a nurse will even ill-treat a larva that does not give up the desired secretion quickly enough; she will seize the larva's head in her jaws, draw it towards her and then suddenly jam it back into the cell; this treatment, observers report, is usually successful in producing the desired result.

The social wasps belong to the family *Vespidae* and they, like the mason wasps, carry their wings folded longitudinally when at rest.

Spider-hunting Wasps

The spider-hunting wasps form a very large family, the *Pompilidae*, that is well represented in Africa. They may be recognised by their long hind legs, curled antennae and smoky wings, and they can be seen running on the ground with great speed, vibrating their wings and antennae, as they search for the spiders with which they provide for their young. One of our largest and most striking wasps is the black spider-hunter (or, strictly speaking, huntress, as it is only the females that seek out the spiders), *Hemipepsis capensis*, about one and a half inches long, with a black body and legs, and smoky brown wings. Other species have wings of a dark metallic blue and some are quite small, but they are all very similar in their ways.

The big black Pompilid wasp, *Hemipepsis capensis*, hunts the formidable baboon spiders, black and hairy, with red round the mouth and with a stout body about an inch and a half long, or the large ground spiders, *Palystes* species, with the dark bars on the underside of their legs. The female may be seen running tirelessly amid the undergrowth, seeking under dead leaves and beneath fallen logs, under stones, and similar places that are the usual haunts of her prey. When she finds a spider large and bulky enough for her purpose—usually a female like herself, because the male spiders are too small for her needs—she at once attacks it boldly. The French entomologist, Fabre, in describing the habits of a closely related wasp found in Southern France, says that the wasp first stings the spider in the front of the head, thereby paralysing the fangs and rendering them harmless. Then, according to Fabre, she sails boldly in and wrestles with her disarmed foe until she can sting it on the underside of the body, between the bases of the legs. Here, just below the surface, the large nerve centre is lodged that controls the spider's movements and, by stinging it in this precise spot, the wasp paralyses the spider, but does not kill it.

These observations of Fabre's, made more than half a century ago, have been queried by later observers and it seems that the hunting wasps do not sting their prey precisely in the nerve centres, as he thought, but that stinging in almost any part of the body will produce the required paralysis. It can easily be shown that the victim is not killed for, if a spider is taken away from one of these wasps after she has stung it, the spider will show signs of life by feeble movements of its legs for some days and it may recover sufficiently to be able to walk, or it may die after a week or so.

After the fight the wasp cleans herself and then off she goes to look for a hole or crack or crevice of sufficient size to receive the bulky spider. Having found such a place she may do some digging and scraping to enlarge the hole, but she saves herself as much trouble as possible by looking for a ready-made hole in a dry, sheltered spot. If it is reasonably near, she will return to the self same spot where she herself was reared and prepare her nest there. Often she will return again and again to the same spot with her prey and make her cells close together in the soil.

Having chosen the site for her nest she flies back to the paralysed spider and, in doing this, she shows the remarkable memory and sense of direction that is characteristic of most of the higher Hymenoptera. She flies without hesitation back to the spot where she left the spider and then, walking backwards, she drags her heavy burden over the rough ground to the hole, it may be many yards distant. From time to time she may leave the spider and fly back to the hole, as though refreshing her memory of its location. Arrived at the hole she drags the spider down into it and lays her large, oval white egg on its abdomen. Then she comes out and fills in the hole by scraping soil into it, levelling off the surface carefully and dragging small twigs and dead leaves over it so that no trace of her nest can be seen at the surface. Finally

she flies off to repeat the whole performance again elsewhere, perhaps
to bring her next victim back to this same spot and bury it close beside
the first, or perhaps to make her next nest some distance away if her
hunting takes her too far afield.

The egg hatches in about ten days and the larva feeds on the
paralysed spider, which provides enough food for the whole of its
larval life. By the time the spider is consumed, only the legs and the
skin being left, the larva is fully grown and it spins a dense cocoon of
brownish silk. It now cleanses its alimentary canal of waste matter,
the stomach opening into the intestine for the first time at this period
of its career, and then it lies motionless inside its cocoon for months,
all through the winter, until the arrival of warmer weather in the
following summer. Lastly it changes into a pupa and two or three
weeks later the adult wasp emerges.

Sand Wasps

Among the solitary wasps that are found in our gardens there is
none more deserving of the gardener's interest and protection than the
slender-bodied black and red sand wasps of the family *Sphecidae*.
There are several species
that are quite common and
they vary in size from about
three-quarters of an inch to
an inch or more in length.
All have a black head, thorax
and hind tip of the abdo-
men, with a long, slender,
red waist.

A female sand wasp
may often be seen digging
her nest at the side of a path
or in a sunny bank. If she
is not disturbed she will sink
a tunnel in the hard soil to
a depth of about two inches
and at the bottom she will
hollow out a chamber about

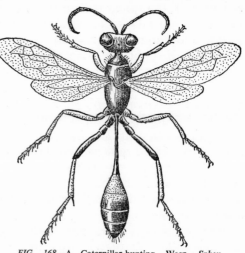

FIG. 168—A Caterpillar-hunting Wasp, *Sphex*
(*Ammophila*) *capensis*, female. She is black and red
and about an inch long.

three-quarters of an inch in diameter. The soil and sand particles
are carried up between her head and front legs and then swept away
by vigorous kicks of her hind legs. Small stones and other obstacles
are dragged out in her jaws and she flies away with them to drop
them a foot or so away from her dwelling, where they cannot get in
her way.

When she has finished digging, she rests for a time, basking in the hot sunshine, and carefully polishing her body and wings and sweeping the dust off her feelers by means of the tiny brush and comb she carries on each front leg. Certain species of *Sphex* (*Ammophila*) carefully cover the entrance to the nest with a small, flat stone before leaving, a truly remarkable instinctive action that seems to indicate intelligence—but they do not all do this. She now sets off to hunt for her prey, running quickly over the ground, searching amid the dense undergrowth, under clods of earth and amid dead leaves for the big, smooth caterpillars that are known as cutworms. When she finds a caterpillar she immediately falls upon it and there is a short fierce struggle. Despite the wild writhings of the caterpillar the wasp swings her slender abdomen round and stings her victim several times on the underside of the body, thereby paralysing it.

The caterpillar is then dragged along the ground to the nest; it is too big for the wasp to be able to fly with it. Arrived at her tunnel she drags it down into the chamber below and lays her oval white egg on it, usually fixing it across the body about a third of the way back from the head, where there are no legs. Then she comes up again and fills in the entrance to the nest by sweeping sand into it. After all is smooth at the surface she flies away never to return to the spot or to bother about that particular nest again. She repeats the whole operation about a dozen times before her work is completed and then she dies.

The egg hatches in two or three weeks and the larva feeds on the paralysed caterpillar. By the time it has consumed its huge meal it is fully grown and it spins a silken cocoon in which to sleep for several months. Finally, in the following spring or summer it changes into a pupa and about a fortnight later the adult wasp emerges.

The majority of the *Sphecidae* have habits similar to those described above, but there are some that build mud nests and capture spiders instead of caterpillars. One of the commonest of these is the black and yellow mud wasp, *Sceliphron spirifex*, that makes its mud nests beneath verandah roofs, and in outhouses where it can get in and out freely. The nest is easily distinguished from that of the mason wasps, *Eumenes* species, because it consists of elongate cells with the entrance at one end, not in the middle with a neat rim as is the case with the nests of *Eumenes*. The female stocks her nest with a number of small, paralysed spiders and she lays her egg on one of the spiders when the nest is about half filled. Having brought enough spiders to feed her young, she plugs the entrance to the cell with mud and then proceeds to construct another cell alongside the first. So she goes on and, if undisturbed, she may make a group of half a dozen or more cells side by side. Finally she gives them all a thick coating of mud put on roughly as an extra protection. Frequently nests may be found that are incomplete, consisting of only one or two cells without the thick protective coat; these are apparently the work of females that have been disturbed and deserted that particular spot or that have been prematurely killed.

Simple experiments to show the limitations of instinct can easily be carried out with these wasps. For example, if the spiders are removed from a cell, one by one as they are brought by the female, she will go on bringing spiders, provided her victims are removed during her absence so that she is not disturbed or frightened, until she has brought the required number. Then, although only the last spider she has brought is in the cell, and although her egg has been removed on one of the purloined spiders, she will close up the cell as though nothing had happened and all was in order inside the cell. Also, if the cells are removed when they are complete, just before she begins the final plastering with mud, she will on her return plaster over the spot where the cells should be, again as though nothing had happened to ruin all her work.

Bee Pirates

Every beekeeper in this country knows the banded bee pirate *Palarus latifrons*. About half an inch long, with dark brown head and thorax and brown bands on its yellow abdomen, the female may be seen haunting the hives during the summer. The male is smaller and darker in colour and is not usually seen about the hives. The female

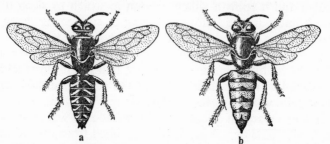

a　　　　　　　　　　　b
FIG. 169—The Banded Bee Pirate, *Palarus latifrons:* (*a*) male; (*b*) female.

bee pirate settles on the ground or on the front of the hive during the hottest hours of the day and she waits there until a worker bee leaves to go out foraging for food. Then the pirate flies after it and swoops down on it like a miniature hawk. They fall together to the ground with the pirate curling her abdomen round to bring the tip of it in the region of the underside of the bee's neck. Here she stings the bee and

PLATE 67

(*a*) THE MOTTLED HORSE FLY, *Haematopota ocellata*

(*b*) AN ASSASSIN FLY

PLATE 68

(*a*) THE DRONE FLY, *Eristalis tenax*

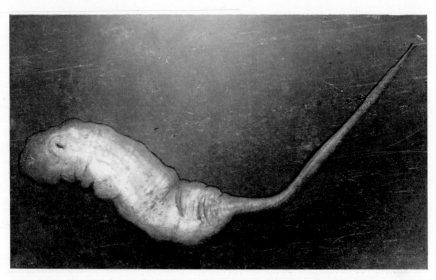

(*b*) Rat-Tailed Maggot, the larva of the Drone Fly, *Eristalis tenax*

it is at once paralysed or killed. Then the wasp may do a ghoulish
thing; sometimes, but not always, she stands astride her victim, which
is lying on its back, legs in the air. She presses her abdomen on the
abdomen of the bee and applies her mouth to that of the bee. The
pressure causes a drop of honey to ooze from the bee's mouth and this
is lapped up by the wasp. She then grasps her prey in her legs and
flies away with it to her nest, which is a long tunnel, a foot or more in
depth, that slants steeply in the side of a sunny bank. Usually a
number of pirates nest in the same vicinity; like other solitary bees
and wasps they seem to like the company of their kind although they
do not co-operate or work together in any way. At the bottom of her
tunnel she has excavated a small chamber and here she stores the dead
bee and lays her egg on it. The larva feeds on the bee but it needs
more than one to bring it to maturity, therefore the mother visits the
nest two or three times, bringing more bees to her young as they are
needed. She does not stock a cell fully, lay her egg and then close it
up, as do most solitary wasps, but she has several cells with young at
various stages of growth, at the bottom of her tunnel, and she brings
the bees to them from day to day.

The harm done by these pirates to the bees is not so much due to
the number killed; this is comparatively small and unimportant. But
the bees are so over-awed by the presence of only one or two pirates
in the vicinity of the hive that they do not go out foraging for food.
The whole colony may be rendered almost completely idle as far as
food-getting is concerned for days on end because the pirates are
about. Most of the few bees that do venture out fall victims to the
swift wasps.

A second species of bee pirate that is very common but that is
never seen at the hives is the yellow bee pirate, *Philanthus diadema*.
This wasp, with its pale yellow abdomen, may be seen haunting the
flowers where it swoops on the bees that are collecting nectar and
pollen and treats them in much the same way as described above for
the banded bee pirate. There are a number of other species of bee
pirates, smaller than the two mentioned, that prey upon solitary bees.
A few species stock their nests with beetles. These solitary wasps form
the family *Philanthidae*.

Fly-hunting Wasps

The fly-hunting wasps of the family *Bembecidae* are all very
similar in appearance and habits and a description of one of them will
serve for all. A common and widely spread species is *Bembex capicola*,
about three-quarters of an inch long, with its abdomen conspicuously
marked with yellow and black bands. The front legs are armed with

NN

stiff spines so that they form efficient rakes. The females make their
nests in sandy soil and, although they never co-operate one with
another, often a number of them may be found nesting close together
in one spot.

When digging her nest the female stands high on her four hind
legs and sends a shower of sand shooting out behind her by the vigorous
use of the rakes on her front legs. Soon she disappears beneath the
surface but the jet of sand still comes spurting out of the hole to show
that she is hard at work sinking her shaft. After a time she makes her
appearance again, backing away from the hole and sweeping ener-
getically to remove the heap of sand that has accumulated at the mouth
of the burrow. Then inside she goes again and the work proceeds at
a great pace, the insect setting up a shrill buzz all the time, until the
slanting burrow is about six inches in depth. At the bottom of the
burrow she hollows out a chamber about the size of an acorn and then
her work is completed for the time being.

Always at the spots she chooses for her nests the sand is cool and
moist a few inches below the surface, although above it is quite dry
and it may be so hot in the blazing sunshine that you cannot bear
your hand on it. When she leaves her nest after the digging is complete,
the dry sand runs into the hole and obliterates it, and she assists in
the concealment by scraping the sand with her feet to remove all traces
of her work. Then away she flies and there is no sign at all on the
surface to reveal the presence of the tunnel and the chamber beneath.
Whilst she is away an animal or a human being may pass that way and
change the appearance of the sand by leaving footprints, but that does
not incommode the wasp in the least. When she returns she drops
down unhesitatingly on the precise spot where the entrance to her
burrow is hidden, locating it by means that are a mystery to us. A
few scrapes with her front legs and the hole is opened once more and
she dives below.

Tucked away below her body and held securely by her middle
legs, she carries a small fly down into the chamber with her. This fly
she has captured and stung whilst on the wing, hunting it in very
much the same way as a hawk hunts and catches a smaller bird. She
deposits this fly in the cool chamber below and then lays an elongated,
white, sausage-shaped egg on it.

She may go off now and start another nest elsewhere, but it is not
known for certain whether this is the case or not. It seems probable
that she restricts her attention to one nest at a time, for if one of these
nests is carefully excavated, a small side tunnel will be found an inch
or so down the main tunnel and in this the female spends a great deal
of her time, resting. After the first small fly has been brought and the

egg laid on it, she probably waits until the egg hatches and then she
goes off to hunt for more food for her young, choosing a larger fly
this time. Any sort of fly will do provided it is moderately large, and
the Bembex wasps do considerable good by capturing such harmful
flies as horse flies, flesh flies and tsetse flies.

From now on she has to provide her ravenous larva with ten or
twelve flies every day for four or five days, some fifty or sixty altogether.
Much in the same way as the parent bird feeds her nestlings, so does
the Bembex wasp provide her larva with fresh food as it is required.
The flies are devoured almost as quickly as they are brought, only the
wings and harder parts of the skin being discarded. When the larva is
five days old and fully grown the wasp stops bringing any more food
and closes up the entrance to the burrow for the last time. She scrapes
sand into the tunnel until it is blocked for the greater part of its length
and then she carefully smooths the sand on the surface so that there
is no external evidence of the nest below. Finally she flies away, never
to return to that particular nest.

The fully grown larva leaves the heap of debris in the chamber
and creeps into the lower end of the tunnel. Here it spins a dense
cocoon of silk round itself, coated on the outside with a layer of sand
grains, each grain placed in position as carefully as a stone-mason
lays stones in a wall. It is not known how the larva forms this strong
protective coat to its cocoon. Although it is inside, the coating of
sand grains is continuous over the whole outer surface of the cocoon.
Near the middle of the cocoon, round its widest circumference, there
are from three to seven black dots. These are thought to be ventilation
pores, constructed by the larva to allow air to circulate between the
outside and the inside of the dense cocoon, but here again we have no
idea how these neat little flask-shaped pores extending through the
silk and between the sand grains are made.

Although each female Bembex makes only some half a dozen
nests during her brief life, she must capture and kill some three to
four hundred flies in order to feed her offspring. The majority of her
victims are harmful flies, such as those mentioned above, therefore
these little wasps must be counted among our friends and allies. There
are a number of different species found in this country and they are
quite common where conditions are suitable for them.

Crabronid Wasps

The large family of small wasps known as the *Crabronidae* includes
many species that prey upon flies and that make their nests in hollow
stems. Some burrow in the ground and some prey upon small caterpillars and other insects. As an example of the group we may take the

little watsonia wasp, *Dasyproctus capensis*, about half an inch long, with four yellow spots on the abdomen and red legs; it has a large square head and short antennae.

When she is ready to lay her eggs the female bores a hole in the side of a Watsonia flower stalk, or the stem of some similar plant with soft pith in the centre. She chooses fresh green stalks for this, not dry stems as do so many of the solitary bees and wasps. She digs out a tunnel inside the stem, both above and below the entrance hole. As a rule the tunnel above the entrance is only about an inch in length, whilst the lower portion may be three or four inches long.

Having completed the construction of her nest she flies off and hunts for flies. She captures her prey by swooping on it like a miniature hawk and stings it. She then flies back to her nest, packs the fly inside and lays her egg on it. The egg is large, white and curved and is invariably fixed across the neck of the fly, between the head and the thorax. Then off she goes again in search of another victim. Five to ten flies form the victuals for one larva, the number of flies depending on their size, for she attacks all kinds that are of a convenient size for her to carry. Having stocked a cell with enough food, the wasp constructs a partition across the burrow, chewing fibres from the inside of the wall of the stem as her building material. Then she stocks a second cell above the first and lays her second egg, and so on up the tunnel. She is not prolific, eight or nine cells being the usual number, and the last few of these may be lodged in the upper part of the tunnel, above the entrance.

When fully grown the larva spins a silken cocoon, pale brown in colour and two or three weeks later the adult emerges. There are a large number of Crabronid wasps found in this country but they have been little studied and there is still much to be learned about their ways.

CLASSIFICATION

ORDER 21: *HYMENOPTERA* (Wasps, Bees and Ants)

Insects with two pairs of membranous wings, hind wings smaller than the front pair and interlocked with them by means of tiny chitinous hooks. Mouthparts adapted for biting and sucking. Abdomen constricted to form a waist and the first joint fused with the thorax. Ovipositor of the female modified for sawing, piercing or stinging. Metamorphosis complete, larvae of most Hymenoptera being legless, blind maggots.

SUB-ORDER 1: *Symphyta*—SAW FLIES

No narrow waist, the abdomen at the base being about the same width as the thorax. Trochanters two-jointed. Larvae with three pairs of thoracic legs and frequently six or more pairs of abdominal limbs, caterpillar-like in appearance. The ovipositor of the female adapted for sawing. These are the most primitive of the Hymenoptera and they are usually divided into four families, of which the *Tenthredinidae* is much the largest.

SUB-ORDER 2: *Apocrita*—WASPS, BEES AND ANTS

This sub-order includes the great majority of the Hymenoptera. The abdomen is always constricted at the waist and the larvae are always legless.

SUPERFAMILY: *Ichneumonoidea*—ICHNEUMON WASPS AND THEIR KIN

The antennae are not elbowed. Trochanters two-jointed. Fore-wings with a stigma (a dark spot on the front edge). Ovipositor issuing some distance before the apex of the abdomen. A very large group of 15,000 or more species, most of which are parasitic on other insects.

FAMILY 1: *Evanidae*—ENSIGN WASPS

Abdomen inserted high up on the back of the thorax so that the abdomen is carried raised in the air. They are parasitic on cockroaches (in the egg-sacs), on beetle larvae and on bees and wasps.

FAMILY 2: *Ichneumonidae*—ICHNEUMON WASPS

Abdomen inserted in the normal manner, at hind end of thorax. A very large family the majority of which are parasitic on caterpillars. The ovipositor of the female is usually long and slender and issues from the apex of the abdomen.

FAMILY 3: *Braconidae*—BRACONID WASPS

Very similar to the *Ichneumonidae*, but the venation of their wings is different. They are parasitic on different kinds of insects.

SUPERFAMILY *Chalcidoidea*

The antennae are elbowed. Trochanters two-jointed. Fore wings without a stigma or closed cells. Ovipositor issues some distance before the apex of the abdomen. A very large group that includes some of the smallest of all insects; most are parasites, but not all.

FAMILY 4: *Agaonidae*—FIG INSECTS

Very small insects that live in figs. Females winged, males wingless. Fore and hind legs stout, middle pair short and poorly developed. These insects play an important part in the pollination of wild figs.

FAMILY 5: *Eurytomidae*

These are small insects, many forming galls on plants, others live in the seeds of various kinds of plants, whilst still others are parasites.

FAMILY 6: *Encyrtidae*

A large family of small insects that are parasites of the eggs, larvae and pupae of other insects of many different kinds. Polyembryony is frequent in this family— the egg is deposited in the egg of the host, which hatches normally, and many embryos develop from the one parasitic egg.

FAMILY 7: *Pteromalidae*

Another large family of small insects that are parasitic on many different kinds of insects. These families are separated one from the other by minute anatomical details that cannot be described here.

FAMILY 8: *Eulophidae*

Yet another large family of small parasites that play a very important part in maintaining the balance of nature.

FAMILY 9: *Trichogrammidae*

Some of the smallest of all insects are included in this family. They are egg parasites and are so small that, in some cases, several individuals can develop in one moth's egg.

SUPERFAMILY *Cynipoidea*

Antennae not elbowed. Trochanters usually one-jointed. Fore wings without a stigma, with very few closed cells and with reduced venation. Ovipositor issues some distance before the apex of the abdomen. These are very small insects, many of which make galls on plants.

FAMILY 10: *Cynipidae*—GALL WASPS

Most members of this family produce galls of various types on many kinds of plants. Some are parasitic.

FAMILY 11: *Figitidae*

Small insects, with peculiar abdominal structure, that are parasites, mostly on the larvae of flies. Some attack aphids and scale insects.

SUPERFAMILY *Proctotrypoidea*
Trochanters two-jointed. Ovipositor issuing from apex of abdomen. Slender, small insects that are nearly all parasites. This group is divided into several families of which only the largest is mentioned below.

FAMILY 12: *Platygasteridae*
Very small insects that are mostly parasites of the gall midges. The females lay their eggs in the eggs of their hosts, but they do not hatch until the fly larvae have emerged and then the parasitic larvae live inside the fly maggots.

SUPERFAMILY *Vespoidea*
First segment of thorax extends back to the tegulae (small scales at base of front wings). Trochanters almost always one-jointed. This large superfamily includes the true social and solitary wasps, that fold their wings longitudinally when at rest, as well as the digger wasps, that do not fold their wings.

FAMILY 13: *Mutillidae*—VELVET "ANTS"
Black insects, marked or ringed with white, yellow, orange or red. Females always wingless, males usually winged. They are all parasitic on solitary bees and wasps, tsetse flies, and other insects.

FAMILY 14: *Scoliidae*
Includes some of the largest of the Hymenoptera. Stoutly built, hairy insects, mostly black with spots or bands of yellow or red. Prey upon the larvae of the *Scarabaeidae*; do not make nests but lay their eggs on the paralysed larvae where found and stung.

FAMILY 15: *Chrysididae*—CUCKOO WASPS
Brilliant metallic coloration, usually green, or blue and red, with coarse punctures in chitin. Convex abdomen on dorsal side, flattened or concave on ventral side, can roll into a ball. Only three or four segments visible in abdomen. They are all parasitic on other solitary bees and wasps.

FAMILY 16: *Eumenidae*—MASON WASPS
Mostly build mud nests in sheltered spots, but some dig tunnels in ground or in dry stems and they partition off their cells with clay. They stock their nests with paralysed caterpillars. These wasps fold their wings longitudinally when at rest. The claws of the feet are toothed.

FAMILY 17: *Vespidae*—SOCIAL WASPS
This family includes the well-known social wasps of the northern hemisphere, as well as the more primitive social wasps, *Belonogaster* species and *Polistes* species, found in Africa and elsewhere in the world. They fold their wings longitudinally when at rest. The claws on their feet are not toothed.

FAMILY 18: *Pompilidae*—SPIDER-HUNTING WASPS
A large family of active wasps with long hind legs that run swiftly over the ground, and their antennae are curled. They nest in the ground and stock their cells with paralysed spiders.

SUPERFAMILY *Sphecoidea*
First segment of thorax does not reach back as far as the tegulae. Trochanters one-jointed. The wings are not folded longitudinally when at rest. This large group includes several families of digger wasps, none of which is social.

FAMILY 19: *Sphecidae*
Slender wasps with a long, narrow waist, usually black with red or yellow markings. Most of them dig tunnels in the ground and stock their nests with caterpillars, but some build mud nests and prey upon spiders.

FAMILY 20: *Philanthidae*—BEE PIRATES
The members of this family burrow in the earth and stock their nests with bees, which they capture on the wing and paralyse by stinging. It includes the two well known enemies of the honey bee, the banded bee pirate and the yellow bee pirate.

FAMILY 21: *Bembecidae*
These wasps burrow in sandy soil and feed their larvae from day to day with flies. They do not stock a cell completely, lay an egg and then close it up, as most solitary bees and wasps do. They are mostly greenish yellow and black in colour and about half an inch long.

FAMILY 22: *Crabronidae*

    Small slender wasps with varied nesting habits. Some make their nests in hollow stems, in holes in palings, walls and tree stumps, and others burrow in the ground. They stock their nests with small caterpillars and other insects.

FAMILY 23: *Oxybelidae*

    Small wasps that burrow in the soil and stock their nests with small flies, which they do not sting but kill or paralyse by crushing the thorax in their jaws.

    (Several smaller families of less importance have been omitted from the above list.)

CHAPTER XXI

BEES

Bees and Wasps

In general it may be said that bees differ from wasps in the nature of the hairs on their bodies and in the nature of the food. The hairs on a wasp's body are simple, without side branches, whilst many of the hairs on a bee's body are feathery, particularly those on the head and thorax. It is thought that the plumose hairs on the bee assist in collecting the pollen. Bees feed on nothing but honey and pollen throughout their lives, whereas wasps in their larval stage are carnivorous. Bees have two pairs of membranous wings, linked together with tiny hooks on the hind pair that fit in a fold on the front wing when

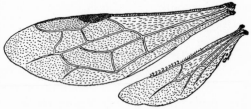

FIG. 170—Wings of a Bee. *Allodape angulata*, showing the small fold on the hind margin of the fore wing and the tiny hooks on the hind wing that fit into it.

the insect is in flight; in this they resemble the majority of wasps, but there are no wingless species among the bees. The tongue of a bee is well developed and adapted for lapping nectar; in the more primitive bees the tongue is short and blunt but in the higher bees it is long and slender; the jaws are well developed in all bees. The larvae of all bees are blind, white and legless, and they are provided with food by the females.

There are a large number of species, most of which are solitary, each female working alone to construct her nest and provide for her young, but some are social and live in highly organised communities. Bees are usually classified as forming a superfamily of the Hymenoptera known as the *Apoidea*, and this is divided into a number of families.

Primitive Bees

The most primitive bees are smallish insects, not more than half an inch long, wasplike in appearance because they have but little pubescence on the body and are generally brown and red in colour. The tongue is very short and they have no special pollen-collecting apparatus such as is found in the higher bees. Their nests are placed in hollow stems, in the ground or in holes in walls and tree stumps. The only material they use for lining their nests and for dividing it into cells is their own saliva which dries and forms a transparent membrane.

342

A common species is the brown membrane bee, *Nothylaeus heraldicus*, of which the female is about three-eighths of an inch long, and the male a little bigger. She is reddish brown and black, with a yellow front to her head and two small yellow stripes on the abdomen. She makes her nest in any suitable dry tubular opening she can find, in hollow stems, in the deserted burrows of wood-boring insects, holes in walls, and so on.

The female starts operations by licking the inside of the tube with her gummy saliva that dries to form a thin, transparent pellicle or membrane. After she has coated the inside of the tube with this water-proof varnish she makes a transverse partition of the same substance near the mouth of the tube, with a small round hole in the middle, just big enough for her to go in and out. This is a long, laborious process that entails several hours licking with her broad, short tongue that she uses as her trowel.

When she begins to stock her first cell at the bottom of the tube the reason for the water-proofing becomes evident. As she cannot carry pollen home on her legs or on the underside of her abdomen, as the higher bees do, she swallows it and brings it home in her crop together with the clear, watery nectar. The two are mixed with saliva and she regurgitates the mixture, which has the consistency and usually the colour of the yolk of an egg, in the bottom of the cell. It is much

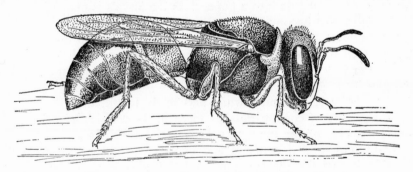

FIG. 171—The Membrane Bee, *Nothylaeus heraldicus*. Female.

more liquid than the food provided by most solitary bees and it would soak into the walls of the nest were it not for the preliminary coating of varnish.

When she has accumulated enough food for her larva she lays her large, sausage-shaped egg in the centre of the mass of food, where it floats. Then, leaving sufficient space for the larva when it is fully grown, she makes a transparent partition across the tube, thus sealing off her first cell, which is about three-eighths of an inch in depth from back to front. And so she goes on, constructing and stocking cell after cell, one above the other. Finally she seals up the mouth of the tube with another membranous partition that looks much like a thin sheet of transparent mica. If her egg-laying is not yet complete, she goes on to find another tube where she can nest. Twelve to fifteen cells are about the limit of her capacity. Often a female will go on working after her ovaries are exhausted and she has no more eggs to lay. She will construct more cells and stock them with food and seal them off, but all this labour is in vain because the cells contain no eggs.

The egg hatches in from five to ten days, depending on the temperature, and the larva, coiled up like a letter "C", feeds whilst floating on the mixture of honey and pollen. It grows rapidly and devours its huge meal in from six to twelve days. As is the case with the larvae of most Hymenoptera that feed in a confined space on a store of food, the stomach of the larva, whilst it is feeding, is blind, with no connection with the intestine; it is like a bag, open in front and closed behind. As a result the larva cannot evacuate and contaminate its food. The waste material accumulates as a dark mass at the hind end of the stomach and this shows as a discoloration through the translucent body-wall of the larva. Only when it is fully grown and has stopped feeding, and whilst it is resting motionless in its cell for a week or ten days prior to changing into a pupa, does the larva's stomach join with the intestine and become open at the hind end. Then, and then only, can it evacuate and all the waste material is expelled at once. There is not much of it because of the nature of the food and it is pushed out of the way to the end of the cell, where it dries as small yellow granules.

The larva is now pure white and ready to pupate. It does not make any sort of cocoon but lies loose in its cell. After about two weeks the eyes of the pupa turn brown and then black. Slowly the body darkens until it is brown and finally, after three to four weeks, the skin is cast for the last time and the adult emerges, about two months after the egg was laid. There are two generations a year of these bees, the first generation nesting during the latter half of October and November, and the second during January and February. The larvae of this second generation reach full size in April and they rest motionless in their cells all through the winter, changing to pupae in the spring and giving rise to the first generation of the following season, in October. These bees are heavily parasitised by the ensign wasp, *Gasteruption spilopus* (see page 314).

The primitive bees are placed in a family known as *Prosopidae* (or *Hylaeidae*).

Burrowing Bees

Many solitary bees dig tunnels in the ground, frequently on gravel paths or in banks where the soil is compact and dry. Although solitary in the sense that each works alone, they are gregarious in their choice of a nesting site and frequently a large number of tunnels will be found close together in a suitable spot. The little bronze-coloured bees, *Halictus* species, of which over seventy species have been described from Africa, exhibit this habit of living in colonies to a marked degree. Sometimes a small area on a path will be seen dotted with little heaps of earth, like miniature mole-hills, and each heap marks the spot where a bee is burrowing below the surface.

The females of some species of *Halictus* dig a common burrow, several females working together at the excavation, but a little way below the surface the tunnel branches and each female has her own branch with her own cells at the end; the only communal part of the nest is the main entrance and passage-way. We know little about the habits of our African species, but judging from observations made on closely allied species in Europe, they should be of especial interest and well worthy of study. It is said of certain European species that there are two generations a year. The spring generation consists of females that have survived the winter and that mated the previous autumn, the males dying soon after the mating. These give rise to a summer generation that consists only of females whose eggs develop partheno-genetically and give rise to the males and females of the autumn generation. It is said of other species of *Halictus* that the female of the spring generation survives after her egg-laying is completed and guards the nest. When her daughters emerge they return to the nest and form a small community, with the old female acting as sentry at the entrance, whilst the young females go busily in and out, foraging for food and stocking their cells.

Small bees with black head and thorax, coarsely pitted, and a red abdomen, belonging to the genus *Sphecodes*, may often be seen in the vicinity of the *Halictus* colonies. They are close relatives and belong to the same family and they are parasitic on *Halictus*, the females laying their eggs in the cells of the host after they have been stocked with food; the eggs of the parasites hatch quickly and each larva devours first the egg of the host and then the provisions in its cell.

In addition, there are a large number of species of small bees, *Nomia* and *Nomioides* species, that belong to this family, *Halictidae*, and that, as far as is known, make their nests in the ground.

Leafcutter Bees

Leafcutter bees, *Megachile* species, are very well known because of their habit of cutting neat circular or oval pieces out of the leaves of rose bushes and other plants. There are a large number of different species, varying in size from that of a house-fly to that of a honey-bee, and they are common and widely spread. They are stoutly built, brown, hairy bees with a conspicuous yellow tuft of hairs on the underside of

FIG. 172—The Leafcutter Bee, *Megachile venusta*. Female.

the abdomen, where the pollen grains are collected. Many bees collect pollen on their hind legs, but all the members of the family to which the leafcutter bees belong, *Megachilidae*, have the pollen-collecting apparatus on the underside of the abdomen.

When the female leafcutter bee is ready to lay her eggs she seeks out any sort of tube of the right diameter that is sheltered and dry and that will serve as a home for her young. It may be a hollow stem, a hole in the wall, an abandoned mud wasp's nest, a burrow left in a fallen log by a wood-boring beetle, even a key-hole. Having decided on the site of her home, she commences operations by cutting an oval piece from a leaf of some suitable plant; she needs fairly thin, smooth leaves and the young foliage of rose bushes and certain kinds of gum trees are favoured sources of building material. Some species use the petals of flowers and a few cut pieces from the papery bark of certain trees.

She tucks the oval piece in the bottom of the tube, pressing it into position with her broad head and using her saliva as a cementing medium. Several of these oval pieces form the base and side-wall of her first cell. They overlap in three or four thicknesses and form a receptacle like a small cup or thimble about half an inch deep. This she fills to about three-quarters of its depth with a thick yellow paste of pollen and honey. On top she lays a white, sausage-shaped egg. Then she closes the thimble with a lid made of circular pieces of leaf, cut to size with amazing accuracy.

After a lid consisting of three or four circular pieces of leaf has been fitted on her first thimble, the bee proceeds to make another cell

on top of it, the lid of the first forming the base of the second. This is
in turn stocked with food and an egg laid on it, and so it goes on until
the tube is nearly filled with thimbles. To finish off her work the bee
now brings a number of pieces of leaf of assorted shapes and sizes and
she pushes these in anyhow, to form a barrier at the mouth of the tube.
Finally she seals off the entrance with a plug of chewed leaf cemented
with her saliva.

There seems to be only one generation a year of these bees. The
fully grown larva spins a cocoon, lining the inside of its cell, and then,
after it has emptied its alimentary canal and coated the inside of its
cocoon with a thin brown layer of excrement that dries to form a
water-proof varnish, it sleeps for months in its snug cell until the
following season, when it pupates and two or three weeks later the
adult emerges.

The little carder bees, *Anthidium* species, belong to the same
family as the leafcutter bees. They are mostly black with a conspicuous
white pollen brush on the underside of the abdomen, and in some
species the males are bigger than the females, an unusual feature among
insects. Most of them make their nests in tubular openings, choosing
sites similar to those utilized by the leafcutters, and they line their cells
with cottony fibres which they strip from various hairy plants by their
mandibles.

The female carder bee arrives at her home with a little bundle of
white fluff carried between her front legs. She takes this into her nest
and cards the fibrous material by pressing it with her head and working

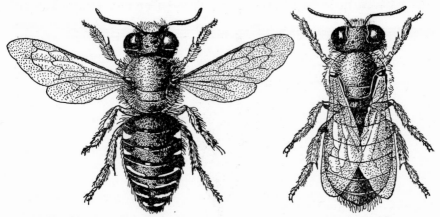

FIG. 173—The Carder Bee, *Anthidium junodi*. Male on left, female on right.

it with her jaws until it forms a thin, uniform, thimble-shaped lining
to the bottom of the tube. Several journeys are made before her
beautiful white thimble is complete and ready to receive its store of

food. The cell is then stocked with a mixture of honey and pollen, the pollen being carried back to the nest on the underside of her abdomen and the honey in her crop. It takes her about two days to construct and stock one cell; then she lays an egg on top of the food and closes the cell with a pad of fluff, well carded and felted together. She fills the tube with cells to within about half an inch from the entrance and then she seals off the lot with a thick pad of fibres, pressed down firmly by her head and jaws to form a protective barrier to keep out enemies.

The egg hatches in seven to eight days and the larva has eaten all the food provided by its mother and is fully grown in ten days. From the time it is about half-grown it begins to excrete waste matter in the form of flattened yellow pellets which it pushes behind it and arranges neatly in a single layer lining the inside of the cotton wallet. By the time it is fully grown these pellets of dry excrement form a layer covering almost the whole of the inner surface of the cell and the larva now proceeds to spin a cocoon of brown silk, with the yellow pellets adhering to the outer surface. The cocoon is dense and smooth, almost spherical, being only slightly longer than it is broad and at the head end there is a curious little nipple which, when examined under the lens, is seen to have a tiny circular opening; it is probably constructed by the larva as a ventilation hole. The adult bee emerges two or three weeks after pupation. There are two generations a year and the larvae that reach full size late in the summer spend the winter months as resting larvae inside their cocoons.

Some species of this family make remarkable nests of matted plant fibres, in some cases as big as a large orange, attached to the

FIG. 174—The Cuckoo Bee, *Coelioxys capensis*. Female. Parasite of *Megachile venusta*.

branches of trees. If such a nest is broken open it is found to consist of a number of cells embedded in the thick, warm, protective coat of fibres. Still other species, of the genus *Osmia*, make their nests in tunnels made by wood-boring insects, in hollow stems, in clay banks, in holes in walls and in empty snail shells, and they mostly use mud (soil particles glued together with saliva) to form the partitions between the cells. A number of species have become cuckoo bees, not constructing and stocking nests for themselves but laying their eggs in the nests of related bees, their larvae feeding on the honey and pollen stored by the host and starving out the legitimate occupants of the nest. Some of the commonest of these are the striking black and white bees, with pointed abdomen, *Coelioxys* species, that are parasitic on leaf-cutter bees.

Carpenter Bees

There are no bumble bees in Africa south of the Sahara; instead we have a number of species of the big burly bees, known as carpenter bees, that form the family *Xylocopidae*. These include the largest of all bees and they are mostly black, marked with bands of yellow or white hairs. They are all very similar in their life history and habits and we may take as our example of the group the common and widely spread species, *Mesotrichia caffra*.

The female is black, a little over three-quarters of an inch long, and she has two prominent bands of yellow hairs, one on the hind half of her thorax and one on the front of her abdomen. The male is about the same size as his mate, but he is completely covered with a dense coat of yellow hairs. Her wings are a dark smoky brown, his are paler in colour. The female starts nesting in spring, at the end of October or the beginning of November and she usually chooses a dead branch of a tree that has partially rotted so that the wood is soft and easily tunnelled. It must be dry, however, for dampness is one of the chief enemies of these bees, many of them dying of fungus disease if moisture penetrates into their home.

She bores a neat tunnel in the wood, about half an inch in diameter and six or seven inches deep, rasping away the wood fibres with her powerful jaws. Several bees may bore tunnels side by side in a dead branch, but they do not, as a rule, co-operate in the work; each female has her own home from which she jealously excludes all intruders, buzzing loudly in protest and butting vigorously with her head if any other bee should enter her tunnel.

Having prepared her nest, with the walls of the burrow carefully smoothed and polished, she sets about collecting food and she limits her attentions almost entirely to flowers of the pea and bean family, the *Leguminosae*. She brings back the pollen on her hairy hind legs and mixes it, inside the nest, with honey regurgitated from her crop, to form a thick, dull yellow paste that is scarcely moist. On top of this mixture she lays her astonishingly large egg, white, curved and half an inch long. Then she closes the cell with a partition made of sawdust chewed from the side of the tunnel, mixed with saliva.

She constructs six or seven such cells, taking about a month to do it, and then her work is completed. After this she rests in the tube, leaving it only occasionally for a little food, and guards her nest from any intruders. The eggs hatch in about a fortnight and the larvae take three or four weeks to consume all their food and reach full size. Then they pupate in their cells, without spinning any cocoon, and the adults of the new generation emerge at the end of January or the beginning of February. In the meantime the old bee has died or disappeared.

The young adults break down the partitions between their cells soon after their emergence, so that the tube contains the debris of the nest with the six or seven brothers and sisters resting amid it. After a

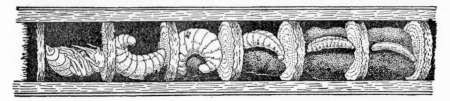

FIG. 175—Development of the Carpenter Bee, *Mesotrichia caffra*. Different stages found in one nest. Egg on the right, pupa on the left.

few days they become active and the rubbish is swept out of the nest. The bees continue to live in the nest amicably as a family party, the various individuals only leaving occasionally to go out and get some food; by far the greater part of their time is spent in the nest, even on bright sunny days. So they spend the autumn and the winter months. When the following spring arrives, and the bees are about ten months old, they become more active. The females begin to show hostility towards the males and the latter are eventually driven out and take up bachelor quarters in an abandoned tunnel; thus early in the spring segregation of the sexes takes place and tunnels can be found crowded with males only. Later the females show hostility to one another and finally only one, apparently the boldest and most aggresive of them, retains possession of the original nest, whilst the others go off to make new tunnels for themselves elsewhere.

Thus there is only one generation of these bees a year and, unlike most other bees, the greater part of their comparatively long life of about a year is spent in the adult state. They can easily be induced to nest in bamboo tubes, about a foot long and from half to three-

PLATE 69

(a) Vinegar Flies, *Drosophila* species, larvae, pupae and adults. The flies are only about one eighth of an inch long.

(b) THE COMMON BLUEBOTTLE, *Chrysomyia marginalis*

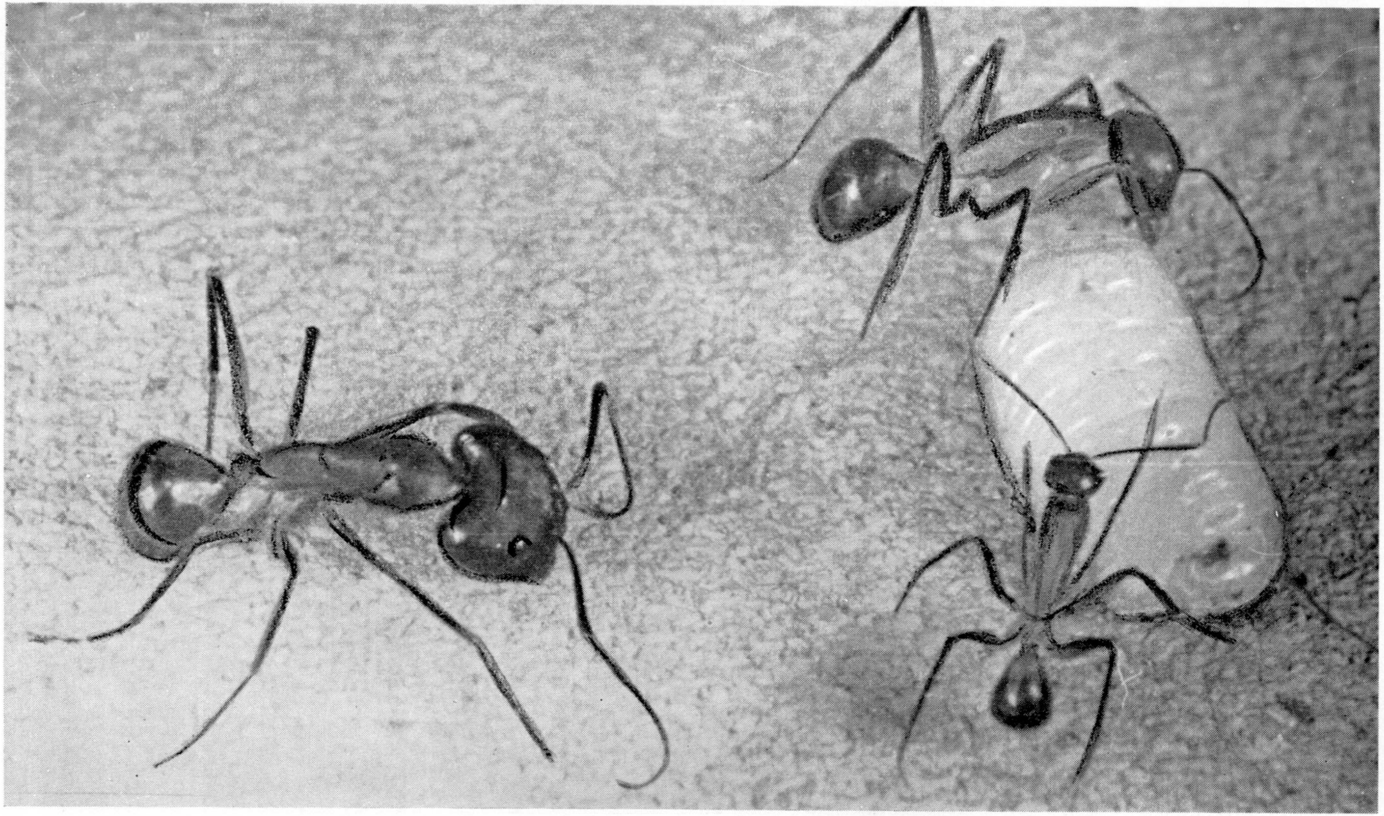

PLATE 70

Ants attending caterpillar in their nest

quarters of an inch internal diameter, if they are taken from their natural homes on a cold day in winter and put into the tubes. The bamboo must be placed in a box where they are quite dry, as the bees quickly desert a damp home. It was from bees nesting in such tubes that the observations recounted above were obtained. Although they are large and strong, their sting is not so painful as that of the honey bee; the sting is not barbed and it is not left behind in the wound.

These bees have some remarkable mites associated with them. Not all carpenter bees have them, but *Mesotrichia caffra* and allied species are all infested with these strange large mites, known as *Dinogamasus* species, that are found only on the bees and in their nests, and nowhere else. If a female *Mesotrichia caffra* is carefully examined, a small hole will be seen at the base of the abdomen, on the dorsal side, just where it is in contact with the hind end of her thorax. This hole leads to a chamber in her abdomen, lined with chitin, and about the size of a lentil. The mites live in this special compartment in her body, packed together like sardines and up to eighteen in number on one bee. She carries them about with her wherever she goes and occasionally one or more of the mites may creep out of the hole and wander over her body, before returning to its retreat. When she constructs her nest, two or three mites leave her body and take up their abode in each cell, so

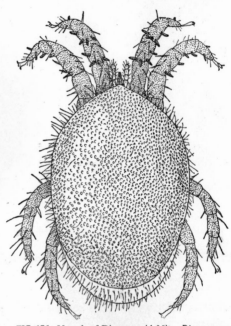

FIG. 176—Nymph of Dinogamasid Mite, *Dinogamasus braunsi*, found on females of *Mesotrichia caffra*. Natural size is one twentieth of an inch long.

that, by the time she has completed her egg-laying, no mites are left in the chamber in her abdomen. The mites lay their eggs on the food mass in the cells and the young mites grow up side by side with the larvae of the bee. Apparently they feed on a fatty exudation they get from the skin of the bee larva but they do not seem to harm their host in any way.

When the young bees emerge from the pupal state the mites in the cells with them creep into the abdominal pockets of the female bees (the males do not have the pockets and never carry the mites about with them). It is not known what is the precise relationship between the bees and the mites. It has been suggested that the mites feed on pollen grains they pick off the hairs on the bee's body, but this is very improbable because of the nature of the mouthparts of the mites. Another suggestion made is that the large Dinogamasid mites feed on the smaller mites that pester these bees, but this again is improbable as one may frequently find a bee badly infested with the small mites and yet with a number of Dinogamasid mites in its pocket.

FIG. 177—The Sub-social Bee, *Allodape angulata*.   Female on left, male on right.

We still have much to learn about this remarkable case of symbiosis between certain species of carpenter bees and the Dinogamasid mites.

A number of species of much smaller bees, ranging in size from about a tenth of an inch to half an inch, with few hairs on their bodies and generally metallic green in colour, belong to the genus *Ceratina* and are sometimes called lesser carpenter bees. They make their nests in hollow stems, such as the dry flower stalks of aloes, watsonias and others. On a much smaller scale, their nests are very similar to those of the carpenter bees, each cell stocked with a mass of a rather dry mixture of honey and pollen and each cut off from the next by a partition of fragments chewed from the wall of the stem and glued together with saliva.

Some remarkable and very interesting little bees, of the genus *Allodape*, are also included in this family. The largest of them is only about half an inch long, brown or black as a rule, whilst others are much smaller. They are common and widely spread through Africa and there are many different species of them. As our example of this group we may take one of the largest as well as one of the commonest species, *Allodape angulata*. The female of this species is easily recognised by her size, a little more than half an inch, and by the three points at the end of her abdomen.

She makes her nest in dry flower stalks similar to those chosen by the lesser carpenter bees, *Ceratina* species. Usually she chooses a stalk that has been broken and she burrows down into it from the top, chewing out the pith to a depth of six or seven inches. Then she lays two or three large oval white eggs which lie loose at the bottom of the burrow. After this she spends most of her time in the tube, guarding her eggs until they hatch. She does not attempt to collect a store of food for her young but, as soon as the first egg hatches, she goes out and collects honey and pollen. Returning to the nest, she scrapes the pollen from her hind legs into a heap on the floor of the nest and then regurgitates some honey on to it and mixes the two into a stiff paste. Picking up this paste in her jaws she places it on the larva, just behind its head, as it lies back downwards. By bending its head, the larva can get at the food lying on its chest, as it were. As soon as this lot of food is finished, the mother fetches some more and, when the other eggs hatch, she feeds her other larvae in the same way. She always arranges them in the tube with the oldest near the entrance, the next in age a little lower down, and so on, while the newly hatched larva and any eggs that may be present are at the bottom of the tube. Usually she will have a family of six or seven being fed day by day.

FIG. 178—Metamorphosis of *Allodape angulata:* (*a*) Egg; (*b*) young larva; (*c*) older larva with food-mass; (*d*) larva ready to pupate; (*e*) pupa, male.

When she is not occupied caring for her young, the mother rests at the mouth of the tube, with the tip of her abdomen just at the entrance, ready to sting any intruder. She carefully removes the excrement passed by the fully grown larvae and keeps her nest spotlessly clean. When the larvae pupate she spends practically all her time in the nest, waiting patiently for a fortnight or more for her sons and daughters to emerge. The family remain together, mother (now with tattered tips to her wings) and her sons and daughters (with undamaged wings), if the tube is commodious enough. If not, some of the young bees will leave their home to go and seek nesting sites elsewhere, but usually one or two of the males and females remain with their mother. In this way small colonies are formed but they never grow larger than three or four individuals. The females work together in caring for the young, the old female spending the greater part of her time in the nest, guarding the entrance. The presence of the males in the nest is tolerated, although they do not assist at all in rearing the young.

Here we see the primitive beginnings of social life among these bees. They are comparatively long lived, each female living for nearly a year in the adult state; it is not known how long the males live, but they also live longer than is the case with most male bees. The females come into contact with their young and they see them grow up into adults. With the great majority of solitary bees, the females never come into actual contact with their young; they seal off the cells after stocking them with food and they die before their family reach the adult state and emerge. Bees of the genus *Allodape* are the only ones that exhibit these interesting habits and they are well worthy of further study. They exhibit striking differences in their ways. For example, the small species, *Allodape halictoides*, that is also very common and that also nests in dry flower stalks, has quite a different method of arranging her eggs from that seen in *Allodape angulata*.

FIG. 179—Eggs and newly-hatched larvae of *Allodape halictoides*

The female *Allodape halictoides* lays her eggs, which are comparatively small, on the wall of the nest, gluing them in an upright position in a circle, jutting towards the centre of the burrow like the spokes of a wheel. She lays half a dozen or more in a short period and,

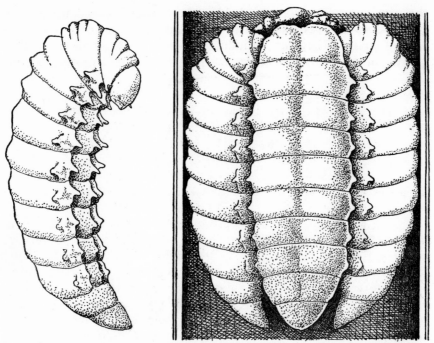

FIG. 180—Larvae of *Allodape halictoides:* isolated larva on left, group of larvae feeding inside nest on right.

when they hatch, the young larvae remain attached to the wall of the nest by their hind end, which is retained in the egg-shell. Thus the larvae all have their heads towards the centre and all at the same level. The mother brings in pollen which she piles in a heap just in front of her young. To feed them, she regurgitates some honey on the heap, mixes some pollen with it to the desired consistency, and then she picks up the sticky mass and thrusts it between the heads of her young, thereby supplying all her family with food at once.

As the larvae grow bigger they come to lie side by side, all with their heads up, pointing towards the entrance, and all at the same level. Therefore throughout their lives the mother can feed her whole family at once by thrusting a lump of food paste in between the heads of the larvae. When they are fully grown she drags the larvae apart and arranges them in a row along the tube, and she now spends most of her time in the nest, with her tail at the entrance to keep out intruders. When the adults of the next generation emerge they remain with the mother for a time but soon, to prevent overcrowding, some members of the family depart to found new nests elsewhere.

Certain species of *Allodape* lay only one large egg at a time and the mother tends the single larva until it is fully grown before laying the next egg. There are probably other variations and these little primitive social bees, that are so abundant in Africa, offer a fruitful field of study. They can be induced to nest in glass tubes, about a quarter of an inch in diameter and six inches long, plugged at the

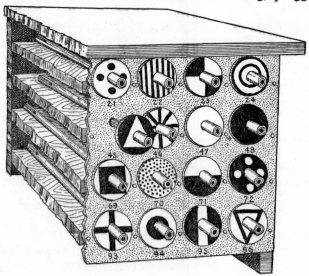

FIG. 181—Artificial nests for the Primitive Social Bees, *Allodape*. The glass tubes have discs with black and white patterns on them to assist the bees in finding their homes.

rear end with a piece of pith or wad of cotton-wool, and lined along the lower half with a strip of paper to afford a foothold for the bees. If such tubes are pushed into holes in the side of a box so that only the mouths protrude and if pupae, collected from nests in the field, are put into them, the bees, when they emerge, will remain in the tubes and nest in them. As they use no sort of building material, all that goes on inside the glass nest can easily be watched.

Anthophorid Bees

There are numerous species of stoutly built, hairy bees that look much like small bumble bees and that belong to the family known as the *Anthophoridae*. Over one hundred species have been described and named from Africa and they are also well represented in other parts of the world. They are very swift on the wing and their flight is erratic, accompanied by a shrill hum. All, as far as is known, nest in the ground, digging very deep burrows, generally in the sun-baked side of a bank. At the bottom, short side tunnels lead to the cell chambers which are stocked with a mixture of honey and pollen in the usual manner. Some species construct a curious curved tube at the mouth of their burrow, made from grains of sand cemented together with saliva. Most of them seem to like the company of their own kind for they form large colonies of nests close together, although each female works entirely alone and unaided in her own nest.

Social Bees

There are well over ten thousand species of bees known from all over the world but, of these, only about five hundred are social bees; all the rest are solitary—they do not form colonies and the females work alone. Excluding the primitive social bees described above, and the bumble bees which do not occur in our region, all social bees are placed in the family known as the *Apidae*, and these, in Africa, include the well known honey bees and the little stingless bees.

The stingless bees, or Mopani bees, as they are often called, that are found in Africa belong to the genus *Trigona*. They are small; indeed, some of them, only about an eighth of an inch long, are among the smallest of all bees. Although they cannot sting, because their stings are vestigial and useless as weapons of defence, they swarm out of their nest if disturbed and buzz about in front of one's face in a very irritating manner, settling in the hair and on the eyebrows and forehead, crawling into the eyes, mouth and nose and being generally very unpleasant; on occasion, they will bite freely.

The stingless bees nest in hollow tree-trunks, in holes in walls and, in the case of some species, in holes in the ground. A few species in Central Africa are said to make their nests in the centre of termite mounds. The nesting material is a dark coloured wax, mixed with earth or resin so that it is black or brown in colour. The workers also gather a great deal of propolis, resins and gums that they use in their nest, to block up cracks and crevices and also in the construction of the curious spout or funnel that marks the entrance to the nest. It has been suggested that the sticky funnel at the entrance prevents the entrance of ants and other unwanted visitors.

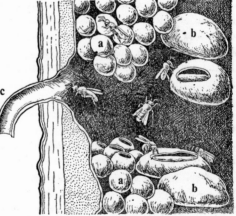

FIG. 182—Portion of nest of Stingless Bee, *Trigona* species, in a hollow tree (diagrammatic): (*a*) Brood cells; (*b*) cells for storage of pollen and honey; (*c*) spout.

Sentries remain on guard at the entrance during the day, as is the case with the ordinary honey bee, but at night the stingless bees close up the funnel with a temporary plug of wax and gum.

The interior of the nest consists of a brood portion and a portion for the storage of food. The combs in the brood portion consist of irregular masses of spherical cells, or of layers of small, hexagonal cells with their mouths facing upwards, and they may be arranged in combs one above the other, or in a spiral, or irregularly, depending upon the species. The combs are sometimes enclosed in a hollow envelope of wax.

Outside the brood area of the nest, the workers construct large elliptical or spherical pots of wax in which the honey and pollen are stored. The workers put a quantity of honey and pollen in each cell of the brood combs and then, after the queen has laid an egg in a cell, it is sealed with a waxen cover. Therefore these little bees, although they are social, rear the young very much in the same way as the solitary bees do. The number of individuals in a colony varies very widely, from a few hundred to several thousands, depending on the species and on the age of the colony. The inhabitants are nearly all sterile females, or workers, although it is said that the presence of large numbers of males is tolerated in the nest because they, unlike all other male Hymenoptera, can assist their sisters in building the nest. The wax is stated to be produced between the dorsal segments of the abdomen, not from the underside, as is the case with the honey bee, and that males as well as females can produce the substance.

The queen differs little in appearance from the workers; her head is smaller and her abdomen slightly more portly because of her active ovaries. There is only one mother queen in a colony, but a number of daughter queens may be present as well to assist the old queen. The bitter jealousy between queens found in the honey bee seems to be absent among the stingless bees. New colonies are formed by swarming, young queens leaving the nest from time to time accompanied by a detachment of workers. This again is somewhat different from the honey bee, where it is the old queen that leads forth the swarm; it is said the old queen of the stingless bees is too fat and heavy with eggs to fly out with a swarm.

The honey bees are separated by a wide gap from the stingless bees. Most authorities consider there are only four species of honey bees in the world, and of these three are found only in the Indomalayan region, whilst the fourth is the well known hive bee, *Apis mellifica*, that has been carried all over the world by man. Several different varieties or races of the hive bee have been named, and no less than six have been recorded from Africa. Of these the two most important are the yellow-banded race, *Apis mellifica adansoni*, which is the commonest type of bee found in apiaries in this country, and *Apis mellifica uni-*

color, the black variety that has the reputation of being vicious and intractable. Hybrids between these two races occur.

One point of special interest about our black bees, the *unicolor* variety, is the fact that competent observers have reported that the workers, during a queenless period, will lay eggs that can develop into workers or even queens. As is well known, workers of other races of honey bees lay infertile eggs that develop only into drones, and workers capable of laying female-producing eggs have not been reported elsewhere in the world. Further work on the *unicolor* race is needed to confirm and extend the earlier observations, made about forty years ago and not followed up since.

CLASSIFICATION

ORDER 21: *HYMENOPTERA* (Wasps, Bees and Ants)

SUPERFAMILY *Apoidea*—BEES

This superfamily includes all the bees. The tarsi on the hind legs are dilated or thickened and some of the hairs on the body are feathery. The food consists entirely of honey and pollen.

FAMILY 1: *Prosopidae*—PRIMITIVE BEES

A small family of smooth, almost hairless bees with short tongues. They have no special pollen-collecting apparatus, the females swallowing the pollen and carrying it back to the nest in their crop. They line their nests with saliva that dries to form a transparent membrane, and they partition off their cells in the same way.

FAMILY 2: *Colletidae*

Also primitive bees, but separated from the *Prosopidae* by their hairiness; they are also larger and more stoutly built than the former. They burrow in the soil and line their nests with water-proof coating of saliva in the same way as the *Prosopidae*.

FAMILY 3: *Halictidae*

A large family of small to moderate sized bees of varied habits, but most of them construct burrows in the ground, with short branches at the lower end giving access to the cells. Some members of this family are parasitic in the nests of other bees.

FAMILY 4: *Megachilidae*—LEAFCUTTER AND CARDER BEES

A large family of moderate sized bees, the best known of which are the leafcutter bees. Other members of the family make their nests or the nest partitions out of plant fibres, resin or mud. Some nest in the ground, others in holes in wood, walls, hollow stems, and so on. Some members of the family are parasitic on other bees.

FAMILY 5: *Xylocopidae*—CARPENTER BEES

The largest of all bees are included in this family although some of them are smaller than the honey bee. They are mostly black with bands of white or yellow hairs and they make their nests in dead branches, dry aloe stems, bamboos, etc. They limit their attention mainly to flowers of the *Leguminosae*.

FAMILY 6: *Anthophoridae*

Burly, hairy bees with a swift, erratic flight. They nest in the ground, making deep tunnels and constructing their cells at the bottom.

FAMILY 7: *Apidae*—SOCIAL BEES

This family includes the little stingless bees, *Trigona* species, and the well known honey bee, *Apis mellifica*.

(A few of the smaller, less important families have been omitted from the above list.)

CHAPTER XXII

ANTS

The Formicidae

Ants form one very large family, the *Formicidae,* of which there are about four thousand species known in the world. They are all social insects; no solitary ants are known. A colony of ants may consist of only a few individuals, or it may be a huge community of hundreds of thousands. It includes a queen or queens, the only individuals in the nest, as a rule, that are fertile and capable of laying eggs, and a number of workers, all of which are sterile females; some of the workers in certain species have large heads and powerful jaws and these are spoken of as soldiers, but they also are sterile females. The only time males are encountered in an ants' nest is when they have been reared for the mating flight; they die soon after mating and are not found in the nests as "kings", as is the case with termites; nor are there ever any male workers. The young are blind, legless and quite helpless and are tended by the workers. It has been found that they give off a salivary secretion of which the workers are very fond, as is the case with the social wasps (see page 330). The larvae of many kinds of ants spin silken cocoons when they are fully grown, others do not and the pupae lie naked in the nest.

All ants have a very narrow waist between the thorax and abdomen, called the petiole or pedicel, and it consists of one or two small joints. The workers are always wingless; some are blind and some have small, compound eyes. Only the fully developed males and females have wings, two pairs similar to those of other Hymenoptera, and they retain them for but a short time after emerging from the pupal state. As soon as the wedding flight is over the males die and the queens shed their wings. The males of all ants have well developed eyes and most queens have eyes. The females of most ants, including the workers, have stings, but among the higher ants the sting is vestigial or absent.

The family is divided into five sub-families, the Ponerinae, Dorylinae, Myrmicinae, Dolichoderinae, and Camponotinae. It is convenient to deal with each separately under the names ponerine ants, doryline ants, myrmicine ants, dolichoderine ants, and camponotine ants.

Ponerine Ants

The ponerine ants are the most primitive of the family and they may be recognised by the one-jointed petiole between thorax and

abdomen, and by the constriction between the first and second segments of the abdomen. Many species are found in Africa and the
workers range in size from about an eighth of an inch in length up to
three-quarters of an inch. The colonies are mostly small but there are
a few species that live in large communities. All are carnivorous,
hunting other insects for food and preying to a large extent upon
termites. The queens and workers are armed with stings and some

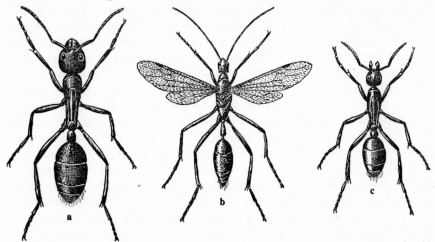

FIG. 183—The Matabele Ant, *Megaponera foetens:*   (a) Major worker; (b) male; (c)
minor worker. All drawn to the same scale. The major worker is three fifths of an inch
long.

of the larger species can inflict a painful wound; some, if not all, can
stridulate by rubbing the roughened surfaces on the first and second
abdominal segments together; the sound made by the largest species
is quite audible to human ears some distance away. The queens look
very like the workers and there is not much difference in size between
them. The larvae are fed by the workers on scraps of insects and they
spin cocoons round themselves when fully grown.

The Matabele ant, *Megaponera foetens*, is one of the largest and
best known members of this sub-family. It is common and well known
in the Rhodesias because of its aggressive ways, its painful sting, its
distinct stridulation and its offensive smell. The workers are of two
sizes, the larger being about three-fifths of an inch long, black with
fine yellow hairs on its body, whilst the smaller is a little less than half
an inch long and more shiny than its big sister. The queen is about
three-quarters of an inch long and looks much like a major worker,
with a stouter abdomen. The nest is in the ground and the entrance to
it is a simple hole without a mound round it.

These ants feed almost exclusively on termites and they make well organised raids to secure their prey. They march in a double file, major and minor workers together, and, when they reach the termite nest that is to be raided, they pour into every hole and crevice that gives access to the galleries below. Each worker seizes a termite in its powerful jaws and brings it to the surface, where it is left, maimed and dying. Then the worker dives below again in search of another victim. After each worker has brought up five or six termites, the army reassembles at the surface and each worker picks up as many of the dead and dying termites as it can carry and returns to the nest—in double file again. This species and other ponerine ants undoubtedly play an important part in keeping down the numbers of termites.

Some species of ponerine ants live in small colonies in hollow stems and they are nocturnal, creeping out at night to hunt their prey. A few species are known that prey almost exclusively upon beetles, but others will destroy any insects they can overcome, and still others, like the Matabele ant, seem to limit their attentions almost entirely to termites. Several of them have an unpleasant smell, which has been likened to that of a foul tobacco pipe, and also to a strong smell of cockroaches. The majority of the species nest in the ground, some at a depth of a foot or more, and the entrances to the nest are often marked by mounds of excavated earth; some nest under stones and others in the walls of termite mounds.

Driver Ants

The members of the sub-family *Dorylinae* are commonly known as driver or legionary ants. They are found throughout Africa, from the Cape to the Sahara, but they are not often seen because of their secretive, subterranean ways, except when they are on the march in dense columns on the surface on dull days. Countless hordes of them may suddenly appear in a garden, in the neighbourhood of the manure or compost heap, moving along in a slow, never-ending stream just beneath the surface of the soil or under piles of dead leaves. They stay for a time and then disappear again as silently and unexpectedly as they came. Occasionally a colony may take up its temporary abode in hollows in the walls of old houses, particularly if they are built of sun-dried bricks. Gardeners sometimes complain about the damage done by these insects to such plants as cabbages and dahlias, but as their stay in any particular spot is not of long duration and as they are almost entirely carnivorous, they usually do little harm to plants in the garden. They may, on the other hand, do good by destroying such pests as cutworms and root-eating beetle larvae. Stories are told of great armies invading houses in Central Africa and driving every living thing out, whilst they swarm everywhere in their ceaseless hunt for prey, but the driver ants in the Union do not seem to indulge in this unpleasant habit.

The most common and widely spread of the driver ants in Africa is *Dorylus helvolus*. There are four types of workers in this species, the largest measuring about a quarter of an inch in length, while the smallest are midgets of less than one-eighth of an inch. They are red-

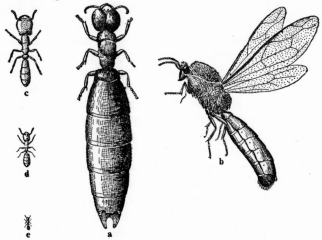

FIG. 184—The Driver Ant, *Dorylus helvolus:* (*a*) Queen; (*b*) Male; (*c*) Major worker, or soldier; (*d*) Medium worker; (*e*) Minor worker. All drawn to same scale and a little larger than natural size.

dish brown and all are completely blind, yet they move along when on the march with uncanny precision, disciplined and orderly and purposeful, but nobody has succeeded in finding out who or what it is that guides and rules the countless throng.

Somewhere in the neighbourhood is the nest, a temporary resting place probably deep below the surface of the ground, at the base of some buried stone or tree stump as a rule. From this central spot the marauding columns radiate, hunting for any living things they can overcome, cut up and carry back to their nest as food. When the surrounding area has been thoroughly searched for all available food, when there are no more victims to be caught, the order to move on is given, by some means or other, and the great throng treks in orderly fashion to seek fresh hunting grounds.

They carry their young and their queen with them. Even their pets go with them, for these ants generally have a great number of beetles and other insects (see page 220) living with them. Because they are hunters, depending on the chase for their living, and because they live in communities consisting of many thousands of individuals, these driver ants are doomed to be always on the move; they can never settle for any time in one place because the food supply is soon exhausted.

The doryline ants and their South American relatives are the only hunters that have succeeded in forming large communities. Even man, in his primitive hunting state, such as the Bushmen of to-day, can only live in small family groups.

The queen of the driver ant is an amazing insect; she is also one of the rarest of insects, as only about a dozen specimens are to be found in all the museums of the world, yet these ants are common and widely spread throughout the continent. She is a fat, clumsy creature, brown in colour and about an inch and a quarter long. Her large, heavy abdomen, distended with eggs, impedes her movements so that she can only walk with difficulty. How, then, does she get along when her countless offspring decide that it is time to shift camp? We do not know. It has been suggested that she is dragged and carried along by the workers, and as proof of this it is said that the specimens in collections mostly have bits of their legs missing and show scratches on the underside of the body, as though they had been pulled along over rough ground. It is exceedingly strange that nomadic creatures such as the driver ants should have such sluggish, helpless queens.

The queen is also remarkable in that she is quite blind and never has wings. Among the great majority of ants the young males and females have two pairs of wings and a pair of compound eyes, as well as simple eyes on top of the head; there are very few exceptions to this rule. The queen driver ant obviously can never take part in a wedding flight. In fact, she is not a real queen at all; she is nothing more or less than an enormously over-grown, specially developed worker. That is why she has no wings or wing muscles or eyes. The real queens have disappeared from among the doryline ants and their places have been taken by these monstrous workers, dichthadiigynes, as they are called.

The male driver ant is also an extraordinary creature. He is about an inch long, with a brown, fluffy head and thorax, and a brown, cylindrical abdomen which, when you pick him up, he waves about in a threatening manner, but, like all male ants, bees and wasps, he has no sting. He has a pair of sharp jaws but he never attempts to bite; it is doubtful whether he ever feeds after leaving the nest. His four wings are transparent and he is a strong flier. He alone of all the driver ant throng has a pair of compound eyes and three small, simple eyes on top of his head. Frequently these large, wasplike males will come flying into a room at night, attracted by the light, and will flop heavily on to the floor. Probably these blundering males have left their nest to hunt for other colonies with virgin queens, and they are led astray by the light. As the queens cannot fly, can scarcely walk even, it is obvious that the males must seek them out, or that mating takes place inside the nest between brothers and sisters. Probably the males are guided to the virgin females by the sense of smell.

There are a number of species of driver ants found in Africa and all, as far as is known, have habits similar to those described above.

Dolichoderine Ants

The ants belonging to the sub-family *Dolichoderinae*, are small and soft bodied. The petiole between the thorax and abdomen is only one-jointed; the workers cannot sting, because the sting is vestigial or absent, but they have special glands at the hind end of the abdomen which produce a secretion that hardens on exposure to the air and that usually has an unpleasant smell. This secretion is used when fighting and it serves to clog the legs of their enemies. They are mostly shy, inconspicuous insects that live in small or moderate-sized colonies, but there is one introduced species belonging to this sub-family that has become a very serious pest wherever it has established itself.

This is the Argentine ant, *Iridomyrmex humilis*, that was first officially recorded as being present at the Cape in the year 1908, and it is generally supposed that

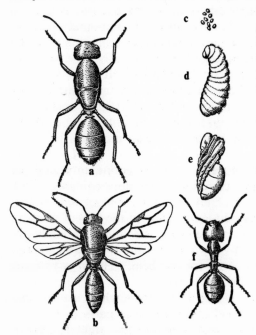

FIG. 185—The Argentine Ant, *Iridomyrmex humilis:*
(*a*) Queen; (*b*) Male; (*c*) Egg; (*d*) Larva; (*e*) Pupa; (*f*) Worker. The queen is brown and about one quarter of an inch long.

it got here during the Anglo-Boer War, in forage imported from South America, but there is no evidence either for or against this theory. It was first collected near Buenos Aires in 1868 and described and named, but after this nothing more was heard about it until it suddenly burst into world prominence as a major and widely distributed pest early in the present century. Between 1900 and 1910 it was recorded from the United States, Chile, Madeira, Portugal, South Africa, and other places, and it is still spreading; in recent years it has found its way to Western Australia and become a serious pest there. It is not known at present how far it has spread in South Africa as no survey has yet been carried out, but it is very abundant and harmful in the south-west Cape.

During the winter months the ants do not attract much attention as they remain in their sheltered nests during the cold, wet weather, beneath large stones, in the middle of the compost heap, in logs tunnelled by other insects, and so on, and very little breeding goes on. But when the warmer weather of spring arrives they become active and troublesome.

Most ants live in separate colonies and the inhabitants of one colony are antagonistic to the members of others, but this is not the case with the Argentine ants. They live in huge compound colonies, the nests in different parts of the garden communicating one with the other and the ants all working together in friendly co-operation. Argentine ants are, however, fiercely intolerant of all other kinds of ants and, where they are numerous, they quickly exterminate all our native ants. It is, in fact, difficult to find any South African ants on the Cape Peninsula to-day, unless you go up to the mountain slopes above a thousand feet or so, where the South American intruders have not yet penetrated.

As a rule, there are many queens in an Argentine ants' nest, as many as fifty or more being quite common in populous colonies. They are small, only about a quarter of an inch long, brown and active. Occasionally some of them may be seen running in the files of workers on the surface of a warm evening. When food is coming in abundantly they lay large numbers of small, oval white eggs and these are gathered into heaps by the workers and cared for by them. The eggs will not hatch if taken away from the workers.

The eggs hatch into blind, legless, white larvae which are fed and cleaned by the workers and carried about to those parts of the nest where temperature and moisture conditions are just right for them. The fully grown larvae, after having emptied the alimentary canal, rest for a few days and then change into pupae; they do not spin any cocoons. About a fortnight later the adults emerge. It is probable that the workers and queens develop from the same kind of egg; the remarkable differences in size and structure of the workers and queens are determined apparently by the nature and quantity of food given to the larvae by the workers. The great majority of the larvae are more or less starved so that their growth and development are stunted, and sterile females, the workers, are the result. When more queens are required, some of the larvae are fed on a more abundant and richer diet and they develop into fully grown females, with functional sexual organs, that we call queens. The male ants are almost certainly reared from unfertilised eggs, as is the case with the honey bee.

At about mid-summer, on warm, sultry evenings when rain is threatening, male Argentine ants fly from the nest and are often attracted to lights. They may be recognised by their dark brown colour, by their hump-backed appearance and by their size; they are about three-sixteenths of an inch long. There is no wedding flight with the Argentine ants.

Most ants rear a number of males and females in the nest during the summer. These are winged and, when weather conditions are favourable, they leave the nest in a swarm on their mating flight, much in the same way as termites do. The males die soon after mating and the fertilised females seek out sheltered spots where they can found new colonies, usually each female settling down alone. She lays a few eggs and then watches over them until they hatch, never leaving the nest. The larvae are fed from secretions from the mother's body, from special glands and from her broken-down wing muscles which she no longer requires. As the queen takes no food herself during this period, the food for her young is limited, therefore the first workers that develop from the first half a dozen or so eggs are small, much smaller than normal, but, as soon as they emerge, the dwarf workers take over the work of enlarging the nest and foraging for food and water. Thus the queen can now lay more eggs and so the size of the colony increases at a progressive rate. This is the way new colonies are founded among the majority of ants, but it is not the case with the Argentine ant.

Apparently the winged females of the Argentine ant never leave the nest but shed their wings soon after the adult state is reached. It seems that mating usually takes place between brothers and sisters, but the males that leave the nests on warm summer nights probably find their way to other colonies and so continuous inbreeding is avoided. More observations are needed on this point.

As the numbers increase rapidly during the summer, new nests are formed in the neighbourhood of the parent colony, some queens and workers take up their abode in the new position, but they still go to and fro between this and the old nest, and so the compound colonies are formed that are so characteristic of the Argentine ant. Often the ants move their home so as to be nearer an abundant food supply and they will make their nests almost anywhere where they can find darkness and a certain amount of moisture. This need for moisture becomes urgent towards the end of the long, dry summer and this is when the ants invade the kitchen in swarms and become a great nuisance round the kitchen sink.

They are extraordinarily catholic in their taste in food and will eat meat, cakes, sweets, honey, fruit and other insects. They will swarm on fruit trees, not only for the juice of any damaged fruit on the trees, but also for the honey-dew they collect from aphids and scale insects and mealie-bugs. Eucalyptus trees in flower supply them with an abundant food supply in the form of nectar from the blossoms. The refuse bin in the yard is a rich hunting ground for them. When food is plentiful the queens lay large numbers of eggs and the colonies may grow to an enormous size of hundreds of thousands of inhabitants.

Apart from the Argentine ant, we have no Dolichoderine ants in this country that are of any great importance. There are not many native species and they live in small colonies and attract little or no attention.

Myrmicine Ants

The ants of the sub-family *Myrmicinae* are very numerous, with nearly three hundred species in South Africa alone. They have a two-jointed petiole between the thorax and abdomen. The members of this group show a greater variety of habits and structure than are

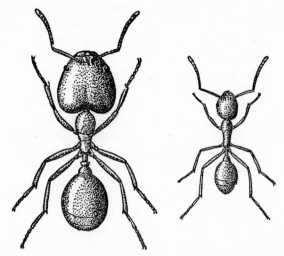

FIG. 186—The Brown House Ant, *Pheidole megacephala*. Major and minor workers drawn to the same scale and magnified six times.

found in any of the other sub-families. The females are armed with stings and the larger species can inflict quite a sharp wound which has, however, no lasting effect.

One of the commonest and most widely spread of the Myrmicine ants is the brown house ant, *Pheidole megacephala*. It is very widely distributed throughout South and Central Africa and in places may become a serious household pest. The workers are small, a little less than an eighth of an inch long, and brown in colour; in a large colony several thousands of these may be present. The soldiers, or major workers, are about a sixth of an inch long, and they have large square heads armed with powerful jaws. It is misleading to speak of these larger workers as soldiers because they do not play an important part in the defence of the nest. If a stone is turned over and a nest exposed beneath it, the so-called soldiers run away and hide, whilst the minor workers are much more aggressive. Apparently these large-headed workers function more as labourers to remove material from the nest that is too heavy for the minor workers, to cut up hard-bodied insects and perhaps to crush seeds with their powerful jaws. The queens are dark reddish-brown in colour and about a third of an inch long; there are usually several of them present in a nest.

These ants nearly always make their nest in the soil, under stones as a rule, and they are shallow, never more than a few inches deep. The entrances to the nest are often marked by small heaps of loose soil carried out by the ants in making their irregular, shallow cavities in which they live. The ants are most active in the evening and at night, visiting aphides, scale insects and mealie-bugs for their honey-dew, capturing and cutting up insects and foraging for any other food they can find. They are almost as catholic in their taste in food as the Argentine ants.

There is little or no breeding during the winter but early in the spring the queens begin to lay freely. The tiny white eggs hatch in from two to four weeks, according to the temperature and the larvae are fed by the workers for about the same length of time. Then they pupate, without cocoons, and again in about two to four weeks the adult workers emerge. Larger larvae, destined to develop into winged males and females are found in the nests from October to December. The sexual individuals that develop from these are present at mid-summer. Possibly the wedding flight takes place at night for so far there are no records of such flights by day. The winged individuals have all disappeared from the nest by autumn. Paussid beetles (see page 220) and other guests are frequently found in the nests of these ants.

Closely allied species of the brown house ant are the well known harvester ants. A common and widely spread harvester ant is *Messor barbarus*, with large-headed soldiers, or major workers, a little less than half an inch long, and small-headed minor workers about a quarter of an inch long, both brown in colour. The dark brown queens are about three-fifths of an inch long. These ants form large nests in the soil and they feed mainly on the seeds of different kinds of grasses.

The husks removed from these seeds by the ants are deposited in a circle round the entrances to the nest and, in the case of large colonies, these heaps may be two or three inches deep and cover an area of a square foot or more. The workers seem to have well-trodden pathways which they use regularly in passing to and from their harvesting grounds. Frequently, if a nest is opened in the autumn or winter, heaps of the heads of major workers will be found piled in a chamber at one side of the nest. Possibly the major workers are slaughtered and eaten (except the heads) by the minor workers at the end of the season, when food is becoming scarce and there is no more work for the majors to do.

The thief ant, *Carebara vidua*, is a remarkable myrmicine ant, with tiny yellow workers, less than a twelfth of an inch long, and with

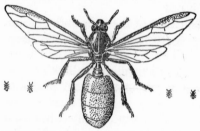

FIG. 187—The Thief Ant, *Carlbara vidua*. A young queen as she leaves the nest and four workers. They are sisters. All natural size. The queen is black and brown, the workers are pale yellow.

giant queens an inch long, with black head and thorax and reddish brown abdomen. These ants are only found nesting in termite mounds and the tiny workers make very narrow tunnels through the mound, large enough for them to get through, but too small for the termites. The little thief ants, it is believed, creep into the chambers of the termite nest and carry off the eggs and young as food, being secure from pursuit and harm when they get back into their narrow tunnels.

These ants are common over the Ethiopian region and they offer a promising field of study. It is thought that the giant queen is incapable of caring for her eggs and feeding her tiny young when she starts a new colony. Therefore she has dense tufts of hairs on her tarsi and young queens, on their wedding flight, have been caught with several tiny workers clinging to these hairs. The huge female carries them easily with her and it is suggested they are necessary to help her with the founding of the new nest because her large mouthparts are far too clumsy to tend the very small larvae of her first brood.

There are many species of the black cocktail ants, *Cremastogaster* species, that are easily recognised and well known because of their habit of carrying the abdomen raised over the back when alarmed or disturbed. The petiole is joined at the back to the dorsal surface of the abdomen and the joint between the two is very flexible, hence the ease with which these ants cock their tails. Also when they are disturbed these ants expose small white glands at the tip of the abdomen and a sticky whitish fluid is given off from them with an unpleasant odour.

Most of the cocktail ants are tree dwellers, making their nests under the bark, in hollow branches, or in carton nests attached to the

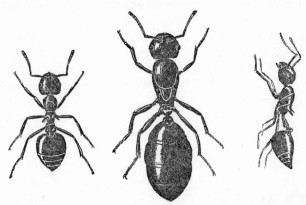

FIG. 188—The Black Cocktail Ant, *Cremastogaster peringueyi.* Queen and workers. The worker on the right shown in side view. Magnified six times.

branches. The carton nests are more or less spherical in shape, black, and they vary in size according to the size of the colonies. They are made of chewed vegetable fibres mixed with the secretion of the maxillary glands of the workers, which blackens the material and acts as a cement. The walls are thin and papery and the interior consists of irregular cells, like a coarse sponge. If the wall of one of these nests is broken open, the workers swarm out, with their tails in the air and their repugnatorial glands exposed.

All the cocktail ants are fond of sugary substances and they attend aphids, scale insects, mealie bugs and other members of the *Hemiptera* for the sake of the honey-dew given off by them. Frequently small shelters made of carton will be built over these insects by the ants, to protect them from the elements and from enemies, with only small round holes through which the ants can reach them; without much exaggeration it might be said that they build stables for their pets.

The *Cremastogaster* queen is black, like the workers, but larger. In the case of Peringuey's cocktail ant, *Cremastogaster peringueyi*, for example, the workers are from one-eighth to a fifth of an inch in length, whilst the queen is about a third of an inch long. The males are much smaller, only a sixth of an inch long, also black, and slenderly built. These ants make black, spherical carton nests, varying in size from that of an apple to rugby football. Usually they build in low bushes or among reeds, with a stem running through the centre of the nest to support it.

These ants readily adapt themselves to the artificial nests shown in figure 189. The nest consists of a sheet of plywood as a base, with a piece of cork lino glued in one half by a water-proof glue. Circular holes an inch in diameter are punched in the lino and grooves cut in

FIG. 189—Artificial Ant's nest, made of cork lino and three-ply wood with D.D.T. to keep ants in.

the cork to connect these cells one with the other. The nest is raised on four screws with their heads in small containers of 10 per cent. D.D.T. powder; this forms an effectual barrier to the escape of the ants. If a carton nest is broken up and the ants shaken on to the tray, they soon find their way into the darkness of the nest and carry their young stages inside and settle down. They will eat honey, scraps of meat, dead insects, and, if a plant with scale insects or aphids is placed on the tray, the ants will visit them eagerly. They never attempt to construct any carton cells in the artificial nest, possibly because the necessary raw material is not available, but otherwise they behave normally and their habits and the rearing of the different stages can be studied with ease. Sometimes young queens just commencing a new nest may be found in hollow stems; if they are removed with their young and placed in a small artificial nest, they also will settle down and the establishment of the new colony can be watched. It is a slow process for, at the end of a year, the colony consists only of the queen and perhaps a dozen dwarf workers, together with some eggs, larvae and pupae.

Camponotine Ants

The ants of the sub-family *Camponotinae* have a one-jointed petiole. The workers have no sting but the poison gland is still present and functional; some species can squirt their poison at their enemies when fighting, turning their abdomen forward between their legs to do so, whilst others bring the tip of the abdomen forward and touch the wound when biting, thus bringing the poison into contact with it. The pupae of these ants are usually enclosed in cocoons.

Perhaps the commonest and most widely spread of the campono-tine ants in South Africa is the pugnacious ant, *Plagiolepis custodiens*. It is an active, aggressive ant that will attack fiercely if its nest is disturbed. The workers vary in size, the smallest being about one-sixth of an inch long, whilst the largest are about two-fifths of an inch in length. They are brown. The queens are about half an inch long and darker in colour than the workers.

These ants usually nest in the ground but frequently they may be found living in the walls of termite mounds. The nest entrances are small round holes, rarely surrounded by any material excavated by the ants, such material usually being spread out thinly for some distance round the entrances. The colonies are large as a rule. The ants are

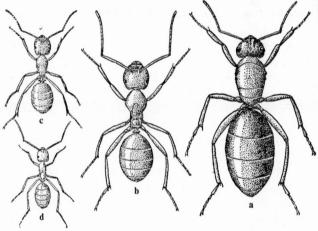

FIG. 190—The Pugnacious Ant, *Plagiolepis custodiens:* (*a*) Queen; (*b*) Major worker; (*c*) Medium worker; (*d*) Minor worker. All drawn to same scale, four times natural size.

mainly carnivorous, living on any other insects they can capture and they may do some good by keeping down the numbers of termites and other noxious insects. But they also attend aphids, scale insects and mealie bugs for the sake of the honey-dew and, as they are so fierce, they keep away the enemies of these insects and so allow them to multiply much more freely than would be the case if they were not protected by the ants.

It is well known that many ants are in the habit of collecting nectar and honey-dew, storing it in their distensible crops to carry back to the nest, and then distributing it by regurgitation to the workers and larvae there. This habit is most highly developed among the camponotine ants and often the workers may be seen hurrying back to the nest with the abdomens distended and translucent because of liquid in the swollen crop. Now, ants have no cells in their nests in which they can store liquid food, as bees have, but certain species have solved the problem by converting some of the workers in the nest into living honey-pots. These honey ants, or repletes, as they are called, are to be found among certain species closely related to the pugnacious ant.

For example *Plagiolepis trimeni* is fairly common from Natal and Zululand northwards. It is an active insect with erratic movements, much like the pugnacious ant, and it nests in sandy soil. The workers are straw yellow and vary in size from an eighth of an inch to about a quarter of an inch in length. The queen is pale brown and about a quarter of an inch long. If a nest of these ants is carefully opened, the repletes may be found in a chamber about a foot below the surface. They are major workers, with their abdomens swollen and shiny and translucent because of the large quantity of nectar and honey-dew contained in the crop. Because of the heavy abdomen such a replete can hardly walk about and it does not leave the nest. Workers coming in with liquid food go to these repletes and give it to them by regurgitation. The repletes lap it up until their crops are full almost to bursting point. Thus these ants are able to store liquid food in their nests and the repletes give it up again as it is required.

Another remarkable member of the *Camponotinae* is the tailor ant, *Oecophylla smaragdina*, which is common in some parts of tropical Africa. This ant makes its nest between the leaves of trees, which are fastened together by a fine, white web of silk. The workers are from a third to half an inch in length, slender, yellowish red in colour, and they are very vicious and aggressive. The queen is about three-quarters of an inch long and grass green in colour, whilst the males are dark brown. If two of the leaves covering a nest of these ants are torn slightly apart, their method of constructing their home can be witnessed. The workers swarm out of the damaged nest, to defend it, but after a time some of them line up, side by side, along the edge of one of the leaves where the nest has been exposed. Seizing the edge of the other leaf in their jaws, and clinging to the first leaf by their legs, they pull in unison and slowly draw the two edges closer together again.

No adult insects are known that can produce silk; only larvae can do this, therefore the adult workers cannot bind the two edges together with silk. As soon as the straining workers have succeeded in pulling the two edges together, however, other workers appear from inside the nest, each carrying a larva in its jaws. These workers line up along the inner edge of the slit, opposite to the workers holding the edges together on the outside. Then, by waving the larvae from side to side, touching each edge with their mouths, the larvae are made to give off silken threads from their large silk glands and so the web is made that binds the two edges together. This might well be called an instance of child labour in the ant world, the larvae being used as spinning shuttles in the construction and repair of the nest. Unlike most other camponotine ants, the larvae of the tailor ants do not spin cocoons; possibly their supply of silk is exhausted in nest building.

The sugar ant, *Camponotus maculatus*, is very common and widely spread, not only through Africa but also in other parts of the world. It is often a nuisance in houses, where it is attracted by sweet food-stuffs in the kitchen and pantry. These ants nest in the soil, often beneath a stone, and the entrance to the nest is usually surrounded by a low crater of excavated earth. The workers are of various sizes, the smallest being about a third of an inch long, pale brown, with indistinct yellow spots on the abdomen, the largest are half an inch long, with a black head and thorax and brown abdomen with yellow spots. The queens are about three-fifths of an inch long and brown in colour, with dull yellow spots on the abdomen. The workers are active in the evening and at night.

There are a large number of other species of camponotine ants found in Africa and they differ widely in their habits. Some are timid, others are aggressive, some are active only at night, others may be seen foraging by day; many nest in the soil, many in hollow stems and in cavities in dead wood; some live in populous colonies, whilst other species have nests with comparatively few individuals; some are mainly carnivorous in their diet, whilst others seem to obtain their sustenance chiefly from honey-dew and nectar.

CLASSIFICATION

SUPERFAMILY *Formicoidea*—ANTS

Social insects with different castes of females, including queens and major and minor workers. Thorax and abdomen separated by a petiole of one or two joints. There is only one family, *Formicidae*, which is divided into five sub-families.

SUB-FAMILY 1: *Ponerinae*—PRIMITIVE ANTS

Workers always armed with well developed sting. Petiole nearly always one-jointed. First segment of abdomen usually narrowed behind so that there is a slight constriction between the first and second abdominal segments. Pupae always enclosed in cocoons. Carnivorous ants, mostly living in small colonies, but some species form large nests with numerous inhabitants.

SUB-FAMILY 2: *Dorylinae*—DRIVER OR LEGIONARY ANTS

Workers armed with a sting. Petiole one- or two-jointed. Males large, females large, blind and wingless. Pupae naked or enclosed in a cocoon. Workers are blind and they live almost entirely on insects and any other creatures they can capture and cut up.

SUB-FAMILY 3: *Myrmicinae*

Workers armed with a sting. Petiole distinctly two-jointed. Males usually winged (they are wingless in a few species), females winged and with compound eyes. Pupae always naked, without cocoons.

SUB-FAMILY 4: *Dolichoderinae*

Sting of workers absent or vestigial; anal glands that produce a secretion with a characteristic odour. Petiole one-jointed. Pupae naked, never enclosed in cocoons.

SUB-FAMILY 5: *Camponotinae*

Sting of workers vestigial; poison glands well developed and functional. Petiole one-jointed. No anal repugnatorial glands. Pupae usually enclosed in cocoons, but naked sometimes.

INDEX

Abdominal feet 183
Acacia shot-hole borer 233
Acanthopsyche junodi 151
Acanthoscelides obtectus 242
Achaea lienardi 178
Acherontia atropos 164
Achroia grisella 158
Acraea horta 205
Acraeidae 205, 210
Acridiidae 29, 35
Adenophlebia peringueyella 77, 79
Adephaga 259
Aedes aegypti 270
Aegocera fervida 179
Aeschnidae 90
African caddis flies 139
African cockroaches 14
African dragon-flies 89
African earwigs 37
African Monarch 193, 207
African plume moth 161
African thrips 93
Agaonidae 321, 339
Agrionidae 90
Agrionympha psiliaema 145
Alder flies 128, 135
Aleurodes ricini 112
Aleyrodidae 112, 127
Alimentary canal 12
Allodape 352
Allodape angulata 353
Allodape halictoides 354
Aloe red scale 121
Amauris albimaculata 193
Amauris dominicanus 193
Ambrosia beetles 253, 261
American bollworm 176
American cockroach 7
Amitermes atlanticus 41
Ammophila species 333
Anaphe panda 171
Anaphe reticulata 171
Anatomy of cockroach 8
Androconia 198, 208
Anisoptera 82, 90
Anisops varia 104
Anobiidae 232, 260
Anobium punctatum 231
Anopheles funestus 269
Anopheles gambiae 269
Anophelines 266
Anoplura 71, 76
Antestia bug 94
Antestia variegata 94
Anthia beetles 215
Anthia decemguttata 214
Anthidium species 347

Anthidium junodi 347
Anthomyidae 290, 305
Anthophoridae 356, 359
Anthophorid bees 356
Anthrenus verbasci 227
Antihepialus antarcticus 145
Antliarrhinus zamiae 249
Ant lions 128, 131, 135, 136
Ants 2, 312, 360, 375
Ants' guests 220, 260
Ants' nest beetles 220, 260
Anuraphis persicae-niger 113, 116
Aonidiella aurantii 116, 117
Apanteles 319
Apanteles euproctidis 319
Apanteles halfordi 319
Apanteles ruficrus 318
Aphaniptera 306, 311
Aphelinus mali 322
Aphids 113
Aphididae 113, 127
Aphidius testaceipes 318
Aphis gossypii 116
Aphis leguminosae 113
Aphis maidis 113, 116
Aphis sacchari 116
Apidae 357, 359
Apis mellifica 358
Apis mellifica adansoni 358
Apis mellifica unicolor 358
Apocrita 339
Apoidea 342, 359
Aptera cingulata 14
Apterygida coloniae 36
Aquatic bugs 102
Arctiidae 178
Arctiinae 180
Argentine ant 365
Arista 295
Armoured ground crickets 30
Army worm 173
Army worm phases 174
Artificial nests for termites 43
Artificial nests for ants 372
Artificial nests for primitive social bees 356
Ascalaphidae 134, 136
Asclepias species 25, 208
Ascotis selenaris 184
Asilidae 282, 304
Aspalathus borer 323
Aspidiotus perniciosus 118, 121
Aspidomorphus species 243
Assassin bugs 100, 126
Assembling 169, 198
Athalia pelargonii 312
Aucheromyia luteola 297
Aulonogyra capensis 218

377

Australian bug 124, 226
Australian ladybird 124, 226
Autumn brown 199

Baboon spiders 330
Back swimmers 104, 126
Bacon beetle 227
Baetis species 80
Bagrada hilaris 96
Bagrada stink bug 96
Bagworms 151, 185
Balancers 263
Balclutha mbila 110
Bamboo borer 232
Banded bee pirate 334
Banded blow fly 292
Banded gold tip 189
Banded horse fly 281
Bark anobiid 232
Bark beetles 261
Basket worms 151
Batrachotettix species 29
Beaked butterflies 198, 209
Bean weevils 243, 261
Bed bugs 101, 126
Bee flies 282, 304
Bee louse 302
Bee pirates 334, 340
Bees 2, 211, 259, 312, 342
Beetles 2, 211
Belonogaster 329, 340
Belonogaster junceus 329
Belostoma niloticum 102
Belostomatidae 101, 126
Bembecidae 335, 340
Bembex capicola 335
Biological control 124, 158
Biscuit beetle 232
Biting lice 71, 76
Bittacus nebulosus 137
Bittacus species 138
Black beetle 8
Black cocktail ant 195, 371
Black-footed Simulium 277
Black mound termite 41
Black peach aphis 113, 116
Black scale 121
Bladder grasshopper 27
Blastophaga psenes 321
Blatella germanica 8
Blatta orientalis 8
Blattidae 35
Blind bee louse 302
Blind flies 280
Blister beetles 24, 239, 261
Blistering rove beetle 222
Blood-sucking midges 276
Blood worm 273
Blow flies 292, 305
Blues 195 209
Blue bottles 294
Blue commodore 204
Blue tongue 272
Blue winged orange mayfly 77

Body louse 73
Bombardier beetles 215
Bombycidae 169
Bombycomorpha pallida 162
Bombyliidae 282, 304
Bombyx mori 170
Book lice 68
Bostrichidae 232, 260
Bostrychoplites cornutus 232
Bot flies 297, 305
Bracharoa dregei 182
Brachinus species 215
Brachycera 304
Brachycerus obesus 250
Braconidae 318, 393
Braconid wasps 318, 393
Braula coeca 302
Braulidae 303, 305
Braura truncata 171
Break-bone fever 271
Breathing organs 8, 288
Breathing trumpet 269
Brevicoryne brassicae 116
Bristle tails 2 and 3
Bronze and green dung beetles 257
Bronze spinner 77
Brown bristle tail 4
Brown house ants 368
Brown lacewings 136
Brown locust 22
Brown mantis 18
Brown membrane bee 343
Browns 198, 210
Browntail moth 170, 180
Bruchidae 242, 261
Bruchophagus funebris 324
Bruchus pisorum 241
Bruchus quadrimaculatus 243
Bulb weevil 250
Bumble bees 349
Bunaea alcinoe 169
Buprestidae 235, 261
Buprestid beetles 235
Burrowing bees 345, 359
Butterflies 143, 187, 209
Button spider 317
Bymot 164
Bythoscopus cedaranus 110

Cabbage aphis 116
Cabbage-tree Emperor moth 169
Cactoblastis cactorum 159
Cactoblastis moth 124
Caddis flies 139, 142
Caddis worm 140
Cadelle 222
Caeca 11
Calamistis fusca 175
Caliroa cerasi 313
Callosobruchus chinensis 243
Calosoma beetles 215
Calosoma planicolle 214
Calosoma species 215
Cambium 235

Campodea 5
Camponotinae 360, 375
Camponotine ants 373
Camponotus maculatus 375
Cantharidae 231, 260, 239
Cantharidin 239
Cantharis pallidipennis 241
Cape alder fly 129
Cape caddis fly 139
Cape ghost moth 145
Cape gooseberry beetle 245
Cape Tiger moth 180
Capparis species 190
Capri fig insects 321
Carabidae 214, 260
Carcelia evolans 299
Carder bees 347, 359
Carebara vidua 370
Carpenter bees 349, 359
Carpenter moths 153, 185
Carpophilus hemipterus 223
Carton nests 371
Case-bearing clothes moth 147
Cat flea 306
Cecidomyidae 276, 304
Cerambycidae 246, 249, 261
Ceratina species 352
Ceratitis capitata 286
Ceratopsyllidae 311
Cerci 14
Cercopidae 108, 127
Ceroplastes species 122
Chaerocampa celerio 166
Chafers 259
Chalcidoidea 321, 339
Chalcid wasps 321
Charaxes 203, 210
Charaxes pelias 203
Chelonus texanus 320
Chigger flea 309
Chilomenes lunata 224
Chinese weevil 243
Chironomidae 272, 276, 304
Chironomus species 272
Chitin 8
Chlorolestes conspicua 83
Chloridea obsoleta 176
Chloroniella peringueyi 129
Chordotonal organs 247
Christmas butterfly 191
Chrysididae 326, 340
Chrysomela fasciata 246
Chrysomelidae 243, 261
Chrysomyia albiceps 292
Chrysomyia chloropyga 292
Chrysomyia marginalis 294
Chrysopa species 130
Chrysopidae 136
Cicadas 106, 127
Cicadidae 127
Cicindela lurida 211
Cicindela marginella 212
Cicindelidae 214, 259
Cigarette beetle 232

Cimex lectularius 101
Cimex rotundatus 101
Cimicidae 126
Citrus mealy bug 123
Citrus psyllid 111
Citrus swallow tail 191
Clearwing ant lion 132
Clearwings 154, 185
Click beetles 235, 261
Cliffortia strobilifera 274
Cloeon lacunosum 80, 81
Clothes moths 146
C.M.R. beetles 239
Coccidae 116, 127
Coccinellidae 224, 260
Cochineal insects 124, 160
Cockroaches 1, 7, 35
Cocktail ants 196, 371
Codling moth 149
Codling moth egg parasite 323
Coelioxys capensis 348, 349
Coleoptera 211, 259
Collembola 5, 6
Colleterial glands 11
Colletidae 359
Colophon cameroni 255
Colophon haughtoni 254
Colophon izardi 255
Colophon primosi 255
Colophon species 254
Colophon stokoei 254
Colophon westwoodi 254
Commodore 204
Common furniture beetle 231
Communal moth 171
Compound eyes 12
Confused flour beetle 237, 238
Congo floor maggot 296, 297
Conopidae 305
Convolvulus hawk moth 166
Copifrontia xantherythra 179
Coppers 195
Coptotermes formosans 67
Cordylobia anthropophaga 296
Coreidae 98, 125
Corixidae 105, 126
Cornicles 114, 116
Corydalidae 135
Coryphodema tristis 153
Cosmoglyphus kramerii 66
Cossidae 154, 185
Cotton aphis 116
Cotton stainer bug 98
Cotton stainers 126
Cottony cushion scale 125
Cowpea weevil 243
Coxa 13
Crab louse 73
Crabronidae 337, 341
Crabronid wasps 337, 341
Crane flies 263, 304
Cremaster 191
Cremastogaster peringueyi 371
Cremastogaster species 195, 370

Cricket-grasshoppers 33
Crickets 7, 33, 35
Crocydoscelus ferrugineum 161
Cryptocerata 103
Cryptotermes brevis 60, 67
Ctenocephalus canis 306
Ctenocephalus felis 306
Cuckoo bees 348
Cuckoo-spit 108
Cuckoo wasps 326, 340
Cucujidae 224, 260
Cueta lanceolata 132
Culex pipiens 266
Culex quinquefasciatus 266
Culicidae 304
Culicines 266
Curculionidae 249, 261
Cuscuta 15
Cutworms 172, 333
Cybister species 216
Cybister tripunctatus 216
Cycad weevil 249
Cyclopides metis 187
Cyclorrhapha 304
Cydia pomonella 149
Cynipidae 339
Cynipoidea 339

Dactylopius opuntiae 124, 160
Dacus oleae 287
Dacus vertebratus 287
Daddy-long-legs 263
Damsel flies 83, 89, 90
Danaidae 209, 210
Danaus chrysippus 193, 204, 207, 210
Dassies 72
Dasyproctus capensis 338
Death's head moth 165
Death watch beetles 231
Delochilus prionides 246
Dengue fever 271
Dermaptera 36, 38
Dermestes lardarius 227
Dermestes vulpinus 227
Dermestidae 229, 260
Desert locust 22
Diacrisia eugraphica 180
Diadem butterfly 204
Diamond-back moth 147
Diapause 26
Dichthadiigynes 364
Dielis quinquefasciata 326
Digestive canal 11
Dikpens 30
Dinoderus minutus 232
Dinogamasid mites 352
Dinogamasus braunsi 351
Dionychopus amasis 180
Dionychopus similis 180
Diparopsis castanea 176
Diptera 263, 303
Dira (Leptoneura) clytus 199
Distasteful butterflies 205
Dog flea 306

Dolichoderinae 360, 376
Dolichoderine ants 365
Dolichomutilla guineensis 325
Dolichopodidae 304
Donaconethis abyssinica 68
Dorylinae 360, 376
Doryline ants 362
Dorylus helvolus 363
Dragon flies 2, 82, 89
Dried fruit beetles 223
Driver ants 362, 376
Drone fly 284
Drosophilidae 288, 305
Dry-wood termite 62
Dung beetles 255, 262
Duns 77, 79
Dyschimus thrymmifer 139
Dystiscidae 218, 260

Earborer 36
Earwigs 36, 38
Earworm 36
Earworm of maize 177
Echidnophaga gallinacea 311
Egg tube 11
Ejaculatory duct 11
Elateridae 235, 261
Elephantiasis 271
Elytra 211
Embioptera 68, 70
Embryonic diapause 26
Emperor moths 167, 169
Emperor swallow tail 191
Empidae 304
Empusa species 18
Encyrtidae 339
Ensign-wasps 313, 339
Ephemeroptera 77, 81
Ephestia kuhniella 156, 320
Epilachna dregei 226
Epilachna species 226
Eriosoma lanigera 113, 116
Eristalis tenax 284
Ernobius mollis 232
Esphalmenus peringueyi 36
Eucalyptus borer 247
Eucalyptus weevil 252
Eucosternum delegorguei 96
Eulophidae 339
Eumenes caffer 327
Eumenidae 327, 340
Euplexoptera 36
Euproctis fasciata 182
Euproctis terminalis 181, 319
European house borer 248
Eurytomidae 339
Eutermes natalensis 63, 221
Evaniidae 313, 339
Evening brown 200
Eyes 3, 12

False pupa 240
Fannia canicularis 289
Fannia scalaris 290

Femur 13
Fig insects 320, 339
Figitidae 339
Fig tree borer 249
Filaria gallinarum 66
Filariasis 271
Fire-flies 229
Fish moths 2
Flagellates 66
Flat headed borers 235
Flata semanga 111
Fleas 306
Flesh flies 292
Flies 263, 303
Fly belts 294
Fly-hunting wasps 335
Forficula auricularia 37
Formicidae 360
Formicoidae 375
Four-spotted cowpea weevil 243
Fowl flea 311
Fowl midge 277
Foxy charaxes 203
Frenatae 143, 184
Frenulum 144
Friar butterfly 193
Froghoppers 108, 127
Front legs of butterflies 188
Fruit beetles 259
Fruit flies 286, 305
Fruit-piercing moths 177
Fulgoridae 110, 127
Fungus gardens 63
Fungus gnats 276, 304
Fungus-growing termites 63
Furcaspis capensis 120
Furniture beetle 231

Galleria mellonella 158
Gall midges 274, 304
Gall wasps 339
Gamasid mite 65
Garbage flies 290
Garden acraea 205
Gasteruption spilopus 314, 344
Gastrophilus species 298
Gaudy commodore 204
Genitalia 144
Geometers 183
Geometridae 183, 186
Geometrid moth 144
German cockroach 8
Ghost moths 144, 146, 184
Giant water bugs 101, 126
Gizzard 11
Glossina morsitans 295
Glossina species 294
Glow worms 230
Gnats 272
Goat moths 154, 185
Golden eyes 130
Gonimbrasia tyrrhea 168
Gonipterus scutellatus 252
Gonnia 27

Grain weevil 251
Grasshoppers 1, 21, 25, 29
Gregaria phase 174
Gregarious caterpillars 170
Green blow fly 292
Green grain aphis 113
Greenhouse thrips 92
Green jassid bug 110
Green lace wings 136
Green mantis 18
Green stink bug 96
Green-tailed sheep blow fly 292
Grey mantis 15
Groonia 27
Ground beetles 214, 260
Gryllacridae 33
Gryllidae 35
Gryllus domesticus 33
Gynanisa maia 168
Gyrinidae 220, 260

Haematopinus species 74
Haematopota ocellata 280
Halictidae 359
Halobates 99
Halteres 263
Hard scale insects 120
Harpagomantis tricolor 18
Harris fly trap 296
Harvester ants 369
Harvester termites 56, 66
Hawk moths 164, 185
Head louse 73
Head of cockroach 8
Heart 10
Hekiejees 27
Heliothrips haemorrhoidalis 92
Hemerobiidae 136
Hemipepsis capensis 330
Hemiptera 94, 125
Henicus monstrosus 31
Hepialidae 146
Heraclia africana 184
Herse convolvuli 166
Hespagarista echione 179
Hesperiidae 188, 189, 209
Heterocera 143, 187
Heterohyrax 73
Heteroneura 144, 184
Heteronychus species 259
Heteroptera 125
Hetrodes pupus 30
Hexachrysis concinna 327
Hexachrysis lyncea 327
Hippobosca rufipes 302
Hippobosca struthionis 302
Hippoboscidae 302, 305
Hodotermes 56
Hodotermitidae 66
Holopterna vulga 97
Homoneura 144, 184
Homoptera 107, 126
Honey ants 374
Honey bees 358

Honey gland (butterflies) 195
Hopliinae 259
Hoppers 23
Horn beetles 227
Horned shot-hole borer 232
Horse flies 280, 302, 304
Horse sickness 272
Hottentot gods 7, 15
House fly 290, 305
Household fleas 306
Hover flies 284, 304
Human flea 306
Humeral lobe 187
Hunting wasps 316
Hydrometridae 98, 126
Hylaeidae 344
Hylotrupes bajulus 248
Hymenoptera 312, 338
Hymenopterous parasites 158
Hypoderma bovis 298
Hypoderma lineatum 298
Hypolimna misippus 204
Hypopharynx 266
Hypopus 66

Icerya purchasi 124, 226
Ichneumonidae 339, 316
Ichneumonoidea 339
Ichneumon wasps 316
Imago 79
Indian meal moth 156
Intestinal parasites 62
Ipidae 261
Iridomyrmex humilis 365
Isoptera 41, 66
Italian beetle 248

Japyx 5
Jassidae 109, 127
Jigger fleas 309
Jugatae 143, 184
Jugum 144
Jumping plant lice 111, 127

Kalotermitidae 66
Karoo caterpillar 157, 320
Karoo caterpillar parasite 320
Karoo caterpillar moth 157
Katydid 30
Kiggelaria africana 206
King crickets 33
Koringkrieks 30

Labium 12, 94
Labrum 12
Labrum-epipharynx 266
Lace bugs 98, 126
Lacewings 130, 136
Ladybirds 224, 260
Lagochirus funestus 124, 160
Lampromyia brevirost·is 280
Lantern flies 110, 127
Laphygma exempta 173, 179
Laphygma exigua 175

Lappet moths 161
Larder beetle 227
Large blue-bottle 294
Large click beetles 236
Large fungus-grower 63
Larger plant bugs 125
Large vegetarian ladybird 226
Lasiocampidae 164, 185
Lasiocampid moths 163, 164
Lasioderma serricorne 232
Latrine fly 290
Latrodectus indistinctus 317
Layman 193
Leaf-cutter bees 345, 359
Leaf-eating beetles 243, 261
Leaf-hoppers 109, 127
Leaf insects 18, 35
Leather beetle 227
Legionary ants 362, 376
Lema bilineata 245
Lema trilineata 245
Lepidoptera 143, 184, 209
Lepidosaphes pinnaeformis 119, 121
Lepisma saccharina 3
Leptidae 280, 304
Lesser army worm 175
Lesser carpenter bees 352
Lesser fungus grower 65
Lesser house fly 289
Lesser wax moth 158
Lestes species 86
Lestidae 90
Leto venus 144, 146
Libellaginidae 90
Libellulidae 90
Libythea labdaca 198
Libytheidae 198, 209
Lice 71
Light-producing organ 229
Limacodidae 155, 185
Linognathus gnu 74
Liparidinae 182
Liposcelis divinatorius 69
Loa-loa 281
Locustana pardalina 22
Locustidae 29, 35
Locusta migratoria 22
Locusts 7, 21, 35
Long-horned ant lions 135, 136
Long-horned beetles 246, 261
Long-horned grasshoppers 7, 29, 35
Looper caterpillars 182, 186
Loxostege frustalis 157, 320
Lucanidae 254, 262
Lucern chalcid 321, 324
Luciferase 229
Luciferin 229
Lucilia sericata 292
Luciola capensis 229
Lunate ladybird 225
Lycaena asteris 196
Lycaenidae 188, 195, 209
Lyctidae 235, 261
Lyctus brunneus 234

Lygaeid bug 109
Lygaeidae 126
Lymantridae 182

Machilis species 4
Macrotermes natalensis 63
Macynia labiata 19
Maize aphis 113, 116
Maize leaf-hopper 110
Maize stalk-borer 175
Malacodermidae 231
Malaria 266
Malaria carriers 269
Mallophaga 71, 76
Malpighian tubes 11, 133
Mandibles 12
Mantichora ferox 212
Mantichora species 214
Mantidae 35
Mantis 7, 15, 35
Mantispas 134
Mantispidae 135, 136
Margarodes scale 122
Mask (Dragon fly) 85
Mason wasps 327, 340
Mastotermitidae 66
Matabele ant 361
Maxentius pallidus 33
Maxillae 12
May flies 2, 77, 81
Meal moths 156
Meal worms 237
Mealy bugs 122, 127
Mecoptera 137, 138
Mediterranean flour moth 156
Mediterranean fruit fly 286
Megachilidae 346, 359
Megachile species 345
Megachile venusta 346
Megaloptera 135
Megaponera foetens 361
Melanitis leda 200
Meloe angulatus 240
Meloidae 239, 261
Melophagus ovinus 301
Membracidae 109, 127
Membrane bee 343
Meneris tulbaghia 201
Mesocelis montana 164
Mesotrichia caffra 349
Messor barbarus 369
Metamorphosis 211, 312
Microdon illuceus 286
Microdon species 286
Microhodotermes 56
Micro-organisms 62
Micropterygidae 145, 184
Midges 272, 304
Migration of moths and butterflies 201
Migratory locusts 22
Mimicry 193
Mimleucania leucosoma 179
Mocker swallow tail 193
Mole crickets 34

Monkey beetles 259
Monstrous cricket 31
Mopani bees 357
Mormoniella brevicornis 322
Mosaic vision 13
Mosquitoes 265, 304
Moth flies 264, 304
Mottled horse fly 280
Mountain beauty 201
Mountain cockroach 14
Mouthparts 12
Mud wasps 333
Multivoltine 170
Musca domestica 290
Muscidae 292, 305
Museum beetle 227
Mushroom gland 11
Mussel scale 119, 121
Mutillidae 324, 340
Mycetophilidae 276, 340
Mylabris species 239
Myrmeleonidae 136
Myrmicinae 368
Mystery worm 173

Nagana 294, 295
Natal fruit fly 286
Nematocera 303
Nemopteridae 136
Nepa species 104
Nepidae 102, 126
Nervous system 12
Neuroptera 128, 135
Nezara viridula 96
Nitidulidae 224, 260
Noctuidae 172, 178, 186
Nomadacris septemfasciata 22
Nomidaes arion 197
Nomia 345
Nomioides species 345
Nothylaeus heraldicus 343
Notodontidae 172, 186
Notonectidae 104, 126
Novius cardinalis 226
Nudaurelia cytherea 167
Nymphalidae 188, 199, 203, 205, 210

Oak slug caterpillar 155
Ochthopetina transvaalensis 39
Odonata 82, 89
Odynerus species 328
Oecophylla smaragdina 374
Oesophagus 11
Oestridae 299, 305
Oestrus ovis 298
Oil beetles 239, 240, 261
Old-fashioned clothes moth 147
Olfactory organs 12
Olive fly 285
Omophron beetles 215
Omophron species 215
Onion thrips 91
Onitis aygulus 257
Ophion species 318

Orange tips 189
Oriental dampwood termite 67
Orthetrum caffrum 82, 86
Orthoptera 7, 18, 35
Orthorrhapha 303
Orzaephilus surinamensis 222, 224
Osmeterium 191
Osmia 349
Osteomyelitis 293
Ostrich fly 302
Oviducts 11
Ovipositor 29, 31, 32
Ovios capensis 179
Owlet moths 172
Oxybelidae 341

*P*achypasa gonometra 164
Paederus subaeus 222
Paedogenesis 276
Paida pulchra 179
Painted lady family 201, 210
Palarus latrifrons 334
Pallid king cricket 33
Palpares speciosus 133
Palystes species 330
Pangonia 281
Papilio antimachus 191
Papilio dardanus 193
Papilio demodocus 191
Papilionidae 188, 189, 191, 209
Papilio ophidicephalus 191
Pappataci 265
Paracorotoca akermani 221
Parasa latistriga 155
Parasa johannes 155
Parasa vivida 155
Parasitic wasps 95, 122, 206, 316
Pardalaspis cosyra 286
Pardalaspis quinaria 286
Parthenogenesis 21, 113, 115, 122, 125, 153, 170, 313
Passalidius fortipes 214, 215
Passerina vulgaris 163
Paussidae 220, 260, 369
Paussus arduus 220
Paussus barberi 220
Pea aphis 113
Pear slug 313
Pea weevils 241, 261
Pedicel 360
Pediculidae 73
Pediculus humanus 73, 75
Pelargonium saw fly 312
Pephricus capicola 98
Pentatomidae 125
Pentzia incana 320
Pepper tree catterpillar and moth 162
Perigea grandirena 179
Periplaneta americana 7
Peringuey's alder fly 129
Peringuey's cocktail ant 371
Pernicious scale 118, 120
Petiole 360
Penzomachus latrodectiphagus 317

Phasmidae 21, 35
Phasis chrysaor 195
Pheidole megacephala 368
Philanthidae 335, 340
Philanthus diadema 335
Phlyctinus callosus 251
Phorocantha semipunctata 247
Phryneta spinator 249
Phthirus pubis 73
Phthorimaea operculella 148
Phylloxera vitifoliae 116
Phylopsyche abdominalis 316
Phymateus morbillosus 25
Physopoda 91
Pieridae 188, 189, 209
Pine brown tail moth 181
Pine tree emperor moth 167
Pine tree moth 162
Pin-hole borers 252
Plagiolepis custodiens 197, 373
Plagiolepis trimeni 374
Plague 308
Planipennia 136
Plant bugs 94, 125
Plant lice 113, 127
Platychila pallida 212, 214
Platygasteridae 340
Platypus species 253
Plecoptera 39, 40
Plodia interpunctella 156
Plume moths 161
Plum slug caterpillar 155
Plutella maculipennis 147
Pneumorinae 27
Polistes species 329, 340
Polyembryony 323
Polyphaga 260
Polyplax cummingsi 74
Pompilidae 330, 340
Pond skaters 98, 126
Ponerinae 360, 375
Ponerine ants 360
Potato tuber moth 148
Powder post beetles 234, 261
Praying mantes 7, 15, 35
Precis octavia 204
Precis octavia natalensis 205
Precis octavia sesamus 205
Prickly pear beetles 124
Prickly pear moth 159
Primary kings and queens (Termites) 50, 55
Primitive ants 360, 375
Primitive bees 342, 359
Primitive insects 1, 6
Primitive moths 145
Proboscis 94
Procavia capensis 72
Procavicola supparvus 73
Procavicola vicinus 73
Procaviphilus serraticus 72
Proctarrelabris capensis 134
Proctotrypoidea 340
Prolegs 183
Prosopidae 314, 344, 359

Protura 5, 6
Proxenus leuconephra 179
Psammodes species 237
Pseudococcus citri 123
Psocids 69
Psocoptera 69, 70
Psychidae 151, 185
Psychodidae 264, 304
Psyllidae 111, 127
Pterocroce storeyi 133
Pteromalidae 339
Pterophoridae 161, 185
Pterygota 1, 7, 35
Ptilinum 292
Ptinidae 260
Pugnacious ant 373
Pulicidae 311
Pulex irritans 306
Pumpkin fly 287
Puparium 288, 292
Pyralidae 159, 185
Pyrrhocoridae 98, 126

Quince borer 153
Queen driver ant 364

Ranatra species 102
Raphidiiae 135
Rat fleas 308
Rat-tailed maggot 285
Rectal gills 88
Rectal glands 11
Red bollworm 176
Red border-wing 77, 80
Red commodore 205
Red locust 22
Red scale 116
Reduviidae 126
Red water mites 104
Repletes 374
Reproductive nymphs 52
Reproductive organs 11
Reproductives (termites) 50, 51, 60
Repugnatorial glands 371
Respiratory horn 268
Respiratory system 10
Respiratory tube 104
Rhinotermitidae 67
Rhodesian fruit fly 286
Rhoizema spinosum 141
Rhopalocera 143, 187
Rhopalomenus angusticollis 215
Rice weevil 251
Rift valley fever 272
Robber flies 282, 304
Rodolia cardinalis 124
Rondanio-oestrus apivorus 300
Rosette disease 114
Rostrum 249
Rove beetles 221, 260
Ruby wasps 326

Sacred scarab 255
Saissetia oleae 121

Sand flies 264, 304
Sand wasps 332
Sarcophagidae 305
Sarcopsyllidae 311
Saturniidae 169
Saturniinae 169
Satyridae 199, 201, 210
Satyrinae 199
Saw flies 312, 338
Saw-tooth grain beetle 222, 224
Scale patterns and colouration 202
Scaly-winged insects 143
Scarabaeus sacer 255
Scarabaeus rugosus 255
Scarabeidae 255, 262
Sceliphron spirifex 325, 333
Scent gland 165
Scent scales 208
Schistocerca gregaria 22
Scoliidae 325, 340
Scoliid wasps 325
Scolytidae 252, 261
Scorpion flies 137, 138
Seasonal dimorphism 204
Secondary kings and queens (Termites) 54
Selago serrata 196
Semiothisa interrupta 144
Sensory hairs 12
September brown mayfly 77
Serrodes partita 178
Sesiidae 185
Setae 178
Seventeen-year locust 107
Sheep blow flies 292
Sheep ked 301
Sheep maggot flies 292
Sheep nasal flies 298
Shield bugs 94, 125
Short-horned grasshoppers 7, 21, 25, 35
Shot-hole borers 232
Sialidae 135
Sigara meridionalis 105
Silken tunnel dweller 68, 70
Silk worms 170
Silver fish 2
Silver-lined hawk moth 166
Silver-spotted ghost moth 145, 146
Simple eyes 13
Simuliidae 277, 304
Simulium damnosum 278
Simulium nigritarsis 277
Sinion hageni 141
Siphonaptera 306, 311
Siphunculata 73, 76
Sitodrepa panicea 232
Sitophilus granarius 251
Sitophilus oryzae 251
Skin beetles 227
Skippers 187, 209
Sleeping sickness 294
Slug caterpillars 154
Small alder flies 135
Snake flies 135
Snake's head swallow-tail 191

Snake worms 276
Snout beetle 249
Snouted harvester termites 58
Social bees 357, 359
Social wasps 316, 328, 340
Soft scale 121
Solitary bees 342, 354
Solitary grasshoppers 24
Solitary phase locusts 24
Solitaria phase 175
Solitary wasps 316
Sound-producing organ 106
Spanioza erythreae 111
Spanish fly 241, 246
Sphecidae 332, 340
Sphecodes 345
Sphecoidea 340
Sphex 333
Sphingidae 167, 185
Sphingomorpha chlorea 178
Sphodromantis gastrica 18
Spider-hunting wasps 330, 340
Spinners 77, 79
Spiracles 10
Spotted-wing ant lion 133, 135
Spring-tails 5
Stable fly 294
Stag beetles 254, 262
Staphylinidae 221, 260
Star blue butterfly 196
Stegomyia fasciata 270
Stick insects 2, 7, 18, 35
Stick tight flea 311
Stingless bees 357
Stink bugs 97
Stink flies 130
Stink sprinkaan 25
Stomoxys calcitrans 294
Stone flies 2, 39
Straight-winged insects 7
Stridulation 28, 29, 324, 361
Stridulatory combs 105
Stripsipher zebra 259
Sub-imago 79
Suboesophageal ganglion 12
Sucking lice 71, 76
Sugar ant 375
Sugar-cane aphis 116
Swallow-tails 191
Swarm phase locusts 24
Swift moths 146, 184
Symbiosis 352
Sympetrum fonscolombei 90
Symphyta 338
Synhoria hottentota 241
Synhoria rhodesiana 241
Syrphidae 284, 305
Syrphus cognatus 285
Systoechus scabrirostris 283

*T*abanidae 280, 304
Tabanus kingi 281
Tachinidae 299, 305
Tachinid flies 20, 158, 299

Taeniochauliodes ochraceopennis 128
Tailor ant 374
Tarachodes perloidea 18
Taragama concolor 162
Tarsus 14
Tassel worm 177
Telephoridae 231
Tenebrioides mauritanicus 222
Tenebrio molitor 237
Tenebrionidae 237, 261
Tenebrio obscurus 237
Tent caterpillars 164
Tenthredinidae 338
Teracolus eris 189
Termes badius 64
Termes latericius 65
Termes transvaalensis 65
Termitacarus cuneiformis 65
Termite guest fly 297
Termite mound 45, 47
Termites 2, 41, 66
Termitidae 67
Termitometopia skaifei 297
Tertiary kings and queens 55
Tetralobus rotundiformis 236
Thief ant 370
Thorn-tree brown-tail moth 182
Thorn-tree Emperor moth 168
Thorn-tree goat moth 154
Thread-winged ant lions 135, 136
Three-day fever 265
Thrips 91, 93
Thrips tabaci 91
Thysanoptera 91, 93
Thysanura 6
Tibia 13
Tiger beetles 211
Tiger moths 178
Timbals 106
Tinea pellionella 147
Tineidae 149, 184
Tineola biselliella 146
Tingidae 98, 126
Tip-tail ants 370
Tipulidae 263, 304
Toad grasshoppers 29
Tobacco bud worm 117
Tobacco slugs 245
Toktokkie beetles 237
Tomato fly 287
Tomato fruit worm 177
Tortoise beetle 243
Tortricidae 151, 185
Toxoptera graminum 113, 116
Trabata species 164
Tracheae 10, 78
Tracheal gills 18, 85, 86, 268
Transiens phase 174
Transvaal fungus grower 65
Tree cricket 35
Tree hoppers 109, 127
Tribolium confusum 237, 238
Trichogrammatoidea lutea 323
Trichogrammidae 339

Trichophaga tapetiella 147
Trichoptera 139, 142
Tricorythus discolor 79, 80
Tridacus pectoralis 288
Trigona species 357
Trinervitermes species 58
Triungulins 240
Trochanter 13
Trogostidae 223, 260
Trox 259
Trypanosoma parasite 295
Trypetidae 287, 305
Tsetse flies 294
Tunga penetrans 309
Tumbu fly 296
Tussock moths 182
Twig wilters 97, 125
Tympanal organs 25, 30
Typhoid 290
Typhus 308
Tyroglyphidae 66

Vanessa cardui 201
Vegetarian ladybird 227
Velvet ants 324, 340
Vespidae 330, 340
Vespoidea 340
Vine calandra 251
Vinegar flies 288, 305
Vine phylloxera 116

Warble flies 297
Wasps 2, 312, 338, 342
Water beetle 216, 260
Water boatmen 104, 126
Water bugs 101
Water measurers 99
Water scorpions 102, 126
Watsonia wasps 338
Wattle bagworm 151
Wax moth 158
Wax scales 122
Weeding flight (Termites) 52

Weevils 249, 261
West African swallow-tail 191
West Indian dry-wood Termite 60, 67
Wheat louse 116
Whirligig beetles 218, 260
White ants 41
White flies 112, 127
Whites 189, 209
Willow tree moth 168
Wire worms 236
Witches broom 110
Wood-eating termite 60
Wood-inhabiting termites 60, 66
Woolly aphis 113, 116
Woolly aphis parasite 322
Woolly bears 178
Worcester dark blue 77, 80
Worm lions 278, 304
Wrigglers 268
Wrinkled scarab 255

Xenopsylla brasiliensis 309
Xenopsylla cheopsis 308
Xenopsylla eridos 309
Xenopsylla erilli 309
Xiphodontus antilope 255
Xyleborus celsus 253
Xyleutes capensis 154
Xylion adustus 233
Xylocopidae 349, 359
Xyloperthodes nitidipennis 233

Yellow bee pirate 335
Yellow dun 77
Yellow fever mosquito 270
Yellows 189
Yellow-spotted ghost moth 145

Zebra beetle 259
Zonocerus elegans 29
Zygaenidae 185
Zygoptera 82, 90